PASCAL
Selections

THE GREAT PHILOSOPHERS

Paul Edwards, General Editor

PASCAL
Selections

Edited,
with Introduction, Notes, and
Bibliography, by
RICHARD H. POPKIN
University of California

A Scribner/Macmillan Book

Macmillan Publishing Company
NEW YORK

Collier Macmillan Publishers
LONDON

17731584

Macmillan Publishing Company
866 Third Avenue, New York, New York 10022

Collier Macmillan Canada, Inc.

Library of Congress Cataloging-in-Publication Data

Pascal, Blaise, 1623–1662.
  [Selections. English. 1989]
  Pascal selections / edited, with introduction, notes, and
bibliography by Richard H. Popkin.
    p.   cm. — (The Great philosophers)
  ISBN 0-02-396161-9
  1. Philosophy—Early works to 1800. 2. Theology—Early works to
1800. 3. Mathematics—Early works to 1800. 4. Science—Early works
to 1800. I. Popkin, Richard Henry, 1923–   . II. Title.
III. Series.
B1900.E5 1989   88-7032
194—dc19   CIP

Printing: 1 2 3 4 5 6 7   Year: 9 0 1 2 3 4 5

Contents

Introduction   1

I. Scientific Writings   19

    Letter to the Chancellor about the Adding Machine   21

    Necessary Advice about the Adding Machine   24

    Letter to Queen Christina   30

    New Experiments about the Vacuum   33

    The Great Experiment   42

    Reply to Father Noel   49

    On the Equilibrium of Fluids and Weight of Air   56

    Preface to the Treatise on the Vacuum   62

II. Short Religious and Philosophical
    Writings   67

    The Memorial   69

    On the Conversion of the Sinner   71

    Three Discourses on the Condition of the Great   74

    Conversation with M. De Saci   79

    The Provincial Letters   90

    On the Geometrical Mind and the Art of Persuasion   173

    The Pensées   195

Bibliography   265

v

Introduction

Blaise Pascal (1623–1662), the brilliant mathematician, physicist, inventor, philosopher, and theologian, was born in Clermont, Auvergne, in south-central France. His father was of the minor nobility and held government office, working on state financial affairs. Pascal's mother died three years after his birth, leaving her grief-stricken husband to raise two daughters and one son.

In 1631 the father, Etienne, moved his young family to Paris, the center of cultural life in France. But because he opposed some financial regulations of Cardinal Richilieu, the country's chief minister, he was forced to leave the city in 1638. However, he was pardoned after one of his daughters took part in a children's play given for Richilieu. On his return to Paris, Etienne Pascal became the royal tax commissioner at Rouen.

The elder Pascal was a man of wide interests with great concern for his children. He decided to educate them himself, without tutors. It was evident from the outset of this experiment that young Blaise was a prodigy, with strong mathematical interests. However, the father did not want to teach the son mathematics before he had become a master of Greek and Latin. He feared that Blaise would be too distracted by mathematics and would neglect other subjects.

And so, without any training or instruction, young Pascal, at age twelve, began to work out the principles of geometry by himself. He had reached as far as the thirty-second proposition of the first book of Euclid when his father found out what he was doing. Etienne then abandoned his original plan for the boy's education and gave him a copy of Euclid's *Elements of Geometry*. Soon after, the father and son joined a group of participants at weekly lectures on mathematics and science, which had been organized by Father Marin Mersenne, a leading mathematician in his own right and a friend of such eminent philosopher-scientists as René Descartes, Pierre Gassendi, and Thomas Hobbes.

PASCAL AS MATHEMATICIAN

Young Pascal's mathematical achievements were astounding. At the age of sixteen, he wrote his major mathematical work, *Essai pour les coniques (Essay on Conic Sections)*, which was published the following year. In her later biography of her brother, one of his sisters reported that people thought what Blaise had done was "so great an intellectual achievement that people said that they had seen nothing as mighty since the time of Archimedes" in ancient times.

In 1642, at age nineteen, Pascal invented the calculating machine. After watching the arduous way in which his father added up the fiscal accounts of the French government, Pascal figured out the mathematical principles needed to construct a machine that would do the calculations. This machine (described in two of the selections in this book) was one of the first genuine achievements of the "new science" that was developing in the seventeenth century. It was basically the same as the calculating devices used up until the development of the computer, and is, in fact, considered the grandfather of the computer, since the latter is actually a much extended use of Pascal's principles, aided by power sources unknown until three centuries later. In recognition of this, one of the better-known computer languages is called PASCAL.

As indicated by the writings included in this book from 1645 and 1652, Pascal had inordinate difficulties in putting his calculating machine theory into practice. At that time the gulf between mathematical theory and physical capability was very great, the state of metallurgical work not being up to the theory. It was extremely difficult to make the appropriate gears and to keep them in alignment as the machine was moved from place to place. Pascal was so proud of his mathematical machine that he offered a model to Queen Christina of Sweden, who was developing a great center of learning at her court in Stockholm.

Pascal continued his mathematical researches throughout the remainder of his life. He made very important contributions to the theory of probability, to number theory, and to geometry. And he helped prepare the way for the discovery of calculus by Gottfried Wilhelm von Leibniz and Isaac Newton shortly after him.

After his religious conversion in 1654 (discussed below), Pascal did little serious mathematical work. He kept up his correspondence with some of the leading mathematicians of the time, however, and he reported that as the result of a night of insomnia in 1658, he worked out an important analysis of the nature of the cycloid curve. During his religious period, he wrote his basic work on the philosophy of mathematics, *L'Esprit géométrique (The Geometrical Mind)*, about 1651–1658 (see pp. 173–194 of this volume). It was probably intended as the preface to a textbook in geometry, which was to be used at the Jansenist school at the abbey of Port-Royal.

Also, in the *Pensées*, we see that important mathematical ideas are interwoven in Pascal's philosophical and theological reflections.

PASCAL AS PHYSICIST

Pascal was interested in both experimental physics and in applying the power of mathematics to explaining physical events. In 1646 he learned of the experiment performed with a barometer in Italy by physicist Evangelista Torricelli. This involved setting an inverted tube filled with mercury in a bowl that was also filled with mercury. The mercury in the inverted tube did not all flow into the bowl; some of it remained in the inverted tube. Pascal repeated the experiment and confirmed the result. Then he asked, what could account for some of the mercury remaining suspended in the tube? And what could be the content of the space in the tube above the column of mercury?

Several scientists of the time believed that the atmosphere must be responsible for keeping some of the mercury in the tube. But they were unable to offer any proof. They also were all in agreement that the space in the tube above the column of mercury must contain some type of rarified and invisible matter, since nature, according to the Aristotelian tradition, abhors a vacuum. Pascal, in 1647, published his *Experiences nouvelles touchant le vide (New Experiments Concerning the Vacuum)*, parts of which are included in this book; see pp. 33–41). He described a series of experiments he had performed using tubes of different shapes and sizes, and various kinds of liquids. From the experiments he was able to set forth the basic laws about atmospheric pressure, showing how much water and how much mercury could be supported by the pressure of the air surrounding the tubes. He also showed how large a siphon had to be for it to be able to function. And he presented his reasons for believing that a genuine vacuum not only could, but did, exist on top of the column of mercury or other fluid supported in a barometric device.

Pascal's results and his conclusions were genuinely novel, and in some ways disturbing, at the time. He was challenged by one Father Estienne Noël, the rector of the Collège de Clermont in Paris. Father Noël reiterated the accepted view that nature abhors a vacuum. Since that was so, the space that Pascal claimed to be empty on top of the column of fluid in the barometer must in fact contain some special kind of matter. Pascal's reply (see pp. 49–55 in this book) presents what he saw as the conditions for judging scientific hypotheses. It is perhaps the clearest statement in the seventeenth century on scientific method. Pascal insisted that confirming an hypothesis — showing that all the known facts fit with it, or follow from it — does not show that the hypothesis is true. It only shows that the hypothesis is possible or even probable. On the other hand, one could show that an hypothesis is false if one could derive a contradiction from it, or if a conclusion from the hypothesis was counter to known facts. If it leads, Pascal asserted, "to something contrary to a single one of the phenomena, that suffices to establish its falsity." (Pascal's view here is close to that of Sir Karl Popper in his principle of falsification.) Having set forth his criterion for disproving hypotheses, Pascal then went on to show that the hypothesis of Aristotle and Father Noël (that nature abhors a vacuum) is false because conclusions that are contrary to experimentally established facts follow from it. Pascal's theory that there is a genuine vacuum above the mercury column fit the facts, and hence is a possible or probable explanation of the phenomenon observed in the barometer.

Shortly after writing his unfinished piece on the vacuum, Pascal's brother-in-law performed the famous experiment of taking a barometer up a mountain (1648). He carried an inverted tube of mercury in a bowl of mercury up Le Puy-de-Dôme, outside of Clérmont-Ferrand. By measuring the height of the column of mercury from start to finish, it was shown that the level of the mercury in the tube decreased as one climbed higher. Pascal checked the results at different heights by carrying the materials up church towers in Paris. On the basis of these experiments, he announced that nature does not abhor a vacuum. The effects attributed to the alleged abhorrence were, in fact, due to atmospheric pressure. Thus Pascal was able to combine ingeniously designed experiments with a careful analysis of possible explanatory hypotheses in order to reach one of the significant achievements of seventeenth-century science — the development of a mechanical explanation of air pressure and gas pressure in general — and to eliminate some of nature's alleged occult qualities and alleged personality. Only the preface of Pascal's *Treatise on the Vacuum* survives, and is included in this volume (see pp. 62–66).

In his preface, as well as scattered through his other scientific and religious writings, Pascal defended the "new science," both in terms of its theory of what nature is like and in terms of the method to be used in learning about nature. Although it is often claimed that there was an opposition between science and religion, even a warfare between them, Pascal, both as a scientist and as a devout believer, saw the experimental science of the seventeenth century as the most fruitful way of finding out about nature. He maintained that in the study of nature one should not allow respect for authority to take precedence over either reasoning or experience. In understanding God and His relationship to humankind, the reverse was the case; traditional authority took precedence over new reasoning and new data.

In his scientific and philosophical views, Pascal accepted a type of fundamental skepticism about what we could know about the world. Nature, which he thought of as always active, could not be known directly. In the *Pensées* as well as in scientific writings, he emphasized the many reasons why we could never penetrate to knowing the secrets of nature, reasons that involved our limitations and the nature of nature. As a result, said Pascal, we can study nature only through its effects. But we cannot know all of these effects since they are endless; also they are infinitely large and infinitely small. We can, however, through experience and reasoning about experience, discover in the course of time more and more about the natural world. And we can codify this in terms of laws of nature. As we collect more and more data, we should reasonably expect that many of the previously accepted views and hypotheses about nature are no longer tenable and must be replaced by newer ones. At any given time in the world's history, our interpretation of nature is limited by how much experience we have collected. The truths about nature itself are unchanging. But our understanding of these truths is a part of the development of human history, and it varies as our historical development changes. Hence the history of science as a human enterprise is different from science, a body of fixed truths about nature. The latter is what we are seeking but only approximating at each stage in our history. In view of this, there is no particular reason for preferring ancient scientific views, or thinkers like Aristotle, to the views of modern scientists, based on more recent investigations. Hence Pascal was on the side of the scientific innovators and was one of the most important of them at the time. He defended Copernicus and Galileo for their scientific views, and followed in their footsteps in seeking mechanical and mathematical accounts of how nature behaved.

RELIGIOUS VIEWS

Although Pascal's achievements in mathematics and physics are highly significant, his religious and philosophical views have had even greater influence. His writings on these subjects grew out of his activities in the Jansenist movement, with which he became involved in 1646 after his father was injured. Two Jansenists took care of his father, and this led the whole family, including Blaise, to become interested and concerned with the group.

Jansenism was a reform movement within Catholicism. It has had an important influence both openly and clandestinely in European religious affairs, especially in France. The movement gets its name from Cornelius Jansen (1585–1638), who was the bishop of Ypres. Strongly attracted to the views of St. Augustine, especially concerning the all-important role of divine grace in human salvation, Jansen opposed what he saw as a lax moral view being espoused by the Jesuits to the effect that human beings could take steps that aided in their salvation. Jansen's views were published in his book, *De Augustinus*, in 1641 by one of the leading French Jansenists, Antoine Arnauld (1612–1694). This set off a controversy that led to the condemnation of certain of Jansen's views, and finally to the suppression of the movement, which went underground in France, but survives today in The Netherlands and Germany.

The abbey of Port-Royal, which had been spiritually and morally reformed by Arnauld's sister, Angelique, from its dissolute condition early in the century, became the center of Jansenist activities. People moved there to concentrate on their spiritual lives. The leading Jansenist in France, Jean Vergier Du Hauranne, the abbé de Saint-Cyran (1591–1643), was its spiritual adviser. The Pascals went to the abbey to hear sermons, and Blaise became interested in the Jansenist theology.

After his father's death in 1651, Pascal's sister Jacqueline decided to become a nun at Port-Royal in spite of her brother's opposition. Possibly as a reaction to his father's death, Pascal turned away from religious activities from 1652 to 1654 and became a *libertin*, associating with free-thinkers, gamblers, and womanizers. Nonetheless he frequently visited his sister at Port-Royal and told her that he had great contempt for the ordinary world and the people in it, but that he did not feel drawn to God. Then, on the night of November 23, 1654, when crossing a Paris bridge in a carriage during a storm, he had an overwhelming religious experience. Immediately afterward he wrote down what he recalled of it, in the statement called the *Memorial* (pp. 69–70). He carried it sewn into his clothes from then on, and it was found shortly after his death. In the statement Pascal indicated that he felt himself in the presence of the god of Abraham, Isaac, and Jacob, and not the god of the philosophers. He determined to devote the rest of his life primarily to religious activities and to remain forever in the presence of the living God.

At the beginning of 1655, Pascal went on a retreat to Port-Royal-des-Champs, one of the two Port-Royal convents. There he met the Jansenist theologian, Isaac Le Maistre de Saci, and had a discussion with him, which was published as *Entretien avec M. de Saci* (see pp. 79–89). Pascal presents what he found positive and negative in the views of Montaigne and Epictetus. In the course of the discussion, one finds that many of the basic themes of Pascal's central religious work were already at least partially worked out.

From this time onward, Pascal was a frequent visitor at one or the other of the Port-Royal convents and was in contact with Arnauld and others about the challenges being made to Jansenism, either in terms of what was in Jansen's book or what Arnauld had written in defense of Jansenism. As Arnauld's defense was leading to an attempt in early 1656 to revoke his doctoral degree, Pascal, in cooperation with Arnauld and Pierre Nicole, began a series of defenses, the *Lettres provinciales (Provincial Letters)*. Eighteen of these were published (1656–1657), and notes for a nineteenth exist. The letters try both to defend the Jansenists from persecution and to challenge the moral theory of their chief opponents, the Jesuits.

The *Provincial Letters* were published secretly, unsigned, one at a time. They are a series of satirical polemics with Pascal as the main author, although Arnauld and Nicole apparently supplied him with most of the documentation, which helped to make the satire so forceful and comical. The work begins as a series of letters to Pascal's brother-in-law who lived in the country (the provincial). The first three were intended as a last-minute effort to head off the condemnation of Arnauld by the theology professors of the Sorbonne. In spite of the brilliance of these letters, Arnauld was condemned on January 31, 1656, and his title of "doctor" was taken away. The fourth to the tenth letters present a counterattack, challenging the moral theory of the Jesuits by showing the apparent immoral and ludicrous results of their casuistry.

The eleventh to the sixteenth letters were no longer addressed to the "provincial," but to the Jesuit fathers, attacking their views and political activities, and also defending their anonymous author against his opponents. This indicates that the *Letters* had an immediate effect. The last two were addressed to the king's confessor, and they amount to a plea in favor of the Jansenists at Port-Royal. Pascal made some notes for another letter, but apparently gave it up because it became obvious that the king and his advisers had sided against the Jansenists. The *Letters* were published as a collection in 1657 and have become a classic example of philosophical and theological argument by satire. (Voltaire considered them as great as the satires of Molière.)

The Jansenists lost their battle for survival as a legitimately accepted Catholic group during 1656–1657. Soon after, they were forced to sign a statement abjuring Jansen's views. Port-Royal was destroyed, and those who would not give in, such as Arnauld, fled from France. Others continued their views underground and reappeared in French history around the time of the French Revolution, which began in 1789. (Important revolutionary figures such as the abbé Henri Grégoire were Jansenists.) In exile they kept up what they called the Old Catholic Church, which merged in the 1870s with those who would not accept the doctrine of papal infallibility. Only after Vatican II, the ecumenical council of 1962–1965, convened by John XXIII, was a truce worked out with the Church of Rome. The Jensenists, who had been very powerful in mid-seventeenth-century France, went into a long eclipse, occasionally reappearing on the scene. The *Provincial Letters*, a classic of French literature, has made the Jansenists a continuous part of the literary world. Pascal, in defending them, left a brilliant and thought-provoking work on the basis of morality and Christian theology. (Substantial selections from the *Letters* are included in this volume.)

Besides the *Provincial Letters*, Pascal worked on a variety of subjects after becoming immersed in the Jansenist movement, mostly religious and philosophical, but also including mathematical work. In 1659 he became seriously ill and wrote relatively little thereafter. Prior to his illness he composed his *Écrits sur la Grâce (Writings on Grace)*, *De l'Esprit géométrique (On the Mathematical Mind)*, *De l'art de persuader (On the Art of Persuasion)*, the work on the cycloid curve, and portions of his *Apologie de la religion chrétienne*, the unfinished work that was published after his death as the *Pensées*.

Pascal had a short period of improvement in his health in 1660 and wrote his three discourses on the condition of the great (see pp. 74–78), dealing with role of accidental fortune in human affairs. The next year, during the final Jansenist struggle with their enemies, his sister Jacqueline died, apparently from a heart attack resulting from the bitterness and hopelessness of the contest. Pascal then wrote his last work on Jansenism, urging the Jansenists not to yield and not to sign the *formulaire*, the statement denying their principles. After this, Pascal withdrew from any further controversial activities.

One of the last things Pascal did in his short life was to propose another invention, that of an omnibus, a large horse-driven carriage that would carry many people from one point in Paris to another for a fixed fare. This would have been the first busline in European history. (Unfortunately it did not come to fruition, since the people who could pay the fare had their own carriages and the others just walked. The first actual functioning busline came into being in London at the beginning of the nineteenth century.) One of Pascal's reasons for proposing the introduction of the bus was that he wanted to earn some money in order to give it away to the poor. In his final years, Pascal gave away practically all of his possessions. In his will he bequeathed portions of the anticipated earnings from the bus to different hospitals.

PHILOSOPHY OF MATHEMATICS AND SCIENCE

When Pascal died, two very important unpublished works were found — the *Pensées* and *De l'Esprit géométrique*. The first (discussed later) was published in 1670, eight years after his death. The second became known from a copy in the possession of Pascal's nephew. Two short extracts were published in 1728. Condorcet, in his important edition of Pascal of 1776, published half of the text, and the rest, except for a few lines, was published three years later. The complete text was finally published in 1844. It is believed that *De l'Esprit géométrique* was probably intended as a preface to a geometry text that Pascal was asked by Arnauld to prepare for the students at the school at Port-Royal. It was not so used, and Arnauld wrote his own preface. The accompanying *De l'Art de persuader* was published in full in 1728. Themes from these two works run through the *Pensées*, but it is only in these relatively short presentations that Pascal set forth his theory about the nature of mathematical and scientific evidence.

The ideal method for discovering truths, said Pascal, would be one in which we were able to define all of the terms used and then were able to demonstrate all propositions from truths that had already been established. Unfortunately, this is not possible because the basic terms that are to be defined presuppose others basic terms, if we are to understand the meaning of the former. It is also the case that basic or fundamental propositions that we are attempting to prove presuppose other basic propositions. And so, we are not able to arrive at first, or primitive, terms and principles. In any mathematical or logicial system, we can start only with such primitive terms that require no additional definitions to make themselves clear but that are not ultimately defined. Similarly, we can start only with principles that we find so clear that nothing clearer can help us in establishing them. Thus, Pascal pointed out, human beings by their own means cannot reach the ideal, and hence are powerless to establish a science in "an absolutely perfected manner."

If we are so limited, the best procedure that humankind can find is the geometrical one. In describing what this is, Pascal set forth the definition of an axiomatic system and its limitations for establishing truths. In this, Pascal, perhaps more than Leibniz, saw what twentieth-century logicians were going to develop. Essentially, Pascal contended, what we can start with are those terms that are clear and are known to everyone. In practice they do not require definition, since everyone knows what they mean. Then, other terms can be defined by using them. Similarly, propositions known by everyone can be assumed, and other propositions can be derived from them. Developing such an axiomatic system would not allow us to claim that we know by natural reason, for instance, that Euclidean geometry is true, since we possess neither the ultimate definitions of the basic terms nor evidence that the premises are true. What we can say, according to Pascal's analysis, is that the geometrical method provides the greatest certitude that human beings are able to attain by their limited capabilities. They can put some of their information into an axiom system, with primitive terms and basic premises or axioms. They can derive propositions in a logical fashion from these. The set of such propositions are true if the axioms are true, *but* human beings cannot tell if this is the case.

The Art of Persuasion complements the study of geometrical method by offering an explanation of how people, in fact, happen to be convinced by first principles, and by the conclusions that are drawn from them. Pascal contended here, and developed the theme in the *Pensées*, that in all our reasonings we are led to a kind of total skepticism, since we cannot by reason and evidence establish the truth of our first principles. Putting them in axiom systems shows what conclusions we can draw from them, but it does not throw any light on their truth. And treating them as scientific hypotheses can, at best, show that they are plausible and have not yet been refuted. We have to turn elsewhere if we are to limit or avoid the constant drift toward skepticism. But where? For Pascal, the answer has to be outside the rational world, by recognizing that we gain our principles, and our assurance of them, by instinct, and as he pressed in the *Pensées*, by revelation. It is through reliance on our feelings and our religious life that we find our certainty.

THE PENSÉES

The most famous and most complete statement of Pascal's philosophy and theology appears in the *Pensées*, his unfinished work. In 1659 Pascal gave a lecture at Port-Royal in which he described the major work he was writing, an apology for the Christian religion. Descriptions of the lecture indicate that Pascal had a fairly well-organized conception of how he would present it. When he died three years later, bundles of notes of various sizes were found pinned together in groups. A copy was made of all of the materials, in the exact form in which they existed at the time. The Port-Royalists, especially Arnauld, felt that only those portions of notes that seemed to them to be complete should be published. They also felt that the notes should be put in what the editors thought to be a coherent order.

Although the work was an immediate success and quickly became one of the classics of philosophy and religion and a masterpiece of French literature, the various editors involved for the next century and a half thought that the *Pensées* was an unfinished collection of notes left in a disordered state because the author died before he could put the material together. Therefore each editor felt free to put them together as he saw fit. And as a result, the work kept being re-edited in differing orders. A leading French historian of philosophy, Victor Cousin, in 1842 pointed out that no complete edition of Pascal's greatest work existed and that each edition had been embellished or re-ordered as the editor desired, without regard for Pascal's intention. Cousin urged that a definitive edition be prepared, based on the manuscripts in the Bibliothèque Nationale, which included the actual notes in Pascal's hand pasted on large sheets of paper. New editions were prepared, including the one by Léon Brunschvicg, which became the standard text until World War II. In the 1930s this text was challenged by Zacharie Tourneur on the grounds that it still was not Pascal's intended order because the pasting had been done after he was dead.

During the Nazi occupation of Paris, a paper manufacturer, Louis Lafuma, hid out in the manuscript room of the Bibliothèque Nationale from 1940 to 1944. He studied the manuscripts of Pascal there and realized that a nephew of Pascal had copied the notes as they existed at the time of his uncle's death, and that Arnauld and others had made the pasteups. Examining the paper, the glue, the sand, Lafuma established an order of composition. He compared it with the projected description of the work in

Pascal's lecture. After the war Lafuma edited a radically new text in terms of the order of the fragments, and in terms of which ones had been finished and put in categories by Pascal and which ones remained unclassified at his death. Because of the detailed evidence Lafuma had amassed during his enforced study (Hitler's unwitting contribution to Pascal scholarship), his radically revised text was soon accepted by Pascal scholars and became the official text used in the French school system.

Further revision to the *Pensées* has continued, chiefly by Jean Mesnard, in revising the date of Pascal's lecture and in interpreting it relative to the fragments. As Mesnard observed, "The manuscripts of the *Pensées* have not yet given up all their secrets." The dating of the fragments is not finished, and there is still the problem of putting together a completely scholarly edition, as well as a clear and readable one. "The most learned edition," Mesnard said, "can and should be at the same time the most perfectly elegant." He has offered his version, and no doubt other scholars will offer different versions.

The *Pensées* is thus one of the very few classics that keeps being re-edited, and revised. The basic content, however, remains the same. Pascal wrote out 'thoughts,' which vary from a few words, a sentence, a paragraph, to essays. Some seem much more complete and polished than others. He had organized some of the material, and other parts appear almost ready to be incorporated into this organization. The order of presentation makes some difference in terms of continuous argument, or stress on one theme or another. However, the thrust remains the same, and Pascal's analysis of the human situation comes through, as well as his presentation of the religious solution and his "defense" of it.

The *Pensées* in Lafuma's order (which is followed in the selections in this book) begins with a series of sections that set forth the human condition by exhibiting the ways people deal with and react to the ordinary world. This is followed by sections focusing on two basic philosophical concerns — how to find true knowledge and how to find genuine happiness. Pascal developed his case by using paradoxical statements, by using most forceful imagery, and by probing various claims, all gradually forcing the reader to recognize the human situation — an inability to find a satisfactory solution by human means, and the need to turn to a religious solution, even though no rational justification can be given for this. Then Pascal turned to the pedantic task of making his own religion, Christianity, plausible and preferable to paganism, Mohammedanism, and Judaism.

The *Pensées* begins by trying to make people uneasy about their lives by showing that the values, the goals that they seek are not worthwhile and will not make them happy. Part of Pascal's case is built on the assumption that people have some idea of what it would be like to be *really* happy. With this murky, shadowy ideal, all ordinary human attempts to attain happiness appear inadequate. No matter what we do, we end up in a miserable state.

Examining why we cannot find what we seek brings us to consider the human knowledge situation. Pascal, raised on reading Michel de Montaigne and Descartes, developed in poignant and probing fashion questions about the human search after truth that lead to complete skepticism. Questions about the reliability of our sensory and rational faculties, about the adequacy of our rational and/or scientific systems all press toward the realization that human beings cannot find any ultimate and certain basis for knowledge of anything based on their own resources. Using and extending the extreme skepticism introduced by Descartes about whether all life is a dream, whether all of our knowledge is the effect of some universal delusion, Pascal sought to make people realize that rationally they are reduced to extreme skepticism (pyrrhonism). But they are saved from this, not by Cartesian rationalism but by instinct and by revelation.

Nature provides us with principles, which we accept by instinct or intuition, not by evidence. "The heart has its reasons that the reason knows not of." These principles, which are felt or intuited rather than established, may or may not be true. In one of the central *pensées* (Lafuma 131, Brunschvicg 434), Pascal posed the problem in its most extreme form. The reliability of any principles depended upon whether we and our faculties are the result of actions of a chance universe, of some kind of systematic delusion, or the result of divine revelation. In the first case, we would never be able to determine if the principles we believed are true or false; in the second case, we could be systematically deluded in any attempt to find any certainty; but in the last case, we would presumably be aware of what is true. Since we use our faculties in the investigation of this fundamental matter, our results are affected by the character of our faculties. The claim by Descartes that we can rely on our faculties because God, who has given them to us, is no deceiver is presented as a result of using our questionable faculties. And the merits of any attempt to offer reasons justifying reliance on our faculties depend upon the status of our faculties. (Pascal, in developing this theme, was putting forth what David Hume later called "an incurable skepticism," which, if it could ever be entertained, could not be overcome).

As one pursued this skeptical undermining of our faculties, rational and otherwise, Pascal pointed out, as Hume also later did, that what saves us from such excessive skepticism is that nature will not let us sustain it and forces us to believe various things. This natural blockage of complete skepticism does not answer the skeptical problems. It just prevents us from going insane about them. And as one ponders our inability to justify any of our knowledge and our inability to become total skeptics, we see that "Nature confounds the Pyrrhonists and reason confounds the dogmatists." When one realizes this, one should abandon the attempt to find an answer by reason, by nature, and "learn that man infinitely surpasses man, and hear from your master your real state which you do not know." "Hear God!"

At this point, for Pascal the problem of knowledge becomes a religious one. By silencing the rational quest for knowing, by submitting to God's will and accepting divine revelation, certain knowledge is acquired. In contrast, neither mathematics nor science can yield such knowledge, since these studies rest on basic principles known through instinct or intuition, but not provable by reason. Skeptical analysis shows that we cannot ascertain if these principles are reliable and if what we derive from them has any probative merit. This is the predicament of human beings in trying to gain any certainty. In realizing fully the predicament, we should be prepared to submit ourselves to accept a religious solution to our quest for indubitable knowledge.

If this is the state of affairs, Pascal then showed in a wonderful variety of ways how people avoid recognizing, or coming to grips with, their fundamental epistemological problems, through diversion or through useless philosophy. People engage in all sorts of trivial pursuits to avoid facing up to their true condition. They engage in all sorts of mental gymnastics to cover up their basic ignorance of what is going on. They construct a god of the philosophers to solve their problems, like Descartes, a god who has no relation to what is going on in their lives.

The human situation, Pascal kept pointing out, is that we are suspended between the infinity of time before us and after us. We are also suspended between the infinitely small and the infinite, the divine. In our brief existence in this world, we can at our peril ignore understanding our situation, and can divert ourselves by card playing, dancing, dueling, and the like. But, as we get any insight into our situation, we may realize that it may make a difference, an enormous difference, an eternal difference, in our situation if we find an answer to why we are here and what we can do about it. The difference is that one answer, if we can accept it and if it is true, can bring us eternal happiness. By our own reason, we can only find the inadequacy of worldly answers.

In the famous *pensée* of the wager (418 and 233), we are presented with the possible answers, namely that God exists or God does not exist. By our own lights we cannot tell which answer is true, but we can see that there could be an immense difference for us if one answer were true and not the other. If God does exist, this could affect both our present lives and any possible future lives. If God does not exist, we are stuck with our present state of affairs, what Pascal called "the misery of man without God." If we look at the matter as a gambler and consider the probabilities involved, Pascal contended that the prudent person would bet on the religious possibility. If God does not exist, there are no great or momentous consequences of betting either that God exists or He does not. All that could be involved for the religious bettor in a purely natural world is that one might engage in certain kinds of activities, like going to church or praying, whereas the irreligious bettor might be playing golf or lying comfortably on his or her couch watching a video film. "From the aspect of eternity," as a Pascal contemporary, Spinoza, might say, neither set of activities is better or worse. One set might give some people more momentary pleasure than the other, or vice versa.

But if God does exist, then living as a nonbeliever might be dangerous now and forever, and living as a believer might be rewarding now and forever. (This, of course, presumes that the deity cares what we do and will respond favorably or unfavorably.) Even if the odds on the theistic alternative were miniscule, and the odds on the naturalistic, or atheistic, alternative were very great, could one take a chance on the nontheistic since there is so much to gain or lose? And, Pascal insisted, one has to choose which alternative one is betting on. Not betting is itself a decision of momentous consequences, since it precludes one from possible eternal rewards. So, what is involved here is what William James later on, in "The Will to Believe" (which is in part an examination of Pascal's Wager), called a forced option — one cannot avoid taking a stand and opting for one belief or the other. Posed this way, Pascal contended that the prudent person would want to be religious. But being religious is not the result of gambling. The "wager" just makes one realize the merits of the religious alternative.

Some critics have tried to show that the case is not as neat as Pascal made it. The religious alternative is not just one possibility, but it is an unlimited number of theistic hypotheses, many incompatible with one another. The Jewish, Christian, Muslim, Hindu, Buddhist, animist, and other religious views present different kinds of God or gods, some of whom, we are told, detest infidels, believers in false gods (that is, the gods of other religions). And one can construct possible religious views that conflict with any known ones. Then how is the bettor supposed to tell what religious alternative to wager on?

Further, the particular religious view that Pascal posed as the one we had to bet for or against presents us with a God who would punish nonbelievers, even if their nonbelief was due to forces beyond their control (their unredeemed natural state). This deity would punish honest doubters or nonbelievers for their sin of proportioning their belief to the evidence available. Why should we accept that we have to bet for or against the existence of such a God, instead of one who rewards people for their honesty, integrity, and moral character? (These and many more criticisms are developed in the writings of Antony Flew and J.L. Mackie, listed in the bibliography.)

For Pascal, accepting the "wager" does not make one religious, but it should make one want to be a believer. Becoming religious is something one can desire and hope for. One can prepare for it through curbing one's passions, restraining one's pride and one's desire to know everything, and hoping for guidance. But as Pascal argued in the *Provincial Letters*, the grace that can make a person a true believer can come only from God. And when God gives such grace, human beings will find their answers and will see that human means such as philosophizing and doing science and mathematics are futile in arriving at ultimate answers.

For many readers the most impressive parts of the *Pensées* are those that deal with the human predicament, our inability to find the answers we seek, our desire to find these answers, and the realization of our weaknesses in this search. Pascal, however, had found his answers, starting from the event recorded in the *Memorial*. Writing from this perspective, he could then expatiate at length on the content of the religious answers he had found. And a large part of the *Pensées* is a statement of his Christian beliefs, and an attempt to show that these beliefs are more reasonable or plausible than beliefs of other religions. This is the apology for the Christian religion that was his grand plan in writing the *Pensées*. Using historical data, interpretations of scriptural passages, claims about miracles, evidences of the fulfillment of prophecies offered in scripture, and moral contentions, Pascal asserted that the Bible is the statement of true religious knowledge. Studying the predictions about the messiah in the Old Testament should make one see that these predictions were fulfilled in the coming of Jesus Christ. Using a host of materials from the then recently rediscovered work of Raymund Martin, *Pugio fidei*, written at the end of the thirteenth century to convert the Jews, Pascal tried to show the reasonableness of accepting Christianity as the fulfillment of Judaism. Using other materials, he tried to show how unreasonable it would be to accept Mohammed as a true prophet. As a man of his times, Pascal also tried to show that one should not be impressed by the claims of Chinese religions, which were just being reported in Europe by the missionaries. The great variety of apologetic materials, Pascal admitted, were not conclusive, but should be persuasive to an unprejudiced person not blinded by sin or ignorance. In *pensée* 835 (564), Pascal pointed out that the prophecies, miracles, and other evidences are not "absolutely convincing," but at the same time "it cannot be said that it would be unreasonable to believe them." Those who are unconvinced are so not by reason, but by lust or malice. And those who are convinced are so by grace. And, if they have received grace, then presumably Pascal's Christianity will not only sound plausible but will be a statement of what one has found through one's own religious experience.

CONCLUSION

Pascal was obviously one of the most brilliant figures of the seventeenth century and one of the greatest writers of the French language. His achievements in mathematics, science, philosophy, and theology are remarkable, especially coming from one person in such a brief career. However, when one examines them, one must admit that his views overall hardly constitute an organized intellectual system. Most of his works are fragmentary. Many are unfinished and represent exciting, original thoughts at specific points in his several different careers, as mathematician, scientist, philosopher, theologian, and Christian apologist. One finds, especially in the *Pensées*, attempts to put some continuity into the different stages of his development. But by that time his basic orientation was as an apologist and expositor of Christianity. Philosophy from that vantage point led only to complete skepticism. Mathematics and physics were inadequate ways of trying to find ultimate truth and ultimate happiness. Pascal's total immersion in religion made him end up as basically antiphilosophical and antirational, although he was still brilliant in using rational, philosophical arguments to demolish opponents like the Jesuits and to develop the skeptical implications involved in the human search after truth.

In the development of modern philosophy, Pascal does not have a fixed place. He was neither an empiricist nor a rationalist. He was a reader of Montaigne and Descartes, and strongly developed some of their skeptical themes. He influenced the skeptics who followed after him. Both Pierre Bayle and Hume read him and seem concerned to comment on his views about the limits of human knowledge and its relation to religious belief. If the history of modern philosophy were written in terms of the development of skeptical ideas, Pascal would have an important place, as a successor of Montaigne and Descartes and as a precursor of Bayle and Hume.

However, since Pascal's most serious concern was with religious belief and with the human predicament of facing an unintelligible universe, he has had the greatest impact on religious thinkers since his time. Voltaire seriously criticized Pascal in his *Philosophical Letters*, chiefly because of Pascal's dismal view of the human situation, his theology, and his religious program. Nonetheless, Voltaire greatly admired Pascal's eloquence, and found his picture of human finitude exciting. It is probably because of Voltaire's interest that the last of the *philosophes*, Condorcet, edited Pascal shortly before the French Revolution, in part to show that his contribution extended beyond just his religious views.

There are also significant similarities between Pascal and the Danish philosopher Sören Kierkegaard. Both of them have inspired modern existentialist writers, religious and irreligious.

Finally, for anyone who uses a computer and has any idea of the theory on which it is based, Pascal is still a vital force in our scientific world. After much neglect, his scientific and philosophical works are beginning to be studied again in their own right. It is being realized that in bits and pieces Pascal came as close as any seventeenth-century thinker to some of the central issues in the twentieth-century philosophy of science and mathematics.

His many-sided genius and his amazing command of the French language still make Pascal one of the most inspiring, exciting, and thought-provoking of writers. Although he is unsystematic in the formal sense, there are themes and threads from his work that can clearly be observed in the development of the modern mind. He has helped to emphasize the dark side of scientific optimism and the bright side of religion based on faith. In the present world, shorn of so many hopeful illusions, Pascal may seem more in tune with the times than many of the other great thinkers of the last three hundred years.

Unless otherwise indicated, all texts were translated by Richard H. Popkin.

I
Scientific Writings

Letter to the Chancellor
about the Adding Machine

Dedicatory Letter to My Lord, the Chancellor, on the Subject of the Machine invented by B.P, Esquire, for doing all sorts of arithmetical operations by a regulated motion without pen or counters, with a necessary advice for those who will have the curiosity to see the aforementioned machine and to make use of it. (1645)

TO MY LORD CHANCELLOR,
MY LORD,

If the public receives any benefit from the invention that I have found for performing all sorts of rules of arithmetic by a manner as new as it is convenient, they will be more obliged to Your Highness for it than to my petty efforts, since I can only boast of having conceived of it, and since it absolutely owes its birth to the honor of your commands. The length and difficulties of the ordinary means which are employed having made me think of some more rapid and easier help to aid me with the large calculations to which I have been engaged for several years in various matters which are involved in some of the tasks with which it pleased you to honor my father in order to serve his Majesty in Upper Normandy, I employed in this research all the knowledge that my bent and the work in my early studies had led me to acquire in mathematics; and after a profound meditation, I realized that this help was not impossible to find. Knowledge of geometry, physics, and mechanics furnished me the design for it, and assured me that the employment of it would be infallible if some workmen could make the instrument whose model I had conceived. But it was at this point that I encountered difficulties as great as those that I wanted to avoid, and to which I was seeking a remedy. Not having the skill to manipulate metal and the hammer like the pen and the compass, and the artisans having more knowledge of the practice of their art than of the science on which it is based, I saw myself reduced to giving up my whole undertaking, which only brought me much weariness without any real success. But, My Lord, Your Highness, having kept up my courage, which was giving up, and having done me the favor of speaking of the simple sketch that my friends had presented to you in terms which made me see it completely otherwise than it had previously appeared to me, with the new strength that your praises gave me, I made new efforts, and suspending all other activities, I no longer thought of anything except the construction of that machine, that I have been so bold, My Lord, to present to you, after having put it in condition to do, with it alone and without any mental effort, the operations of all the parts of arithmetic, as I had intended. It is then to you, My Lord, that I owe this slight achievement, since it is you who made me do it, and it is to you also that I look for an honorable protection of it. Inventions which are not known always have more censors than approvers: those who have found them are blamed, because people do not have genuine understanding of them; and due to an unjust prejudice, the difficulty that people imagine about extraordinary things, makes it the case that instead of considering them in order to appreciate them, they claim that they are impossible in order to reject them thereafter as irrelevant. Besides, My Lord, I well expect that among so many learned men who have penetrated into the ultimate secrets of mathematics, it may be the case that there will be found some who will at first consider my achievement as bold, seeing that as young as I am, and having so little strength, I have dared to attempt a new path in a field bristling with thorns, and without having any guide to show me the way. But I prefer that they accuse me, and even condemn me, if they can show that I have not accomplished exactly what I had promised; and I only ask them the favor of examining what I have done, and not that of approving it without knowing it. Also, My Lord, I can tell Your Highness that I have already the satisfaction of seeing my little work, not only authorized with the approbation of some of the leaders in this true science, which by a very special preference, has the advantage of teaching nothing that it does not demonstrate, but is yet honored by their esteem and their recommendation; and that even the one amongst them, who most of the others admire all the time and accept his achievements, has not judged unworthy to take this trouble, in the midst of his important duties, to teach both the arrangement and employment of it [the arithmetical machine] to those who have some design to make use of it. These are really, My Lord, the great rewards for the time I have spent, and for the expense that I have gone to in order to put the thing into the condition in which I have presented it to you. But allow me to flatter my vanity to the point of saying that they would not completely satisfy me, had I not received a much more important and delightful one (a reward) from your Highness. In fact, My Lord, when I contemplate that this same voice, which every day pronounces oracles on the throne of justice, has deigned to give praise to the initial effort of a twenty-year-old man, that you have judged it worthy to be more than once the subject of your conversation, and to have placed it in your cabinet among so many other rare and precious things with which it is filled, I am overwhelmed with glory, and I do not find the words to show my gratitude to Your Highness, and my joy to everybody. To this impotence in which the excess of your kindness has placed me, I shall content myself by revering it by my silence; and the entire family whose name I bear, being interested as well as myself by this kindness and by various other favors, in making vows all the time for your prosperity, we do it sincerely and so ardently and continually, that no one can boast of being more attached than we to your service, nor of bearing more genuinely than I the title, My Lord, of your most humble and obedient servant.

B. Pascal

Necessary Advice about the Adding Machine

Necessary advice for those who will have the curiosity to see the arithmetical machine and to make use of it. (1645)

Dear reader, this notice will serve to make known to you that I am putting before the public a small machine invented by me, by means of which alone, you can, with no difficulty whatsoever, do all the operations of arithmetic, and relieve yourself of the work which has often tired your mind, when you have had to do it by counters or by pen; I can, without being presumptuous, hope that it will not displease you, since My Lord, the Chancellor, has honored it with his esteem, and in Paris, those who are best versed in mathematics have not judged it unworthy of their approval. Nevertheless, in order not to seem negligent about acquiring yours also, I believed myself to be obliged to enlighten you about all the difficulties that I regarded as capable of shocking your intelligence should you take the trouble to consider it.

I do not doubt that after having seen it, it will immediately occur to your mind that I ought to have explained in writing both its construction and its use, and that, to make such discourse intelligible, I was also obliged, following the method of the geometers, to show by diagrams, the dimensions, the arrangement and the relation of all the parts, and how each ought to be placed in order to make up the instrument, and to allow perfectly for its motion; but you ought not to think that after having spread neither time, nor trouble, nor expense to put it in condition to be useful to you, I would have neglected to what was necessary to satisfy you on this score, which seemed lacking for its completion, had I not been stopped from doing so by a consideration so powerful that I dare to hope it will lead you to forgive me. Yes, I hope that you will approve of my abstaining from such a discourse, if you take the trouble to reflect on the one hand, on the case of explaining orally and of understanding by a brief conference the construction and use this machine, and, on the other hand, on the fuss and the difficulty that there might have been in expressing in writing the measure, forms, proportions, locations and the remainder of the properties of so many parts; then you will appreciate that this doctrine is of the number of those that can only be taught orally: and that a discourse in writing of this type would be both as much more useless and puzzling than the one that we would use for the description of all of the parts of a watch whose explanation nevertheless is so easy, when it is done by word of mouth; and that apparently such a discourse could produce no other effect than that of an unfailing chagrin in the minds of many, making them conceive of thousands of difficulties where there are none at all.

Now (dear reader) I think that it is necessary to warn you that I foresee two items capable of forming some clouds in your mind. I know that there are a number of people who make a profession of finding fault everywhere, and that among those, some will be found who will tell you that this machine could be less complicated. This is the first haze that I think needs to be dissipated. That proposition can only be asserted to you by certain intellects who actually have some knowledge of mechanics and geometry, but who, due to not knowing how to join one with the other, and both together with physics, flatter or deceive themselves in their imaginary conceptions and convince themselves of the possibility of many things which are not such, due to possessing only an imperfect theory of things in general, which is not sufficient to make them foresee in particular the troubles which occur, either because of the material or the locations that the parts of a machine ought to occupy whose motions are different so that they may be free and that they cannot interfere with one another. When then these imperfect scientists inform you that this machine could be less complicated, I implore you to give them the answer I would myself give to them had they made such a claim to me, and to assure them on my behalf that I will show them, whenever it pleases them, several other models, and even an entire and perfect instrument, much less complicated, which I made use of publicly for six whole months, and thus, that I am not unaware that the machine can be less complicated, and particularly if I had wished to begin the motion of the operation by the front surface, which could only take place with an annoying and intolerable inconvenience, instead of having it done by the upper surface with all the convenience that could be desired, and even with pleasure. You may also tell them that my plan never aimed at anything but reducing to regulated motion all the operations of arithmetic, at the same time I convinced myself that my plan would only bring about my own confusion if this motion were not simple, easy, convenient and prompt in execution, and if the machine were durable, solid and capable of undergoing without change the rigors of being transported, and finally, that, if they had meditated as much as I have on this matter, and explored all the routes that I have pursued in order to reach my goal, experience would have made them see that a less complicated instrument could not possess all those conditions that I have happily given to this small machine.

As to the simplicity of the motion of the operations, I have managed so that although the operations of arithmetic be in some measure opposite to one another, as addition is to subtraction, and multiplication to division, nevertheless they are all done on this machine by a single and unique motion.

As to the ease of this same motion of operations, it is completely apparent, in that it is as easy to make a thousand and the thousand wheels move at the same time if they were there, although all accomplish their motion most perfectly, as to make a single one of them move (I do not know whether, after the principle on which I based this facility, there is a further one in nature). That if you wish, besides the facility of the motion of operation, to know what is the facility of the operation itself, that is to say, the facility that there is in operation by this machine, you can do this if you take the trouble of comparing it with the methods of operating by counter and by pen. You know as, in operating by counter, the calculator (especially when he lacks ability) is often obliged, for fear of falling into error, to make a long series and extension of counters, and as necessity forces him afterwards to cut down and pick up those which are uselessly spread out; in which you see two useless troubles, with the loss of two times. This machine facilitates and cuts short by its operation all this excess; the most ignorant find as much advantage in it as does the most experienced, the instrument makes up for the defect of ignorance or of slight ability, and by necessary motions, it alone makes, without even the intention of him who makes use of it, all the short cuts possible naturally, and as often as numbers are arranged for it. You know also how, in working with a pen, one is at all moments obliged to carry over or borrow the necessary numbers, and how many errors slip in amongst these remember-ings and borrowings unless one has had a very long practice and besides pays profound attention, which tires the mind in a short time. This machine liberates him who operates it from this vexation; it suffices that he have good sense; it (the machine) relieves the defect of memory; and without either carrying over or borrowing anything, it does itself what the user wishes without him having even to think about it. There are a hundred other quick accomplishments that use of it exhibits, reporting on which would be boring.

As to the convenience of this motion, it suffices to say that it is uncon-scious, going from left to right, and imitating our ordinary way of writing, except that it goes on circularly.

And, finally, as to its speed, it likewise appears in comparing it with that of the other two methods of counters and of pen, and if you wish a still more exact account of its quickness, I will tell you that it is equal to the agility of the hand of him who operates it: this promptness is based, not only on the ease of the motions which cause no resistance, but further on the smallness of the wheels that are moved by hand, making it that as the route being shorter, the motor can traverse it in less time; from which results further the convenience that, due to this, the machine being re-duced to smaller size, it is easier to handle and to carry around.

And, as to the durability and solidity of the instrument, the hardness of the metal of which it is made up should make one sure; but to obtain a complete assurance about it and to give it to others, I have only been able to do it after having made the experiment of transporting the instrument to more than two hundred fifty places, without there being any alteration.

Thus (dear reader) I implore you once more not to take it as an imperfection that this machine is made up of so many parts, since without this composition, I would not have been able to give it all the conditions formerly stated, which moreover were all necessary for it; in which you will be able to note a kind of paradox, namely, that to make the motion of operation simpler, it was necessary that the machine be constructed with a more complicated movement.

The second reason that I foresee capable of causing you distrust is (dear reader) the poor copies of this machine which might be produced by the presumption of artisans: on these occasions, I implore you to sustain carefully the spirit of distinction, to keep yourself from surprise, to distinguish between one leper and another, and not to judge the genuine originals by the imperfect productions due to ignorance and temerity of the workers: the more that they excel in their craft, the more it is to be feared that vanity only lifts them up by the conviction they give to themselves too easily of being capable of undertaking and executing new achievements all by themselves, of which they do not know either the principles or the rules; then intoxicated by this false conviction they work by groping, that is to say, without definite measurements and propositions guided by skill: from which it results that after much time and effort, either they produce nothing like what they have undertaken to do, or at the most, they create a small monster which lacks the principal parts, the others being misshapen and without any proportion: these imperfections rendering it ridiculous, never fail to draw the contempt of all those who see it, which most people, without justice, throw back the fault on him who first had the ideas of such an invention, instead of having it explained by him and then blaming the presumption of those artisans who, by a false audacity, dare to undertake more than their match, produce these useless abortions. It is of concern to the public to make them recognize their weakness and teach them that, for new inventions, it necessarily must be that skill be aided by theory until use has made the theoretical rules so common that it finally has reduced them to skill and that continual exercise has given artisans the habit to follow and make use of these rules with assurance. And just in the same way that it was not in my power, with all the theory imaginable, to execute by myself alone my own design without the aid of a worker who possessed perfectly the use of the lathe, the file and the hammer in order to reduce the parts of the machine to the measurements and proportions that according to the rules of theory I had given to him: it is in the same way absolutely impossible for all the simple artisans, as capable as they may be in their skill, to put into perfection a new part which consists — as the latter — in complicated motions, without the aid of someone who, according to the rules of theory, provides them with the measurements and proportions of all the parts of which it has to be composed.

Dear reader, I have a special reason to give you this final warning, after having seen with my own eyes a false execution of my idea done by a worker from the city of Rouen, a clockmaker by profession, which, on the basis of the plain report made to him of my first model that I had completed a few months earlier, had sufficient daring to undertake another of them, and which moreover is of another kind of motion; but as the simple man possesses no other talent than that of adroitly using his tools, as he does not but know whether geometry and mechanics exist, also (although he may be most capable in his craft, and even most industrious in some aspects which are not at all part of it) has he only made a useless item, truly neat, polished, and very finished on the outside, but so imperfect on the inside that it is of no use; and nevertheless, due solely to its novelty, it was not without esteem amongst those who know nothing about it, and notwithstanding all the basic defects that testing reveals about it, this did not prevent it from finding a place in the cabinet of an interested person of the same city, a cabinet which is filled with several other rare and curious items. The sight of this small abortion displeased me so completely and so cooled the ardor with which I was then working for the accomplishment of my model; that at that very moment I dismissed all the workers, resolved to give up my undertaking completely by the just apprehension that I had that a similar audacity might occur to several others, and that the false copies that they might produce of this new idea should not destroy the esteem for it as early as its birth in view of the value the public could receive from it. But, some time afterwards, My Lord, the Chancellor, having deigned to honor with his perusal my first model and to give evidence of the esteem that he had for this invention, commanded me to put it in perfect shape; and in order to drive away the fear that had gripped me for some time, it pleased him to cut off the evil from its roots and to halt the course that it could take to the prejudice of my reputation and to the disadvantage of the public by the favor that he did me of according me a license (patent), which is not usual, and which stamps out before their birth all these illegitimate abortions which could be engendered from elsewhere than the legitimate alliance of theory with skill.

Besides, if sometimes you have exerted your mind at inventing machines, I will not have great difficulty in convincing you that the form of the instrument, in the condition in which it is at present, is not the first effect of the thoughts I had on this subject: I had begun the execution of my project with a very different machine from this one, both in its materials and in its form, which (although in condition to satisfy some) did not give me complete satisfaction; which led to that in correcting it little by little, I imperceptibly made a second one of them, in which still encountering drawbacks that I could not permit, in order to find a remedy for them, I composed a third one of them which works with springs and which is very simple in its construction. It is that one of which, as I have already said, I have made use several times, as an enormous number of people know, and which is still in condition to be used as much as ever. Nevertheless, in constantly improving it, I found reasons for altering it, and finally realizing in all of them, either the difficulty in operating, or the unevenness of the motions, or the tendency to become damaged by weather or transportation, I had the patience to make more than fifty models, all different, some of wood, others of ivory or ebony, and others of copper, before having come to the achievement of the machine that I now present, which, although composed of so many different small parts, as you can see, is nevertheless so solid, that after the experiment that I have spoken of above, I dare to give you assurance that all the stresses that it may receive in transporting it so far as you wish, can neither damage it nor make it undergo the slightest alteration.

Finally (dear reader), now that I consider that I have put it in condition to be seen, and that even you can, if you have the curiosity for it, see it and use it, I beg you to permit the liberty that I take of hoping that the idea alone of finding a third method for performing all the arithmetical operations, completely new and which has nothing in common with the two ordinary methods of pen and counter, will receive from you some esteem, and that in approving the hope that I had of pleasing you by assisting you, you will be grateful to me for the care that I have taken to make it the case that all the operations, which by the other methods are laborious, complicated, long and not too certain, become easy, simple, quick and certain.

Letter to Queen Christina

LETTER TO THE MOST SERENE
QUEEN OF SWEDEN (JUNE 1652)

Madame,

If I had as much health as zeal, I would go myself to present to Your Majesty a production of several years, that I dare to offer you from so far away; and I would not allow that other hands than mine had the honor of carrying it to the feet of the world's greatest princess. This production, Madame, is a machine for doing arithmetic without pen and without counters. Your Majesty is not unaware of the time and trouble that new products involve, especially when the inventors want to carry them to the final perfection; that is why it would be useless to relate how long I worked on this one; and I cannot better express it than by saying that I applied myself to it with as much ardor as if I had foreseen that it would one day appear before as august a person. But, Madame, if that honor was not the true motive of my work, it will at least be the reward for it, and I will consider myself too happy if, after so many mighty labors, it is able to give Your Majesty a few moments of satisfaction. I will not trouble Your Majesty at all with the details about what this machine is composed of: if You have some curiosity about it, You can satisfy it in a discourse that I have addressed to M. de Bourdelot; there I have described in a few words the entire story of this work, the object of its invention, the occasion for the investigation, the value of its applications, the difficulties of its execution, the steps in its progress, the success of its accomplishment and the rules for its use. I shall then only speak here of the reason that leads me to offer to Your Majesty, which I consider as the crown and the final happiness of its career. I know, Madame, that I could be suspected of having sought honor by presenting it to Your Majesty, since it can only be considered as extraordinary when it is seen that it is addressed to You, and instead of it only being offered to you by consideration of its excellence, it will be judged that it is excellent solely because it has been offered to you. It is not however this hope that has inspired me with this plan. It is too great, Madame, to have any other aim than Your Majesty yourself. What has really led me to this is the combination that is found in your sacred person of two things which seem to me equally admirable and respectable, which are supreme authority and solid knowledge; for I have a special veneration for those are raised to the highest degree either of power or of knowledge. The latter can, if I am not mistaken, as well as the former, be considered as sovereigns. The same gradations are found among geniuses as in conditions, and the power of kings over their subjects is only, it seems to me, an image of the power of minds over those minds that are inferior to them, over whom they exercise the power of persuasion, which is amongst them what the power of commanding is in political government. This second empire even seems to me of an order so much more elevated, than minds are of an order more elevated than bodies, and so much more equitable, that it can only be distributed and preserved by merit, while the other can be so by birth or by chance. It must then be admitted that each of these empires is great in itself, but, Madame, let Your Majesty permit me to say it: they are not completely damaged if one of these without the other seems defective to me. However powerful a monarch may be, something is missing from his glory, if he does not have pre-eminence of mind; and however enlightened a subject may be, his condition is always lowered by dependence. Men, who naturally desire what is more perfect, have up to now continually hoped to encounter this sovereign *par excellence*. All the kings and scholars have been so many faint shadows of it, who only fulfill half their expectation, and our ancestors have hardly been able to see in the whole history of the world a king who is tolerably learned; this masterpiece has been reserved for your times. And so that this great marvel might appear accompanied with all the possible objects of wonder, the position which men were not able to attain is filled by a young Queen, in whom are found together the advantage of experience along with the tenderness of age, the leisure for study with the occupation of royal birth, and the eminence of knowledge with the weakness of sex. It is Your Majesty, Madame, who furnishes to the universe this unique example which it was lacking. It is You in whom power is dispensed by the light of knowledge, and knowledge exalted by the lustre of authority. It is this so marvelous a combination that makes it such that as Your Majesty sees nothing which is beyond your power, you also see nothing which is beyond your mind, and that you will be the admiration of all the ages to come, as you have been the achievement of all the ages past. Reign then, incomparable princess, in a completely new way; let your genius make subject to you all that does not submit to your arms: reign by right of birth for a long period of years over so many triumphant provinces; but always reign by the force of your merit over the whole expanse of the world. As for myself, not having been born under the first of your empires, I wish everyone to know that I glory in living under the second; and it is to bear witness to this that I dare to raise my eyes up to my Queen, in giving her this first proof of dependence.

This is what, Madame, has led me to give this present to Your Majesty, although unworthy of You. My weakness has not shaken my ambition. I have fancied that even though the name alone of Your Majesty seems to put away from You all that is disproportionate from You, nevertheless You may not reject all that is inferior to You; otherwise Your greatness would be without homages and Your glory without praise. You may be satisfied to receive a great effort of mind, without demanding that it be the effect of a mind as great as Yours. It is by this condescension that You deign to enter into communication with other people; and all of these considerations together make me protest to You with all the submission of which one of the greatest admirers of Your heroic qualities is capable, that I wish nothing with so much ardor but to be able to be acknowledged,

Madame,

by Your Majesty,

as Your very humble, most obedient and most faithful servant.

Blaise Pascal

New Experiments about the Vacuum

*New experiments concerning the vacuum made in tubes, syringes,
bellows and siphons of several lengths and shapes; with various fluids,
such as quicksilver, water, wine, oil, air, etc. with a discourse on the
same subject, in which it is shown that even the largest vessel can be
made empty of all materials known in nature, and which are perceived
by the senses; and what force is needed to create this vacuum.
Dedicated to Monsieur Pascal, adviser of the king in his state and
privy councils. By M. B.P. his son, the whole summarized and
presented in advance of a much larger treatise on the same subject.*

TO THE READER

My dear reader, since several considerations prevented me from setting
forth at the present time a complete *Treatise* in which I deal with many new
experiments that I have made concerning the vacuum, and the conclusions
I have drawn from them, I wished to make a report of the chief ones in this
summary in which you will see in advance the plan of the complete work.

This is the occasion for these experiments: *Around four years ago in Italy it
was shown that a four foot glass tube, one end of which is open and the other
hermetically sealed, being filled with quicksilver, then the opening plugged up by a
finger or something else, and the tube inclined perpendicularly to the horizon, the
plugged up opening being towards the bottom, and immersed two or three fingers
depth in other quicksilver, contained in a vessel half full of quicksilver, and the
other half of water; if the opening is uncorked, remaining continually immersed in
the quicksilver in the vessel, the quicksilver in the tube partly descends, leaving an
apparently empty space at the top of the tube, the bottom of the same tube
remaining full of the same quicksilver up to a certain height. If the tube is lifted up
a bit until its opening was previously steeped in the quicksilver of the vessel,
leaving this quicksilver, reaches the region of the water, the quicksilver in the tube
rises in height with the water: and these two fluids mix together in the tube: but
finally all the quicksilver falls, and the tube is completely full of water.*

When the experiment was sent from Rome to Father Mersenne in Paris,
he divulged it in France in the year 1644, and it received the admiration of
all the learned and interested persons. The communication of this having
become well-known everywhere, I learned of it from M. Petit, Superintendent of Fortifications, and a man well versed in all belles-lettres, who
had learned of it from Father Mersenne himself. We then did it together at
Rouen, the aforementioned M. Petit and myself, in the same way that it

had been done in Italy, and found exactly what had been reported from there, without at that time having observed anything different.

Afterwards, reflecting by myself about the conclusions of these experiments, I became confirmed in the view that I had always had, that a vacuum was not an impossible thing in nature, and that she does not flee from it with as much horror as some imagine.

What led me to this view was the slight basis that I saw from the maxim so well accepted, that Nature will not allow a vacuum, which is only supported by experiments most of which are quite false, although held as most reliable. Of the others, some contributed nothing to prove this maxim, and show that Nature abhors too great a plentitude, and not that she flees from a vacuum. And the most favorable ones do not show anything except that Nature abhors a vacuum, not thereby indicating that she cannot allow it.

To the weakness of this principle, I added the observations that we make every day of the rarefaction and condensation of air, which, as some people have shown, can be condensed down to a thousandth part of the space that it previously seemed to occupy, and which becomes so greatly rarefied that I have found it necessary either that there be a large vacuum between its parts or that there be a penetration of dimensions. But since this was not accepted by everyone as proof, I thought that this Italian experiment was capable of convincing those very people who are the most preoccupied with the impossibility of a vacuum.

Nevertheless the strength of the prejudice was such that objections are still found which will deprive it [the experiment] of the credence that it deserves. Some will say that the top of the blow-tube was full of spirits of mercury; others, of an imperceptible rarefied particle of air; others of a material that only exists in their imagination; and all of them, conspiring to banish the vacuum, vying with one another exercise that mental power, that is called "Subtelty" in the Schools, and which, in order to solve genuine difficulties, produces only vain words without any basis.

I then resolved to perform some experiments so convincing, that they might counter all the objections that could be made about this. At the beginning of this year I performed a great number of them, some of which bear some relation to the Italian one, and others are entirely different, and have nothing in common with it. They have been so exact and successful that I have shown by them that a vessel as large as can be made, can be made empty of all materials that can be observed by the senses, and that are known in Nature; and I have shown what force is needed to create this vacuum. It is also through this that I have tested the necessary height for a siphon to derive the desired effect from it, about which limited height it no longer acts, contrary to the opinion so universally held throughout the world for so many centuries; likewise also the slight force necessary to pull out the piston of a syringe without any material following after it; and many other things that you will see in the complete work, in which I plan to show what force Nature employs to avoid a vacuum, and She admits it and tolerates it in a large space, that can be easily made empty of all material that can be observed by the senses. This is why I have divided the whole *Treatise* into two parts, the first of which comprises a lengthy report of all of my experiments with diagrams, and a recapitulation of what these show, divided into several maxims. And the second, the conclusions I have drawn from them, divided into several propositions in which I have shown that apparent empty space, which has turned up in the experiments, is actually devoid of all material that is observable by the senses, and that is known in Nature. And in the conclusion, I give my opinion on the subject of the vacuum, and answer the objections that can be made about it. Thus, I am satisfied to exhibit a large empty space, and leave it to learned and interested persons to test what happens in such a space; such as, whether animals live there; whether glass diminished its refraction in it; and all the things that can be done there; making no mention of this in this *Treatise*, of which I thought proper to give you this summary in advance, because having made these experiments with much expense, time and trouble, I feared that someone else who would not have taken the time, the money, nor the trouble, might present to the public before I did, things that he might not have seen, therefore, and of which he would not be able to report with the precision and the requisite order to deduce them properly; there being no one who had the tubes and siphons of the length of mine; and few who wished to take the necessary trouble to possess them.

And, as gentlemen join to the common inclination that all people have of keeping their just possessions for themselves, that of refusing the honor that is not due them, you will doubtless approve of the fact that I defend myself equally, both from those who would like to take some of the experiments away from me that I am presenting to you here, and that I promise to present to you in the complete *Treatise*, since they are due to my inventiveness; and of those who attribute to me the Italian one of which I have spoken, since it is not one of mine. For even though I have done it in more ways than any one else, and with tubes twelve and fifteen feet long, nevertheless I shall not speak of it in these writings, since I am not the inventor of it, having the plan of presenting only those which are unique to me and are my own creations.

SUMMARY OF THE FIRST PART IN WHICH THE EXPERIMENTS ARE REPORTED.

Experiments

1. A glass syringe with a very exact piston is plunged completely in water, and in which the opening is stopped up by a finger, so that it touches the bottom of the piston, the hand and arm placed in the water for this effect. Only a moderate force is needed to pull it [the piston] back and

make it such that it separates from the finger without any water at all entering therein (which philosophers believed could not be accomplished with any finite force); and thus the finger feels strongly pulled and pained; and the piston leaves an apparent empty space, and one in which it does not seem that any body has been able to enter, since it is completely surrounded by water which has not been able to enter, since it is completely surrounded by water which has not been able to have access to it, the opening of it being blocked. If the piston is pulled back more, the apparent empty space becomes larger; but the finger does not feel any more pull. And if it is drawn up almost completely out of the water, so that only its opening remains along with the finger that blocks it, then, if the finger is taken away, the water, contrary to its nature, rises violently and completely fills all the space that the piston had left.

2. A bellows well closed on all sides creates the same effect, with a similar preparation, contrary to the view of the same philosophers.

3. A glass tube forty-six feet long, of which one end is open, the other hermetically sealed, being filled with water, or rather with very red wine in order to make it more visible, then closed and raised in this state, and carried perpendicular to the horizon, the opening stopped up at the bottom, in a vessel full of water, and pushed down in it to a depth of about one foot; if the opening is unstopped, the wine in the tube falls to a certain height, which is about thirty-two feet from the surface of the water in the vessel, and empties itself there and mixes with the water in the vessel which it imperceptibly colors, and descending from the top of the glass, leaves a space of around thirteen feet which appears empty, in which likewise it does not seem that any body could enter. And if the tube is slanted so that the height of the wine in the tube becomes less by that inclination, the wine rises until it reaches the height of thirty-two feet; and finally, if the tube is slanted until it is thirty-two feet high, it becomes completely filled by thus taking in as much water as the wine it has lost; so that one sees it full of wine from the top down to thirteen feet from the bottom, and filled with slightly colored water in the remaining thirteen lower feet.

4. A scalene siphon, of which the longer leg is fifty feet, and the shorter forty-five, being filled with water, and the two plugged-up openings being placed in two vessels filled with water, and immersed about a foot, so that the siphon is perpendicular to the horizon, and that the surface of the water in one vessel is higher than the surface of the other by five feet: if the two openings are unplugged, the siphon being in this condition, the longer leg does not draw water from the shorter one, nor therefore from the vessel in which it is, contrary to the view of all philosophers and artisans; but instead the water falls from both legs into the two vessels, until it is at the same height as in the preceding tube, measuring the height from the surface of the water in each vessel. But if the siphon is tilted below the height of

about thirty-one feet, the longer leg draws the water which is in the vessel of the shorter one; and when it is raised above this height, this stops, and both sides disgorge, each into its vessel; and when it is lowered again, the water of the longer leg draws the water from the shorter one as before.

5. If a cord of almost fifteen feet with a thread attached at the end (which is left for a while in water, so that by soaking it in little by little, the air which might be within, leaves it) in a fifteen foot tube, sealed at one end as above, and filled with water, in such a way that there be nothing outside the tube but the thread attached to the cord, in order to pull it from it, and the opening having been placed in quicksilver; when the cord is pulled bit by bit, the quicksilver rises proportionally, until the height of the quicksilver, plus the fourteenth of the height of the remaining water, is two feet, three inches; for, next when the cord is pulled, the water parts from the top of the glass, and leaves a space that appears empty, which becomes still larger, as the cord is pulled further. If the tube is tilted, the quicksilver in the vessel enters it, so that, if it is tilted sufficiently, it is completely full of quicksilver and water which strikes the top of the tube violently, making the same noise and crash as if it were breaking the glass, and which runs the risk of actually breaking it. And to remove the suspicion that there might be air that one could say had remained in the cord, the same experiment is performed with many small wooden cylinders, attached to one another by brass wire.

6. Let a syringe with a perfectly exact piston be placed in quicksilver, so that its opening be immersed there to be a depth of at least one inch, and let the rest of the syringe be raised perpendicularly outside it: if the piston is pulled back, the syringe remaining in this condition, the quicksilver entering by the opening of the syringe, rises and stays joined to the piston, until it be raised in the syringe to two feet three inches. But after this height, if the piston is pulled back further, it does not draw the quicksilver higher, it, remaining constantly at the height of two feet three inches, parts from the piston; so that an apparently empty space is created, which becomes still larger as the piston is further withdrawn. *It is probable that the same thing happens in a suction-pump; and that water only rises there to the height of thirty-one feet, which corresponds to that of two feet three inches of quicksilver.* And what is more remarkable is that the syringe weighed in this state, without removing the quicksilver from it, nor moving it in any way, weighs as much (although the apparent empty space be as small as one wishes) as when, by withdrawing the piston further one makes it as large as one wishes, and that it always weighs as much as the total of the syringe with the quicksilver that it contains up to the height of two feet three inches, without there being any apparent empty space; that is to say, when the piston has not yet left the quicksilver of the syringe, but is ready to disunite itself from it, if it is pulled ever so little. Thus the apparent empty space, even though all the objects that surround it tend to fill it, brings

about no change in its weight, and that, whatever difference in size there be between these spaces, there is none between them in weight.

7. Having filled a siphon with quicksilver, whose longer leg is ten feet, and the other nine and a half, having put the two openings into two vessels of quicksilver, immersed about an inch each, so that the surface of the quicksilver of the one is more than one half foot higher than the surface of the quicksilver of the other: when the siphon is perpendicular, the longer leg does not draw the quicksilver from the shorter one; but the quicksilver, breaking apart at the top, descends in each of the legs, and overflows into the vessels, and falls to the usual height of two feet three inches from the surface of the quicksilver of each vessel. Then if the siphon is tilted, the quicksilver in the vessels climbs up the legs, fills them, and begins to flow from the shorter leg into the longer one, and this empties its vessel; for this tilting in the tubes in which there is this apparent vacuum, when they are in some fluid, always draws the fluids in the vessels, if the openings of the tubes are not stopped up, or it pulls the finger, if it is stopping up these openings.

8. If the same siphon is entirely filled with water, and then with a cord, as above, the two openings being placed in the same two vessels of quicksilver, when the cord is pulled through one of these openings, the quicksilver rises from the vessels into both of the legs: so that the fourteenth part of the height of the water in one leg, plus the height of the quicksilver which has risen into it, is equal to the fourteenth part of the height of the water in the other, plus the height of the quicksilver which has risen into it; which will happen as long as this fourteenth part of the height of the water, plus the height of the quicksilver in each leg be of the height of two feet three inches; for after that, the water will divide at the top, and there will be a visible empty space there.

From which experiments and several others reported in the complete book, in which tubes of various lengths, thickness and shapes are studied, filled with different fluids, immersed diversely in the different fluids, carried from some to others, weighed in several ways, and in which the different attraction felt by the finger which is stopping up the tubes in which a vacuum appears are observed, these maxims are obviously deduced:

MAXIMS

1. That all bodies have a repugnance to separate themselves from one another and to permit this apparent vacuum in the interval between them; that is to say that Nature abhors this apparent vacuum.

2. That this abhorrence or repugnance that all bodies have is not any greater for allowing a large apparent vacuum than a small one, that is to say, to absent itself from a large interval rather than a small one.

3. That the strength of this abhorrence is limited, and equal to that with which water of a certain height, which is around thirty-one feet, tends to flow down.

4. That the bodies that border this apparent vacuum have a tendency to fill it.

5. That this tendency is not any greater for filling a large apparent vacuum than a small one.

6. That the strength of this tendency is limited, and always the same as that with which water of a certain height, which is around thirty-one feet, tends to flow down.

7. That a greater force, as slight as one wishes, than that with which water of the height of thirty-one feet tends to flow downward, suffices to allow for this apparent vacuum, even as great a one as may be desired; that is to say that to disunite bodies with as large an interval as one wishes, provided that there be no other obstacle to their separation, nor to their removal than the abhorrence that Nature has for this apparent vacuum.

SUMMARY OF THE SECOND PART IN WHICH THE CONCLUSIONS OF THESE EXPERIMENTS ARE REPORTED, CONCERNING THE MATTER WHICH MIGHT FILL THIS APPARENT EMPTY SPACE, DIVIDED INTO SEVERAL PROPOSITIONS, WITH THEIR DEMONSTRATIONS.

PROPOSITIONS

1. That the apparent empty space is not filled with external air that surrounds the tube, and that it has not entered there through pores in the glass.

2. That it is not full of the air that some philosophers claim to be enclosed in the pores of all bodies, which would be, in this way, in the middle of the fluid that fills the tubes.

3. That it is not full of the air that some believe to be between the tube and the fluid that fills it, and enclosed in the interstices or atoms of the corpuscles that make up these fluids.

4. That it is not full of a particle of imperceptible air, left by chance between the fluid and the glass, or carried by the finger that stops it up, or admitted by some other means, which rarefies itself extraordinarily, and that some people maintain is capable of rarefying itself sufficiently to fill up the whole world rather than permit a vacuum.

5. That it is not full of a small portion of quicksilver or water, which being pulled on the one hand by the inner surface of the glass, and on the other by the force if the fluid, rarefies itself and converts itself into vapors; in such a way as if this reciprocal attraction had the same effect as heat which converts these fluids into vapor and makes them volatile.

6. That it is not full of the spirits of the fluid that fills the tube.

7. That it is not full of a more subtle air mixed with the exterior air, which by being detached and having entered through the pores of the glass, would always tend to return to it or would be ceaselessly drawn to it.

8. That the apparent empty space is not filled with any materials that are known in nature, and that can be perceived by any of the senses.

SUMMARY OF THE CONCLUSION IN WHICH I OFFER MY VIEW

After having demonstrated that none of the materials which are perceived by our senses, and of which we have any knowledge, fills this apparently empty space, my view will be, until someone may have shown the existence of some material which might fill it, that it is truly empty and devoid of all matter.

That is why I will assert the same about the genuine vacuum as I have shown about the apparent vacuum, and I will maintain the maxims posed above as true, and set forth for the absolute vacuum, just as they have been for the apparent one, namely in this manner:

MAXIMS

1. That all bodies have a repugnance to separate themselves from one another, and to permit a vacuum in the interval between them; that is to say that Nature abhors a vacuum.

2. That this abhorrence or repugnance is not any greater for allowing a large vacuum than a small one, that is to say, to absent itself from a large interval than a small one.

3. That the strength of this abhorrence is limited, and equal to that with which water of a certain height, which is about thirty-one feet, tends to flow down.

4. That the bodies that border this vacuum have a tendency to fill it.

5. That this tendency is not any greater for filling a large vacuum than a small one.

6. That the strength of this tendency is limited, and always equal to that with which water of a certain height, which is around thirty-one feet, tends to flow down.

7. That a greater force as slight as one wishes, than that with which water of the height of thirty-one feet tends to flow downward, suffices to allow for a vacuum, and even as great a one as is desired: that is to say, to disunite bodies with as large an interval as one wishes: provided that there be no other obstacle to their separation, nor to their removal, than the abhorrence that Nature has for a vacuum.

NEXT I ANSWER THE OBJECTION THAT CAN BE MADE TO THIS, OF WHICH THESE ARE THE PRINCIPAL ONES.

OBJECTIONS

1. That that proposition, that space is empty, is repugnant to common sense.

2. That that proposition, that Nature abhors a vacuum, and yet permits it, accuses Her of impotence, or it implies a contradiction.

3. That several experiments, and even everyday ones, show that Nature cannot permit a vacuum.

4. That an imperceptible material, unheard of and unknown to all of the senses, fills that space.

5. That since light is either an accident or a substance, that is not possible that it maintain itself in a vacuum, if it is an accident, and that it would fill the apparent empty space, if it is a substance.

Paris, October 8, 1647

The Great Experiment

Account of the Great Experiment of the Equilibrium of Fluids planned by the Sire B. P. in order to bring about the Treatise that he promised in his Summary concerning the Vacuum and made by Sire F. P. on one of the highest Mountains of Auvergne

When I set forth my summary under the title: *New Experiments concerning the Vacuum*, etc., in which I made use of the maxim about the abhorrence of the vacuum, because it was universally accepted, and because I had not yet any convincing proofs of the contrary, several difficulties remained for me which made me greatly challenge the truth of that maxim. In order to clarify this I thought from then on about the experiment whose account I am here presenting, which could give me a complete knowledge of what I should believe about this. I have called it the *great experiment of the equilibrium of fluids*, because it is the most demonstrative of all those that can be done on this subject, in that it exhibits the equilibrium of air with quicksilver, which constitutes the lightest and the heaviest of all the fluids that are known in nature. But because it was impossible to do it in the city of Paris, because there are very few places in France proper for this effort, and because the city of Clermont in Auvergne is one of the most convenient, I begged Monsieur Périer, Counsellor in the Court of Aids of Auvergne, my brother-in-law, to take the trouble to do it. What my difficulties were, and what this experiment is, will be seen from this letter that I wrote to him then.

COPY OF THE LETTER OF MONSIEUR PASCAL THE YOUNGER TO MONSIEUR PÉRIER, NOVEMBER 15, 1647

Monsieur,

I would not interrupt the constant work which your duties involve you in, in order to converse with you about physical meditations, if I did not know that they would serve to divert you in your hours of relaxation, and that while others would be disturbed by them, you will enjoy them. I find much less difficulty in this since I know the pleasure that you receive from this sort of discussion. This will only be a continuation of those that we have had together concerning the vacuum. You know what view philosophers have had on this subject: All have held for a maxim that nature abhors a vacuum, and almost all, going much further, have maintained that it cannot admit it, and that it would destroy itself rather than allow it. So opinions have been divided, one side being content to say that it only abhors it, the other has maintained that it cannot permit it. I have worked, in my *Summary of the Treatise on the Vacuum*, to destroy this latter view, and I believe that the experiments that I reported there suffice to show clearly that nature can allow and actually suffer a space, as great as one wishes, empty of all materials which are within our knowledge, and which fall under our senses. I am working now to examine the truth of the former, and to look for experiments which might show if the effects that are attributed to the abhorrence of a vacuum, ought really to be attributed to that abhorrence of a vacuum, or if they ought to be attributed to the weight and pressure of air. For, to state my view openly, I hardly believe that nature, which is not animated at all, nor sensitive, may be susceptible of abhorrence, since passions presuppose a soul capable of feeling them, and I incline rather more to imputing all these effects to the weight and pressure of air, because I consider them as particular cases of a universal proposition of the equilibrium of liquids, which should make up the greatest part of the treatise that I have promised. It is not that I did not have these same thoughts during the production of my summary. And nevertheless, for lack of convincing experiments, I did not dare then (and I still do not dare) depart from the maxim of the abhorrence of a vacuum, and I have even employed it as a maxim in my summary. Not then having any other design than to combat the opinion of those who maintain that a vacuum is absolutely impossible, and that nature would rather allow her destruction than the slightest empty space. Actually, I do not think that it is permitted to us to depart easily from the maxims that we have from antiquity, unless we are so obliged by indubitable and incontrovertible proofs. But in this case I hold that it would be an extreme weakness to make the least scruple about it, and that ultimately we ought to have more veneration for evident truths than obstinacy for those accepted opinions. I cannot better indicate to you the circumspection I exercise before turning myself away from ancient maxims, than by recalling to you the experiment that I did some days past in your presence with two tubes, one inside the other, with apparently a vacuum inside a vacuum. You saw that the quicksilver of the inner tube remained suspended to the height which it maintains in the ordinary experiment, when it was counterbalanced and pressed by the weight of the entire mass of air, and that, on the other hand, it completely fell, without any height or suspension remaining, when, as a result of the vacuum with which it was surrounded, it was no longer pressed everywhere nor counterbalanced by any air, this having been removed from all sides. You then saw that this height or suspension of the quicksilver increased or decreased to the degree that the pressure of the air increased or decreased, and that finally all these various heights or suspensions of quicksilver were always proportional to the pressure of the air.

Certainly, after this experiment, there was reason for being convinced that it is not the abhorrence of a vacuum, as we think, which causes the suspension of the quicksilver in the ordinary experiment, but rather the weight and pressure of the air, which counterbalances the weight of the quicksilver. But because all the effects of this latter experiment of the two tubes, which is so naturally explicable solely by the pressure and weight of the air, can still be explained probably enough by the abhorrence of a vacuum, I am keeping to this ancient maxim, resolved nevertheless to seek complete understanding of this difficulty through a decisive experiment. I have conceived of one which alone will be able to suffice to give us the illumination we seek, if it can be carried out carefully. It is to perform the ordinary experiment of the vacuum several times in the same day, in the same tube, with the same quicksilver, now at the bottom and now at the top of a mountain, with a height of at least five or six hundred fathoms, in order to test if the height of the quicksilver suspended in the tube will be found to be similar or different in these two situations. You already see without doubt that this experiment is decisive for the question, and that, if it happens that the height of the quicksilver be less at the top than at the bottom of the mountain (as I have many reasons to believe, although all those who have thought about this matter are opposed to this view), it will necessarily follow that the weight and pressure of the air is the only cause of this suspension of quicksilver, and not the abhorrence of a vacuum, since it is quite certain that there is much more air that weighs down at the foot of the mountain than at its summit: whereas it cannot be said that nature abhors a vacuum at the foot of the mountain more than on its summit.

But as difficulty is ordinarily joined to great things, I see much of it in the execution of the plan, since for this it is necessary to select an extremely high mountain near a city in which there is a person capable of bringing to this test all the precision required. For if the mountain were far away, it would be difficult to carry the vessels, the quicksilver, the tubes and many other needed items to it, and to undertake those laborious trips as many times as would be necessary to encounter calm and pleasant weather on the top of those mountains, which is only infrequently seen there. And as it is as rare to find persons outside of Paris who possess these qualities, as places which possess these conditions, I have greatly esteemed my good fortune in having, on this occasion, met both one and the other, since our city of Clermont is at the foot of the high mountain of Le Puy-de-Dôme, and since I hope that your kindness will grant me the favor of being willing to undertake this experiment there yourself. And on the basis of this assurance, I have led all our interested persons in Paris to hope for this, and among others, the Reverend Father Mersenne,[1] who already has promised, in letters that he has written to Italy, Poland, Sweden, Holland, etc., to report about it to his friends that he has acquired there by his merits. I am not dealing with the means of executing it, because I know well that you will not leave out any of the necessary details for performing it with precision.

I beg you only that it be as soon as you can do it, and excuse this liberty by which I am led by the impatience that I have for learning of the success of it, without which I cannot put the last touches to the treatise that I have promised to the public, nor satisfy the desire of so many people who wait for it, and who will be infinitely obliged to you for it. It is not that I want to diminish my gratitude by mentioning the number of those who will share it with me, since I wish, on the contrary, to partake in that that they will give to you, and to remain all the more grateful, Sir,

Your most humble and obedient servant,

Paris, November 15, 1647 PASCAL

M. Périer received this letter in Moulins where he was on a job which deprived him of the freedom to do what he wanted; so that, whatever desire he may have had for promptly performing this experiment, he was nevertheless not able to do it sooner than during last September.

You will see the reasons for this delay, the report of the experiment, and the precision with which he did it, in the following letter that he did me the honor of sending me.

(The letter of Monsieur Périer to Pascal of September 22, 1648, describes that he was delayed both by business and bad weather until September 19, 1648, from undertaking the experiment. On that date, with some priests and professional persons, M. Périer took two similar tubes, hermetically sealed at one end. At the bottom of the mountain, both were filled with mercury, and the open end placed in bowls of mercury. The height of the columns was measured. Then one tube was left with an observer. The other was carried up to the top of the mountain, where the experiment was again performed, and the height of the column was found to be about three inches less. The experiment was then performed several times more to be sure, in the open and under cover, during various weather conditions. On the way down it was performed again. Then it was checked against the tube left at the bottom, and the mercury interchanged. The next day the experiment was done on the top of the Church of Notre-Dame of Clermont, in a house high in the town, and at some other locations. All of

---

[1] Marin Mersenne, 1588–1648, the leading proponent of the "new science," a friend of Descartes, Hobbes, Gassendi, Herbert of Cherbury, and others.

this showed that the height of the column of mercury decreased at higher positions.)

This report having clarified all of my difficulties, I do not hide that I received much satisfaction from it, and having seen there that the difference of twenty fathoms of elevation made a difference of two lines in the height of the quicksilver, and that six to seven fathoms make about a half line of it, which it was easy for me to test in this city, I made the ordinary experiment of the vacuum at the top and at the bottom of the tower of Saint-Jacques-de-la-Boucherie, 24 to 25 fathoms high. I found more than two lines of difference in the height of the quicksilver. And later I did it in a private home, 90 steps high, in which I found a very noticeable difference of a half-line; all of which corresponds perfectly to the content of the report of M. Périer.

All those interested can test it themselves whenever they wish.

From this experience many consequences follow, such as: The means for knowing if two places are at the same level, that is to say equally distant from the center of the earth, or which of the two is more elevated, no matter how far they are from one another, even if they are diametrically opposite. This would be practically impossible by any other means.

The slight certitude that the thermometer possesses for indicating degrees of heat (contrary to the common view), and that its water sometimes rises when the heat increases, and that sometimes it sinks when the heat diminishes, although the thermometer be kept constantly in the same place.

The inequality of the air pressure which, at the same degree of heat, always presses much more at the lowest places.

All of these consequences will be deduced at length in the *Treatise on the Vacuum*, and many others as useful as they are curious.

TO THE READER

My dear reader. The universal consent of the people and the multitude of philosophers unite in establishing this principle, that nature would rather permit her own destruction than the slightest empty space. A few of the most elevated souls have adopted a more moderate one of them: for although they believed that nature abhors a vacuum, they have nevertheless considered that this repugnance had limits, and that it could be overcome by some force; but there has not yet been anyone who has set forth this third one: that nature has no repugnance for a vacuum, that it makes no effort to avoid one, and that it allows one without difficulty or resistance. The experiments that I have given you in my Summary destroy, in my opinion, the first of these principles; and I do not see how the second can resist those that I now give you; so that I no longer have any difficulty in adopting the third: that nature has no repugnance for a vacuum, that it makes no effort to avoid one; that all the effects that are attributed to this abhorrence arise from the weight and pressure of air; that this is the sole and genuine cause of them, and that, for want of knowing this, people have purposely invented that imaginary abhorrence of the vacuum to explain them. It is not in this sole circumstance that, when men's feebleness has not been able to find the true causes, their subtlety has substituted imaginary ones of them, that they have expressed by specious names that fill the ears but not the mind, it is thus that it is said that the sympathy and antipathy of natural bodies are the efficient and univocal causes of several effects, as if inanimate bodies were capable of sympathy and antipathy. It is the same with the antiperistatis, and with several other chimerical causes, which only bring a vain relief to the avidity that men have for knowing hidden truths, and which, far from uncovering them, serve only to cover up the ignorance of those who invent them, and to sustain that of their followers.

It is not, however, without regret that I depart from those opinions so generally received. I only do it in yielding to the living force that so constrains me. I resisted these new views as long as I had some pretext for following the ancient ones. The maxims I employed in my *Summary* show this sufficiently. But, finally, the evidence of experiments forces me to give up the views which the respect for antiquity had preserved for me. Also I only gave them up little by little, and I only withdrew from them by degrees. For from the first of these three principles, that nature has an invincible abhorrence for a vacuum, I passed to that second one, that it has an abhorrence of it, but not an invincible one. And from there I have finally arrived at the belief in the third one, that nature has no abhorrence for a vacuum.

That is where this last experiment of the equilibrium of fluids has brought me, which I would not have thought of telling you fully unless I had made you see what the motives were that led me to seek it. That is why I presented you with my letter of last November 16 (sic), addressed to M. Périer who has taken the trouble of the hardship with all the care and precision that can be desired, and to whom all those interested persons who have wished it for so long, will be completely obligated.

Since, by a special advantage, this universal wish had made it famous before it appeared, I am sure that it will not become less illustrious after it has been produced, and that it will give as much satisfaction as its expectation caused impatience.

It was not proper to allow those who desired it to languish any longer. And that is why I could not stop myself from presenting it ahead of time, contrary to the plan that I had of doing so only in the complete treatise

(that I promised you in my *Summary*), in which I will deduce the consequences that I have drawn from it, and that I had deferred doing until this
last experiment, because it ought to bring about the accomplishment of my
demonstrations. But since it cannot appear very soon, I did not want to hold
on to it (the new experiment) any longer, as much in order to earn more
gratitude from you through precipitation as to avoid reproach for wrongdo-
ing that I thought you would make as a result of a long delay.

Reply to Father Noel

Reply of Blaise Pascal to the Very Reverend Father Noël, Rector of the Society of Jesus in Paris (1647)

MY VERY REVEREND FATHER,

The honor that you have done me of writing to me makes me depart from the decision I have made of only resolving any of the difficulties that I had reported in my *summary* in the complete treatise on which I am working; for, since the civilities in your letter are joined to the objection that you therein pose, I cannot divide my answer, nor acknowledge one without satisfying the other.

But to do this with more order, allow me to state a universal rule to you which applies to all the particular subjects, in which it is a question of recognizing the truth. I do not doubt that you will agree with it, since it is generally accepted by all those who look at matters without prejudice; and that it constitutes the principal way in which the sciences are treated in the Schools, and the one which is employed by those who seek what is really solid and which fills and fully satisfies the mind. It is that one should only pass a decisive judgment, either negative or positive about a proposition, when one either affirms or denies one of these two conditions: namely, either that it appear so clearly and distinctly by itself to the senses or reason, according to whether it is subject to one or the other, that the mind has no way of doubting of its certitude, and it is what we term *principles* or *axioms*; as, for example, *if equals are added to equals, the sums will be equal;* or that it be deduced by infallible and necessary steps from such principles or axioms, upon the certitude of which all of the conclusions which are well drawn from it depend; as this proposition, *the three angles of a triangle are equal to two right angles*, which, not being obvious in itself, is demonstrated evidently by some infallible conclusions of such axioms. Everything which possesses one of these two conditions is certain and true, and all which does not possess them passes as doubtful and uncertain. And we pass a decisive judgment on matters of the first kind and we leave the others in indecision, so that we name them, according to their merit, sometimes *vision*, sometimes *caprice*, occasionally *fantasy*, other times *idea*, and at most a *fine conception*, and because they cannot be affirmed without rashness, we lean rather towards the negative: ready however to move to the other direction if a self-evident demonstration makes us see the truth of it. And we reserve for the mysteries of faith, that the Holy Spirit has Himself revealed, that submission of spirit which carries our belief to the mysteries hidden to the senses and to reason.

This stated, I come to your letter, in the first lines of which, in order to prove that this space is corporeal, you make use of these words: *I say that it is a body, since it behaves like a body in that it transmits light with refractions and reflections, and in that it brings about the slowing down of the motion of another body*: in which I observe that in the plan for proving that it is a body, you take as principles two things: the first is that it transmits light with refractions and reflections; the second, that it slows down the motion of a body. Of these two principles, the first has not seemed true to any of these who have desired to establish it, and we have always observed, on the contrary, that the ray which penetrates the glass and this space has no other refraction than that which the glass produces, and that, thus, if some material fills it, it does not break the ray in any manner, or its refraction is not perceptible; so that, since doubtless you have established nothing to the contrary, I see that the sense of your words is that the ray, reflected or broken by the glass, passes through this space, and that from this and that bodies fall there in time, you want to conclude that some material fills it, which transports this light and causes this delay in movement.

But, my Reverend Father, if we relate this to the method of reasoning of which we have spoken, we will find that it would first of all have to be kept in accord with the definition of empty space, light and motion, and show by the nature of these items a manifest contradiction in these propositions: "That light penetrates an empty space, and that a body moves there in time." Your proof cannot hold good up to this point, and since in addition the nature of light is unknown, both to you and to me; since of all those who have tried to define it, not a one has satisfied any of those who seek for palpable truths, and since it will perhaps remain forever unknown to us, I see that this argument will remain a long time without receiving the strength which is necessary for it to become convincing.

For consider, I beg of you, how it is possible to conclude infallibly that the nature of light is such that it cannot subsist in a vacuum, when we do not know the nature of light. That if we knew it as perfectly as we do not know it, we would know perhaps that it would subsist in a vacuum with more brilliance than in any other *medium*, as we see that it increases its strength, accordingly as the *medium* in which it is becomes rarer, and this in some way closer to nothing. And if we knew that of motion, I have no doubts that it would appear to us to take place in a vacuum in almost as much time as in the air, whose lack of resistance appears in the equality of the falling of bodies of different weights.

That is why, with the slight knowledge that we have of the nature of these things, if, with a similar freedom, I conceive the idea that I offer for a principle, I am able to say with as much reason: light sustains itself in a vacuum, and motion occurs therein in time; now light penetrates apparently empty space, and motion occurs therein in time; therefore it can actually be empty.

So let us put off this proof until we shall have understanding of the nature of light. Until then I am not able to accept your principle, and it will be difficult for you to prove it; and let us not draw, I beg of you, infallible conclusions about the nature of a thing when we are ignorant about it: otherwise I should fear that you would not be in agreement with me concerning the conditions requisite for making a demonstration perfect, and you would only call that certain which we label doubtful.

In the course of your letter, as if you had invincibly established that this empty space is a body, you do not put yourself to any more trouble than to look for what this body consists in; and to decide affirmatively what material fills it, you begin by these words: "Let us presuppose that as blood is a mixture of several fluids that make it up, so air is made up of air and fire and the four elements that enter into the composition of all the bodies in nature." You *presuppose* next that this fire can be separated from the air, and that on being separated, it can penetrate the pores of the glass; you *presuppose* further that in being separated from it, it has a tendency to return to it, and further that it is ceaselessly drawn to it; and you explain this discourse, quite intelligible in itself, by some comparisons that you add to it.

But, my Father, I believe that you present this as an idea, and not as a demonstration; and no matter what trouble I may have in accommodating the conception I have about it with the end of your letter, I believe that if you desired to present proofs, they would not be based on so little. For at this time when so large a number of learned men are seeking with so much care the material that fills that space; when this problem today agitates so many minds, I should have difficulty believing that in order to bring forth a solution so desired to a great and most justified doubt, you would present nothing but a material, of which you suppose not only the qualities, but further its existence itself; so that he who *presupposes* the contrary, will as necessarily draw a contrary conclusion. If this method of proof is accepted, it will no longer be difficult to resolve the greatest problems. Both the flux of the sea and the attraction of the magnet will become easy to understand, if one is allowed to suppose suitable materials and qualities.

For all things of this nature, whose existence does not reveal itself to any of the senses, are as difficult to believe in as they are easy to invent. Many persons, including some of even the most learned alive today have objected to me about this same material before you (but as a simple idea, and not as an unalterable truth), and that is why I mentioned it in my propositions. Others, in order to fill the empty space with some matter, have imagined one with which they fill the whole universe, because the imagination has this property, that it creates with as little time and trouble the greatest things as well as the smallest; some people have made it out of the same substance as the sky and the elements; and others, out of a different substance, according to their fancy, since they treated it like a creation of their own.

When they are asked, as you are, that they show us this material, they answer that it is not visible; if they are asked to make it produce some sound, they say that it cannot be heard, and so on with all the other senses; and they think they have accomplished a great deal, when they have seized from others who are in the position of not being able to show that it does not exist, withdrawing to themselves all the power of showing that it does exist.

But we discover more reasons for denying its existence, because it cannot be proven except by believing that it suffices for this that it cannot be shown that it does not exist.

For one can believe all of them without making nature into a monster, and as reason can no more lean towards one than towards another, because she finds them equally remote, she refuses all of them in order to defend herself from an unjust choice.

I know that you can say that you have not invented this material all by yourself, and that many physicists have already worked on this; but concerning the characteristics of this material, we do not base anything on the authorities: when we cite authors, we cite their demonstrations, and not their names; we have no regard for them other than as historical data; so much so that if the authors you quote said that they had seen these small igneous bodies, mixed with the air, I would defer sufficiently to their sincerity and their honesty to believe that these [the small bodies] are genuine, and I would believe them [the authors] as historians; but since they only say that they think that air is made up of them, you will allow me to keep my original doubt.

Finally, my Father, consider, I beg of you, that all these men together have not been able to demonstrate that any body takes the place if the one which leaves the apparently empty space, and that it is not yet possible for all these men to show that, when the water climbs back there, some body has left it. Should not that be sufficient according to your maxims to be sure that this space is empty? However, I say simply that my view is that it is empty, and you judge if those who speak with so much restraint about a matter on which they are justified in speaking with so much assurance, will be able to pass a definitive judgment on the existence of this igneous material, that is so dubious and so little established.

After having supposed this material with all the qualities you wished to give it, you account for some of my experiments. It is not a very difficult thing to explain how an effect can be produced, by supposing the material, the nature and quality of it cause: however, it is a difficulty that those who imagine them, defend themselves from a vain complacency and a secret charm that they find in their invention, chiefly when they have so well adjusted it, that from the fictions they have supposed, they necessarily conclude truths as already evident.

But I feel myself obliged to say a few words to you on this topic: these are whenever, in order to find the cause of several known phenomena, an hypothesis is posed, this hypothesis can be of three types.

For, sometimes a manifest absurdity is derived from its denial, and then the hypothesis is true and steadfast; or indeed a manifest absurdity is derived from its affirmation, and then the hypothesis is held as false; and when it has not yet been possible to draw an absurdity either from its negation or its affirmation, the hypothesis remains doubtful, so that, in order to make it the case that an hypothesis be evident, it does not suffice that the phenomena follow from it, instead, if something contrary to a single one of the phenomena follows from it, that suffices to establish its falsity.

For example, if a hot stone is found without the cause of its heat being known, will he be held to have found the genuine one who reasons in this way: Let us suppose that this stone had been placed in a large fire, from which it had been withdrawn a short time ago; then this stone should still be hot: now it is hot; consequently it was placed in the fire? For this to be the case, it would be necessary that fire be the sole cause of its heat; but since it can result from the sun and from friction, his conclusion would be without force. For just as a same cause can produce several different effects, a same effect can be produced by several different causes. It is thus that when we discuss humanly about motion, the stability of the earth, all the phenomena of the motions and retrogradations of the planets, follow perfectly from the hypotheses of *Ptolemy*, of *Tycho*, of *Copernicus* and of many others that can be presented, of all of which only one can be true. But who will dare to make so great a judgment, and who will be able, with no danger of error, to maintain one of them against the others, as, in the analogy of the stone, who will be able, with obstinacy, to sustain that fire caused its heat, without making himself ridiculous?

You see from this that even though all the phenomena in my experience fit with your hypotheses, it would be the case with others; and keeping always within the bounds of probability, it will never reach to that of a demonstration. But I hope to make you see some day at great length that from its affirmation things contrary to experiments follow absolutely. And to indicate one of them here to you in a few words: if it is true, as you suppose it to be, that this space be full of that air, more subtle and igneous, and that it has the tendency that you give to it to return into the air from which it came, and that this exterior air has the strength to pull it back like *a pressed sponge*, and that it be by that mutual attraction that the quicksilver is kept suspended, and that it makes it climb up even when the tube is tilted: it necessarily follows that when the apparent empty space is greater, a much larger height of quicksilver ought to be suspended (contrary to what happens in the experiments). For since all the parts of this interior and exterior air have this attractive quality, it is invariable, by all the rules of mechanics, that their quality, increased to the same degree as the space, should necessarily increase their effect, just as a large pressed sponge attracts more water than a small one.

Then if, in order to solve this problem, you make a second supposition; and you create still another quality expressly avoiding this inconvenience, which not being still sufficiently satisfactory, obliges you to imagine a third of them to save the other two without any proof, without establishing anything: I shall never have any thing to reply to you except what I have already said to you, or rather I shall believe that I have already answered you.

But, my Father, when I say this, and I foresee somehow these last suppositions, I am myself making a false supposition: not doubting that, if something comes forth from you, it will be built on convincing reasons, since otherwise this would be imitating those who only wish to exhibit that they are not lacking in words.

Finally, my Father, to get back to my whole reply, if it were to be the case that this space were a body (which I am far from granting to you) and if the air were filled with igneous spirits, (which I do not find even probable), and if they had the qualities you give to them (which is only a pure thought, which does not seem evident to you or to anyone else): it would not follow from this that space was filled with it. And if it were the case that by supposing that it was full of it (which does not seem so at all), it might be possible to deduce from this all that occurs in the experiments: the most favorable judgment that could be made about this view would be to rank it among the probable ones. But since we necessarily conclude things from it contrary to the experiments, judge what place it ought to have among the three kinds of hypotheses that we have spoken of earlier.

Towards the end of your letter, in order to define body you only explain a few accidents of it, and even relative ones, such as *high, low, right, left,* which properly constitute the definition of space, and which only belong to body in so far as it occupies space. For, according to your own authors, body is defined as that *which is composed of matter and form*; and what we call an *empty space* is a space having length, breadth and depth, immobile and capable of receiving and containing a body of similar length and shape; and that is what is called *solid* in geometry, in which only abstract and immaterial things are considered. So that the essential difference which exists between empty space and a body which has length, breadth and depth is that one is immobile and the other mobile; and that one can receive inside itself a body that penetrates its dimensions whereas the other cannot do so;

for the maxim that the penetration of dimensions is impossible, applies solely to the dimensions of two material bodies; otherwise it would not be universally accepted. From which it can be seen that there is as much difference between nothingness and empty space as between empty space and a material body; and that thus empty space is in the middle between matter and nothingness. That is why Aristotle's maxim that you mentioned, *that non-beings are not different*, applies to real nothingness and not to empty space.

I shall finish with your letter, where you say that you do not see that my fourth objection, which is that a material unheard of and unknown to all the senses, fills this space, *be that of any physicist*. To which I have to answer you that I can assure you of the contrary, since it comes from one of the famous ones of your time, and you could see in his writings that he sets forth in the entire universe a universal matter, imperceptible and unheard of, of similar substance as that of the sky and the elements; and further, that in examining yours, I have found that it is so imperceptible, and that it has qualities so unheard of, that is to any that had never been ascribed to it, that I find that it is of the same nature.

The sentence that precedes your final civilities defines light in these words: *Light is a luminary movement of rays composed of lucid bodies, that is to say, luminous ones*; to which I have to tell you that it seems to me that it would first be necessary to have defined what *luminary* is, and what *lucid* or *luminous body* is; for until then I am not able to understand what light is. And since we never employ in definitions the word to be *defined*, I could hardly accept yours, which says that *light* is a luminary movement of *luminous bodies*. There, my Father, are what are my views, which I always will submit to yours,

Besides, one cannot deny you the glory of having maintained Peripatetic physics as well as it is possible to do so; and I find that your letter is not less a mark of the weakness of the view that you defend than of the vigor of your mind.

And certainly the skill with which you have defended the impossibility of the vacuum with the slight basis that remains for doing so makes it easy to judge that with a similar effort, you would have invincibly established the contrary opinion, given the advantages that the experiments give it.

The same indisposition has kept me from having the honor of seeing and writing to you in my own hand. That is why I beg you to excuse the errors which will be found in this letter, especially in the spelling.

I am with all my heart,

My very Reverend Father.
Your most humble and
obedient servant,
Pascal

Paris, October 29, 1647

On the Equilibrium of
Fluids and Weight of Air

Conclusion of the two preceding treatises (on the equilibrium of fluids *and* on the weight of the mass of air) (1651?)

I have related in the preceding treatise all the effects that are generally thought, up to now, that Nature produces in order to avoid a vacuum; in which I have shown that it is absolutely false that they occur for this imaginary reason. And I have demonstrated, through reasons and absolutely convincing experiments, on the contrary, that the weight of the mass of air is the true and unique cause of them. So that it is now assured that no effect occurs in all that Nature produces in order to avoid a vacuum.

It will not be difficult to pass from that to showing that She has no horror of it. For this way of speaking is not proper, since created Nature, of which we are speaking, not being animated, is not capable of passion. Also it is metaphorical, and one understands by this nothing else but that Nature makes the same efforts to avoid a vacuum as if She had a horror of it. So that in the sense of those who speak in this way, it is the same thing to say that Nature abhors a vacuum, and to say that Nature makes great efforts to prevent a vacuum. There, since I have shown that She does nothing to flee from a vacuum, it follows that She does not abhor it. For, to follow the same figure of speech, since it is said of a man that something is indifferent to him when nothing is observed in any of his actions of any movement of desire or aversion for the thing, it ought also to be said of Nature that She has an extreme indifference for a vacuum, since one never sees that She does anything, either to seek it, or to avoid it. (I always understand by the word, "vacuum," a space empty of all bodies which fall under the senses.)

It is indeed true (and it is this that misled the ancients) that water mounts in a pump when there is no opening by which air can enter, and that thus there would be a vacuum, if the water did not follow the piston, and just as it does not mount there anymore as soon as there are slits by which the air can enter to fill it. From this it seems that it only mounts there in order to prevent a vacuum, since it only mounts when there would be a vacuum.

It is just as certain that bellows is difficult to open, when its apertures are so well plugged that the air cannot enter therein, and that thus, if it were opened, there would be a vacuum. Instead this resistance disappears when the air can enter, so that it is only present when there would be a vacuum. From which it seems that it only happens from fear of a vacuum.

Finally, it is an established fact that all bodies generally make great efforts to be continuous and to keep united whenever there would be a vacuum between them by separating them, and never otherwise. And it is from this that the conclusion is reached that this union results from the fear of a vacuum.

But in order to make evident the weakness of this conclusion, I will employ this example. When a bellows is in water, in the manner in which we often have described it, so that the end of the tube, which I suppose to be twenty feet long, sticks out of the waters and extends up into the air, and that the openings which are at one of the wings are well closed, so that water cannot enter there: one knows that it is difficult to open, and much more so if there is more water above, and that if one uncorks those openings which are in one of the wings, and thus the water enters freely, this resistance ceases.

If we want to reason about this effect in the way that was done with the others, we would also say: when the openings are stopped up, and when it is the case that if they were opened, air would enter therein through the tube, it is difficult to do it; and when water can enter there to fill it instead of air, this resistance ceases. Therefore, since it resists when air would enter therein, and not otherwise, this resistance comes from the horror that it has of air.

There is nobody who would not laugh at this conclusion because it can be the case that there is another cause of its resistance. And actually it is obvious that it cannot be opened without requiring the shifting of the water, since that which would be displaced could not enter inside the body of the bellows; and thus it would have to find its place elsewhere, and it brings about the shifting of the whole mass, and it is this that causes the resistance: which does not happen when the bellows has openings by which the water can enter. For then, whether it (the bellows) is open or closed, the water neither is raised or lowered, because that which is displaced enters proportionally into the bellows. Also it is opened with any resistance.

All of this is clear, and consequently it is necessary to consider that it cannot be opened without two things happening, one that the air actually enters into it; and the other the mass of water is made to rise; and the first is most indifferent to this, although it happens at the same time.

Let us say the same concerning the difficulty one feels in opening a bellows, stopped up on all sides, in the air. If it were opened by force, two things would happen: one, that actually there would be a vacuum; the other, that it would be necessary to lift up and sustain the whole mass of air, and it is the last of these things that causes the resistance that is felt in this, and the first is most indifferent to this. Also this resistance increases and diminishes in proportion to the weight of the air as I have shown.

It is necessary to understand the same concerning the resistance that is felt in separating all the bodies between which there would be a vacuum; for the air cannot insinuate itself there. Otherwise there would be a vacuum; for the air cannot insinuate itself there. And thus, they cannot be separated without the lifting up and sustaining of the whole mass of air, and it is this that causes that resistance.

This is the real cause of the union of bodies between which there would be a vacuum, that has taken so long a time to be discovered, because we have remained for so long with false opinions, which we have only given up by degrees; so that there have been three different views.

There have been three different errors in the world which completely prevented knowledge of this cause of the union of bodies.

The first is that it has been believed almost all of the time that air is light because ancient authors have said so. And those who are committed to believing them and following them blindly, would have remained forever with this view, had not some more capable persons drawn them away from it by the force of experiments. Thus it was not possible to think that it was the weight of the air that was the cause of this union when it was thought that air had no weight at all.

The second is that it is imagined that elements do not possess weight in themselves for no other reason than that the weight of water is not felt when one is in it, and that a bucket full of water which is sunken in it is not difficult to raise so long as it is in it, and one only begins to feel its weight when it is withdrawn from it. As if these effects could not come from another cause, or rather as if these were not beyond plausibility, there being no reason to believe that the water that is drawn in a bucket has weight when it is pulled up from it, and no longer has weight when it is spilled out there; that it loses its weight by being mixed with other water, and it regains it when it leaves that environment. Strange means that men seek to cover up their ignorance! Because they could not understand why the weight of the water is not felt, and they did not want to admit this, they have said that it has no weight there, in order to satisfy their vanity by destroying truth; and it has been accepted in that way. And that is why it was impossible to believe that the weight of the air was the cause of these effects, as long as people had this conception; since even if it were known that it is heavy, it would still have been said that it does not have weight in itself; and thus it would not have been believed that it produced any effect by its heaviness.

That is why I have shown in the *Equilibrium of Fluids* that water weighs in itself as much as it does outside; and I have explained why notwithstanding this heaviness, a bucket is not difficult to lift in it, and why the weight of it is not felt. And in the *Treatise on the Weight of the Mass of Air*, I have shown the same concerning air, so as to answer all doubts.

The third error is of another kind. It is no longer on the subject of air, but on that of the effects themselves that are attributed to the horror of the vacuum, concerning which there are most false views.

For it has been imagined that a pump raises water not only to ten or twenty feet, which is quite correct, but further to fifty, a hundred, a thousand, and as far as one would like, without any limits.

It has likewise been believed that it is not only difficult to separate two polished bodies that are pressed against one another, but that this is absolutely impossible; that neither an angel nor any created power could do it, with a hundred exaggerations that I do not deign to relate; and thus with others.

It is an error of fact so old that the origin of it cannot be found; and Hero himself, one of the ancient and most excellent authors who have written on the elevation of waters, expressly states, as something that cannot be doubted in the least, that the water in a river can be passed over a mountain to bring it to a valley on the other side, provided that it is a little deeper, by means of a siphon placed on the summit whose legs extend the length of the slopes, one in the river, the other on the other side. And he assures us that the water will rise from the river, up the mountain, to descend in the other valley, no matter what the height may be.

All those who have written on these matters say the same thing; and even all our fountain-makers still assert today that they will make suction pumps which will draw water to sixty feet if it is desired.

Neither Hero nor these authors, nor these artisans and still less the philosophers, have pushed these tests very far. For if they had tried to draw water only forty feet, they would have discovered it to be impossible. But they have only seen suction pumps and siphons of six feet, of ten, of twelve, which do not fail to achieve their effect, and that have never seen that water failed to mount there in all the tests that they happened to make. So that they have not guessed that there was a certain level after which it would happen otherwise. They thought it was a natural necessity, whose character could not change. And as they believed that the water mounted because of an invincible horror of a vacuum, they assured themselves that it would continue to rise, as it had started to without ever ceasing; and thus drawing an inference from what they saw to what they did not see, they have taken one and the other as equally true.

And it has been believed with so much certainty that the philosophers have made it one of the greatest principles of their science, and the foundation of their *Treatises on the Vacuum*. It is dictated every day in classes and everywhere in the world, and from all eras from which we have writings, all men together have been firm in this opinion, without anyone having contradicted this up to this time.

Perhaps this example will open the eyes of those who do not dare to think that an opinion may be doubtful, when it has been universally accepted for all time by all men; since simple artisans have been capable of convicting all the great men who are called philosophers of error. For Galileo states in his *Dialogues* that he learned from the fountain-makers of Italy that pumps only raise water to a certain height: after which he tested it himself; and others then did it in Italy, next in France with quicksilver, with greater ease, but which only showed the same thing in several different ways.

Before one learned about it, there was no good reason for demonstrating that the weight of air was what raised water in pumps; since this weight being limited, it could not produce an infinite effect.

But all these experiments did not suffice to show that air produced these effects; because although they had removed us from one error, they left us in another one. For we learned well from these experiments that water only raises itself to a certain height. But we did not learn that it would raise itself higher in deeper places. It was thought, on the contrary, that it always raised itself to the same height, that it was invariable in all parts of the world. And, since the weight of the air was not considered, it was imagined that the nature of a pump is such that it raises water to a certain limited height, and then no more. Also Galileo considered it as the natural height of the pump, and he call it *la Altessa limitatissima*.

Also how would one guess that this height might be variable according to the variations of place? Certainly this was not probable. And moreover this last error made it out of the question to prove that the weight of the air is the cause of these effects; for as it is greater at the feet of mountains than at the summit, it is obvious that the effects there will be proportionately greater.

That is why I concluded that one could only reach this proof by making an experiment of it at two places differing in elevation by 400 to 500 fathoms. And I chose for this the mountain of the Puy-de Dome in Auvergne, for the reason that I gave in a short work that I published in 1648 as soon as it was successful.

This experiment, having shown that water raises itself in pumps to completely different heights, according to the variations in place and weather, and that it is always proportionate to the weight of the air, led to providing perfect understanding of these effects. It ended all doubts. It showed what is the real cause of them. It revealed that it is not the horror of a vacuum. And, finally, it furnished all the illumination that could be desired on this subject.

Let someone explain now, if it is possible, otherwise than by the weight of air, why suction pumps raise water a fourth less on the Puy-de-Dome in Auvergne than at Dieppe.

Why the same siphon raises water and draws it at Dieppe but not at Paris.

Why two polished bodies, pressed against one another, are easier to separate on a steeple than in the street.

Why a bellows, stopped up on all sides, is easier to open on the top of a house than in the courtyard.

Why, when the air is more laden with mist, the piston of a stopped up syringe is harder to pull.

Finally, why all these effects are always proportional to the weight of the air, as the effect to the cause.

Is it that Nature abhors a vacuum more on the mountains than in the valley, when it is damp than when it is good weather? Doesn't She hate it equally on a steeple, in a loft and in the courtyards?

Let all the disciples of Aristotle assemble all that is strong in the writings of their master, and of his commentators, to explain these things by the abhorrence of a vacuum, if they can do it. If not, *let them acknowledge that experiments are the true masters that must be followed in physics*: that the one which has been performed on the mountains has overturned the universal belief of mankind, that Nature abhors the vacuum, and unlocked this knowledge that can never any more perish, that Nature has no abhorrence for a vacuum, that it does nothing to avoid one, and that the weight of the mass of the air is the actual cause of all the effects that have, until now, been attributed to this imaginary cause.

Preface to the Treatise on the Vacuum

The respect that is borne to antiquity being today at such a point regarding matters in which it ought to carry less weight that all its [antiquity's] thoughts are made oracular, and even its obscurities are made into mysteries; that novelties cannot be advanced without danger, and that the text of an author suffices to demolish the strength of arguments . . .

It is not that my intention is to correct one vice by another, and to render no esteem to the ancients because others have rendered too much to them.

I do not claim to banish their authority in order to uphold that of reasoning alone, even though others wish to establish their sole authority to the detriment of that of reasoning . . .

In order to make this important distinction carefully, it is necessary to appreciate that the former depend solely on memory and are purely historical, only having as their object that of knowing what authors have written; the latter depend solely on reasoning, and are completely dogmatic, having as their object that of searching for and finding hidden truths.

Those of the first kind are limited in that the books in which they are contained . . .

According to this distinction, it is necessary to adjust variously the extent of this respect. The respect that ought to be had for . . .

In matters in which one seeks only to know what authors have written, as in history, geography, jurisprudence, language, and especially in theology, and finally in all those areas which have as a basis either a simple fact, or a divine or human institution, one necessarily has to have recourse to their books, since all that one can know about them [these subjects] is contained therein: from which it is evident that one can have complete knowledge about them, and that this it is not possible to add anything more to this.

If it is a question of knowing who was the first king of the French; where the geographers place the first meridian: what words are used in a dead language, and in all questions of this kind, what other means than books can guide us? And who could add anything new to what they teach us, since we only wish to know what they contain?

It is authority alone which can enlighten us about these matters. But it is in theology where this authority has the most strength, because there it is inseparable from the truth, and we only know it through her: so that in order to attain complete certainty concerning the matters that are most incomprehensible to reason, it suffices to show them in the sacred books (just as to point out the uncertainty of the most plausible matters, it is only necessary to show that these are not included therein) because its principles are above both nature and reason, and because man's mind being too weak to reach them by its own efforts, it cannot attain these lofty clear comprehensions unless it is carried thence by an all-powerful and supernatural force.

It is not the same with regard to subjects that fall under the senses or under reasoning; authority is useless here; reason alone is able to know them. They have their distinct rights: the former had all the advantages a little while ago; here the latter reigns in its turn. But as subjects of this kind are suited to the mind's capacity, it [the mind] finds a complete freedom to extend itself here: its inexhaustible fruitfulness continually produces, and its inventions can be entirely without limit and without interruption . . .

Thus it is that geometry, arithmetic, music, physics, medicine, architecture, and all of the sciences which are subject to experience and reasoning, should be augmented in order to become perfect.

The ancients merely found them roughly outlined by those who had preceded them; and we will leave them to those who will come after us in a more completed state than we received them.

Since their perfection depends on time and effort, it is evident that although our effort and time may have accomplished less than their labors did, distinct from ours, nevertheless both joined together should have more effect than each separately.

The clarification of this difference ought to make us pity the blindness of those who offer only authority as proof in questions of physics, instead of reasoning or experiments, and make us horrified at the maliciousness of others who use only reasoning in theology instead of the authority of Scripture and of the [Church] Fathers. It is necessary to restore the courage of those timid people who do not dare to discover anything in physics, and to confound the insolence of those rash persons who produce novelties in theology. However, the misfortune of our age is such that we see many new views in theology unknown in all of antiquity, held with obstinacy and received with applause; while those that are produced in physics, although few in number seem to have to be convicted of falsehood as soon as they shock the accepted views ever so little: as if the respect that is held for the ancient philosophers were a duty, and that which is borne for the most ancient of the Church Fathers were only a matter of propriety! I leave it to judicious persons to note the importance of this abuse which perverts the order of the sciences with so much injustice; and I believe that there will be few such people who will wish only that this [liberty] be applied to other subjects, since the new inventions are infallibly errors in the [theological] subjects which are profaned with impunity; and they are absolutely necessary for the perfection of so many incomparably lower subjects that nevertheless we dare not deal with.

Let us divide our credulity and our distrust more justly; and let us limit that respect that we have for the ancients. As reason gives rise to it, she also ought to measure it; and let us consider that, if they [the ancients] had remained in that cautious state of not daring to add anything to the knowledge that they received, and [if] those of their time had created the same difficulty about receiving novelties that were offered to them, they themselves and their posterity would have been deprived of the fruits of their inventions.

Since they only made use of that which had been left to them as a means for achieving something new, and that this boldness had opened the road for them to great things, we should accept those that they had acquired for us in the same way, and following their example make them the means and not the end of our studies, and thus try to surpass them by imitating them.

For what is more unjust than to treat our ancestors with more reserve than they had for those who have preceded them, and to have that inviolable respect for them that they have only merited from us because they did not have a like one for those who had the same advantage over them!

Nature's secrets are hidden; although she is always active, we do not always discover her efforts: time reveals them from epoch to epoch, and although the same in herself all the time, she is not always equally known.

The experiments which give us an understanding of them [Nature's secrets] multiply continually; and, as they are the sole principles of physics, the consequences multiply proportionally.

It is in this way that we can today hold other views and new opinions without contempt and without ingratitude, since the basic knowledge that they have given to us has served as a stage for our own, and in these advantages we are indebted to them for the ascendency that we have over them; before, having been raised up to a certain level to which they have carried us, the least effort makes us mount higher, and with less difficulty and less glory we find ourselves above them. It is thus that we are able to find out things that it was impossible for them to perceive. Our view is more extended, and, although they knew as well as we all that they were able to observe of nature, they nevertheless did not know it as well, and we see more than they did.

However it is strange in what way their views are venerated. It has been made a crime to contradict them, and an outrage to add to them, as if they have left no more truths to be known.

Does not this amount to treating man's reason unworthily, and to putting it on the same level as the instinct of animals, since the chief difference between them has been taken away, which consists in that the effects of reason augment without end, while those of instinct remain always in the same state? Beehives were as carefully measured a thousand years ago as today, and each of them constitutes as exactly a hexagon the first time as the last one. It is the same with all that animals produce by that occult motion. Nature instructs them to the degree that necessity impels them; but this fragile science is lost with the needs that give it to them. As they receive it without study, they have not the good fortune to conserve it; and every time that it is given to them, it is new to them, since Nature having only the goal of maintaining animals in an order of limited perfection. She inspires this necessary science, always the same, lest they will fall into decay, and She does not allow them to add to it, lest they go beyond the limits She has prescribed for them. It is not the same with man, who is created for infinity. He is ignorant at the beginning of his life, but he is continuously instructed in his progress: for he gains much, not only from his own experience, but also from that of his predecessors, because he always retains in his memory the knowledge that he has acquired, and that of the ancients is always present to him in the books that they have left. And since he guards this knowledge, he can thus easily add to it: so that men are today in somewhat the same state in which those ancients would be, if they had been able to grow old up into the present, while adding to the knowledge they had that which their study would have enabled them to acquire by virtue of so many centuries. Thus it is that by a special prerogative, not only each man advances from day to day in the sciences, but that all men together continually progress in them as the universe grows older, because the same thing happens in the succession of man as [happens] in the different ages of an individual person. So that the entire series of men, during the course of all the centuries, ought to be considered as one and the same man who endures all the time and who continually learns: from which we see how unjust it is to respect antiquity for its philosophers; for as old age is the period most remote from infancy, who does not see the old age of this universal man ought not to be sought for in the times nearest his birth, but in those which are the furthest from it? Those whom we call ancient were really new in all things, and actually constituted the infancy of mankind; and as we have joined to their knowledge the experiences of the centuries that have followed them, it is in us that this antiquity that we revere in the others can be found.

They ought to be admired for the results that they have obtained from the few principles that they had, and they ought to be forgiven for those in which they failed due more to the lack of the good fortune of experiments than to the force of reasoning. For are they not to be forgiven for the view that they had about the Milky Way, when, the weakness of their eyes not having received artificial help, they attributed that color to a very great density in that portion of the heavens that reflected the light more forcibly?

But would it not be unforgivable for us to keep the same view, now that helped by the advantages that the telescope gives us, we have discovered an infinity of small stars there, whose more abundant splendor has made us realize what is the real cause of that whiteness?

Did they not also have reason for saying that all the corruptible bodies were enclosed within the heavenly sphere of the moon's orbit, when during the course of so many centuries, they had still observed neither corruption nor generation outside of that space?

But should we not be sure of the opposite, when the whole world has visibly seen comets light up and disappear far beyond the limits of that sphere?

It is thus that, regarding the subject of the vacuum, they were right in saying that nature would not allow it, because all their experiments had always made them observe that she abhorred it and could not allow it.

But if the new experiments had been known to them, perhaps they would have found grounds for affirming what they had grounds for denying in that the vacuum had not yet appeared. Also in the judgment they made that nature would not allow any vacuum, they only heard about nature in the state in which they knew her, since, to speak generally, it would not suffice to have seen her constantly in a hundred instances, nor in a thousand, nor in any number, no matter how great it might be; since, if a single case remained to be examined, this alone would suffice to prevent the general definition, and if one sole instance was contrary, this alone . . . For in all matters whose proof consists in experiments and not in demonstrations, no universal assertion can be made except by general ennumeration of all the parts or all of the different cases. Thus it is that when we say that a diamond is the hardest of all bodies, we mean that all the bodies that we know of, and we neither can nor ought to include therein those that we do not know of; and when we say that gold is the heaviest of all bodies, we would be rash to include in this general proposition those which are not yet within our cognizance, although it is not impossible that they may exist in nature.

In the same way when the ancients asserted that nature would not allow a vacuum, they meant that she would not allow it in all of the instances they had seen, and they would not have been able, without rashness, to include therein, those of which they were not cognizant. Had they been aware of these, doubtless they would have drawn the same conclusion as we have and would have sanctioned them, by their approval, with that antiquity that some want nowadays to make the sole principle of the sciences.

So it is that, without contradicting them, we can assert the opposite of what they said, and, whatever strength finally that antiquity possesses, truth should always have more, even though just discovered, since it is always older than all the opinions that have been had about it, and that it would be not to know its nature to think that it has begun to exist at the time that it has begun to be known.

II
Short Religious
and Philosophical Writings

The Memorial (1654)

This work was apparently written by Pascal immediately after his great religious experience on the Pont-Neuf in Paris in November 1654. It was found a few days after his death in the lining of his clothes. A servant discovered a small parchment that was folded, written in Pascal's hand. In the parchment was a paper that contained an exact copy of the same text, also in Pascal's hand. The text was recognized as a memorial that Pascal kept with him, carefully preserved, as a remembrance of something that he wished to have always available to read and to think about. It apparently was sewn into his clothes and unstitched each time he changed his clothing. It seems that he carried it with him at all times for eight years.

The text reads as follows:

The year of Grace 1654.

Monday, November 23, the Feast day of Saint Clement, Pope and martyr, and of others in the martyrology.

The eve of Saint Chrysogonos, martyr, and of others.

From about half past ten at night until a half hour after midnight.

FIRE

God of Abraham, God of Isaac, God of Jacob, not of the philosophers and of the learned.

Certitude, certitude, feeling, joy, peace.

(*God of Jesus Christ*).

God of Jesus Christ

Thy God and my God

Thy God shall be my God. [Ruth 1:16]

Oblivious of the world and of everything, except God.

He is encountered only by the ways taught in the Gospel.

Greatness of the human soul.

Just Father, the world has not known Thee, but I have known Thee.

Joy, joy, joy, tears of joy.

I am separated from Him.

"They have foresaken me the fountain of living waters." [Jeremiah 2:13]

My God will you leave me?

Let me not be separated from him eternally

This is the life eternal, that they know thee, the one true God, and the one Thou hast sent, Jesus Christ.

Jesus Christ.

Jesus Christ

I am separated from Him, I have fled him, renounced Him, crucified Him.

Let me never be separated from Him.

He is only preserved by the ways taught in the Gospel.

Renunciation, total and sweet

Etc.

Complete submission to Jesus Christ and to my Director

Eternally in joy for one day of practice on earth

"I will not forget Thy word." [Psalms 119:16] Amen.

On the Conversion of the Sinner (1653)

The first thing that God inspires in the soul that He deigns to touch truly is a knowledge and a completely extraordinary outlook by which the soul considers both things and itself in a totally new way.

This new light gives it [the soul] fear, and causes a disturbance in it that penetrates the repose that it had found in the things that constituted its delights.

It can no longer taste with tranquility the things that had charmed it. A continual doubt wars with it in this enjoyment, and this interior view no longer allows the soul to find this accustomed sweetness among the things in which it had abandoned itself with a complete overflowing of heart.

But it finds still more bitterness in the exercises of piety than in the world's vanities. On the one hand, the presence of visible objects effects it more than the hope of invisible ones, and on the other hand the invisible ones effect it more than the vanity of visible ones. And thus the presence of the ones and the solidity of the others contend for its affection; so that a disorder and confusions arises in it that . . .

The soul considers perishable things as perishing and even already perished; and in the certain prospect of the annihilation of everything that it loves, it is terrified by this consideration, seeing that each moment tears away from it the enjoyment of its good, and what is most dear to it slips away at every moment, and that finally a certain day will come when it will find itself bereft of all the things in which it had placed its hope. . . . So that the soul understands perfectly that its heart being attached only to fragile and vain things, its soul ought to find itself alone and abandoned at the end of this life, since it has not taken care to unite itself to a true and self-subsisting good, which could sustain it during and after this life.

On this basis, it begins to consider as nothingness all that has to return to nothingness, the sky, the earth, its mind, its body, its parents, its friends, its enemies, wealth, poverty, disgrace, prosperity, honor, shame, esteem, contempt, authority, need, health, illness and life itself; finally all that which ought to last less than its soul is incapable of satisfying the desire of this soul which seriously seeks to establish itself in a happiness as durable as itself.

It begins to be astonished at the blindness in which it has lived. And when it considers on the one hand the long time that it has lived without making these reflections and the great number of people who are living in the same way, and on the other hand, how much it is an established fact that the soul, being immortal as it is cannot find its happiness amongst things which are perishable and which will be withdrawn from it at least by death, it enters into a holy confusion and astonishment which brings it to a most salutory trouble.

For it considers that however great may be the number of those who grow old in the maxims of the world, and whatever authority that multitude of examples of those who place their happiness in the world might have, it is nonetheless an established fact that even if the things of this world should have some solid pleasure, which is recognized as false by an infinite number of so disastrous and continual examples, it is inevitable that the loss of these things, or death finally deprives us of them.

So that the soul having amassed treasures of temporal good of whatever kind they may be, be they gold, be they knowledge, be they reputation, it is an indispensible necessity that it find itself bereft of all these objects of its happiness, and that thus, if they were able to satisfy it, they will not always be able to satisfy it: and that, if it is to obtain true happiness for itself, it does not obtain for itself a durable happiness, since it has to be limited to the course of this life.

Thus, through a holy humility that God raises up above pride, the soul begins to ascend above the run of mankind. It condemns their behavior; it detests their maxims, it deplores their blindness. It turns to the search for the true good. It understands that it [the true good] must possess these two qualities, one that it last as long as the soul, and that it can only be taken away from it by its own consent, and the other that there may not be anything more lovable.

It sees that in the love that it had for the world it there found this second quality in its blindness, for it acknowledged nothing as more lovable; but since it does not see the first there, it knows that is not the highest good. It seeks it then elsewhere, and knowing by a completely pure light that it is not in the things that are within it, nor outside of it, nor in front of it, it begins to seek it above itself.

This elevation is so lofty and so transcendent that it does not stop at the heavens: they do not have what will satisfy it, nor does what is above the heavens, nor do the angels, nor do the most perfect beings. It passes over all created things, and cannot stop its heart until it has brought itself up to the throne of God, where it begins to find the repose and that good which is such that there is nothing more lovable, and that can only be taken away from it by its own consent.

For even though it does not feel these charms with which God rewards practice in piety, it understands nonetheless that created entities cannot be more lovable than the Creator, and its reason, aided by the light of Grace makes it know that there is nothing more lovable than God and that He can only be withdrawn from those who reject Him, since to possess Him is just to desire Him, and to refuse Him is to lose Him.

Thus it rejoices at having found a good that cannot be taken away from it so long as it shall desire it, and which has nothing above it.

And in these new reflections it enters into the sight of the greatness of its Creator, and into humiliations and profound adorations. It annihilates itself in His Presence, and cannot form a sufficiently low idea of itself, nor conceive a sufficiently exalted one of the supreme good, it makes new efforts to abase itself to the last abysses of nothingness, by considering God in the immensities that it multiplies; finally in this view, which exhausts its strength, it adores Him in silence; it considers itself as His vile and useless creation, and by its reiterated homages adores Him and blesses Him, and wishes to bless and adore Him forever.

Then it acknowledges the Grace which He has granted to it to manifest His infinite majesty to a lowly worm; and after a firm resolution to be eternally grateful for it, it becomes confused for having preferred so many vanities to this Divine Master, and in a spirit of remorse and penitence, it has recourse to His pity to stem His anger, the effect of which seems frightful to it in the light of His immensities. . . .

It makes ardent prayers to God that from His Mercy, as it has pleased Him to reveal Himself to it, it may please Him to lead it to Him and to create the means for accomplishing this. For since it is to God that it aspires, it aspires also to reach Him only by means that come from God Himself, since it wishes that He Himself may be its path, its object, and its final goal. Following these prayers, it begins to act and seeks among those. . . .

It begins to know God, and desires to reach Him; but since it does not know the means of achieving this, if its desire is sincere and genuine, it does the same thing as someone who wishes to get to some place, having lost his way, and knowing of his straying, would have recourse to those who know the way perfectly and. . . .

It resolves to conform to His will for the rest of its life; but as its natural weakness, with the propensity that it has to the sins in which it has lived, has reduced it to impotence in reaching this happiness, it begs from His Mercy the means of reaching Him, of cleaving to Him and adhering to Him eternally.

Thus it realizes that it ought to adore God as a creature, give thanks to Him as a debtor, satisfy Him as someone who is guilty, pay to Him as someone who is destitute.

Three Discourses on the Condition of the Great (1660)

FIRST DISCOURSE

In order to gain real knowledge of your condition, look at it in terms of this image.

When a man is tossed by a storm onto an unknown island, whose inhabitants were having trouble finding their king who had disappeared; and having a great deal of physical and facial resemblance to this king, he is taken for him, and accepted in this capacity by all of these people. At first he did not know what course to take; but finally he decided to yield himself to his good luck. He received all the homage that they wished to render to him, and allowed himself to be treated as a king.

But, since he could not forget his genuine condition, he bore in mind, at the same time that he was receiving these homages, that he was not that king that these people were looking for, and that this kingdom did not belong to him. Thus he had a double conception, the one in which he was playing the part of king, and the other in which he recognized his true state, and that it was only chance that had put him where he was. He hid this second view, and disclosed the other one. It was in terms of the first that he dealt with the populace, and in terms of the second that he dealt with himself.

Do not imagine that it is any less by chance that you possess the wealth of which you are the master, than that by which that man found himself king. You have no right to it in terms of yourself and your nature, any more than he did: and not only do you find yourself the son of a duke, but you are in the world only as a result of an infinity of chances. Your birth depends on a marriage, or rather on all marriages of those from whom you are descended. But what do these marriages depend upon? A visit made by accident, some idle talk, a thousand unforseen events.

You possess, you say, your wealth from your ancestors; but is it not as a result of a thousand accidents that your ancestors acquired it and that they preserved it? Do you imagine, also, that it is by some natural law that these goods have passed from your ancestors to you? That is not the case. This state of affairs is based only on the sole will of some legislators who could have had good reasons, but none of which is drawn from a natural right that you have over these things. If it had pleased them to order that these goods, after having been possessed by your fathers during their lifetimes, should return to the state after their deaths, you would have no cause for complaint.

Thus the entire title by which you possess your wealth is not a title of nature, but of human institution. Another turn of imagination by those who made the laws would have left you poor; and it is only these fortuitous circumstances which have produced you, with the whim of laws favorable with regard to you, which puts you in possession of all those goods.

I do not mean that they do not legitimately belong to you, and that someone else is allowed to rob you of them; for God who is the master of them, has allowed societies to make laws for dividing them; and when these laws are once established, it is unjust to violate them. This is what distinguishes you a little from that man who only possessed his kingdom as a result of the people's mistake; because God would not authorize that possession, and would oblige him to give it up, while He authorizes yours. But what is completely in common in his and your case, is that that right which you have is not based, any more than his is, on any quality or any merit which is in you and which makes you worthy of it. Your soul and your body are, of themselves, indifferent to the status of ferryman or that of duke; and there is no natural condition which attaches them [the soul and the body] to one status rather than the other.

What follows from this? that you ought to have, like the man we have spoken of, a double conception, and that if you act outwardly with men in accordance to your rank, you ought to recognize, by a more hidden, but more genuine conception, that you have nothing naturally that is superior to them. If the public conception elevates you above the run of mankind, let the other humble you and keep you in a perfect equality with all mankind; for that is your natural state.

The people who admire you, do not, perhaps, know this secret. They believe that nobility is a real greatness, and they almost consider the great as being of another nature than others. Do not reveal this mistake to them, if you wish; but do not abuse this elevation insolently, and especially do not deceive yourself into believing that your being has something more elevated than that of others.

What would you say of that man who was made king as a result of the mistake of the populace, if he came to so forget his natural status, that he might have thought that that kingdom belonged to him, and that he deserved it and that it was rightfully his? You would marvel at his stupidity and foolishness. But is there any less of it among people of rank who live in so strange a forgetfulness of their natural state?

How important this advice is! For all the outburst, all the violence, and all the vanity of great men result from the fact that they do not know what they are, it being difficult that those who see themselves inwardly as equal to everyone else, and who are completely convinced that they have nothing in themselves which merits those slight advantages that God has given them over others, should treat them insolently. One would have to forget oneself for that, and believe that he had some genuine excellence above them, in which the illusion I am trying to make clear to you consists.

SECOND DISCOURSE

It is good, Sir, that you should know what is due you, so that you may not claim to demand from men what is not owing to you: for that is an obvious injustice: however, it is very common to those of your status, because they do not know the nature of it.

There are two kinds of greatness in the world; for there is institutional greatness and natural greatness. Institutional greatness depends on the will of men, who have believed with reason that they ought to honor certain positions and attach certain signs to them. Dignities and nobility are of this type. In one country nobles are honored; in another, the plebians; in this one, the eldest, in the other the youngest. Why is this? Because it has pleased men to do so. The matter was indifferent before the institution of it: after the institution of it, it becomes just, because it is unjust to disturb it.

The natural greatnesses are those that are independent of the whims of men, because they consist in the genuine and actual qualities of the soul and the body, which make one or the other most estimable, such as the sciences, the enlightenment of the mind, virtue, health and strength.

We owe something to each kind of greatness; but since they are of a different nature, we also owe them different kinds of respect.

To institutional greatness, we owe the respect of the institution, that is to say, certain external ceremonies which ought to be, nevertheless, accompanied, according to reason, by an internal recognition of the justice of that order, but which do not make us conceive any genuine quality in those whom we honor in this way. One has to speak to kings on bended knee; one has to remain standing in the chamber of princes. It is foolishness and a baseness of spirit to refuse them these obligations.

But, regarding the natural respects which consist in esteem, we owe them only to natural greatness; and we owe, on the other hand, contempt and aversion to qualities contrary to natural greatness. It is not necessary, because you are a duke, that I have esteem for you; but it is necessary that I bow to you. If you are a duke and a gentleman, I render what I am obliged to one and to the other of these statuses. I shall not refuse you the ceremonies that your status as duke deserves, nor the esteem that that of a gentleman deserves. But if you were a duke without being a gentleman, I would still do you justice, for in rendering to you the external obligations that the human order has attached to your birth, I would not fail to have the internal contempt for you that the baseness of your spirit would deserve.

Therein is what constitutes the justice of these obligations. And injustice constitutes attaching natural respect to institutional greatness, or in demanding institutional respect for natural greatness. M.N. . . . is a greater geometer than I am; in the light of this, he wants to pass in front of me: I will tell him that he understands nothing about the matter. Geometry is a natural greatness; it demands a preference of esteem; but men have attached no external preference to it. Therefore, I will pass before him, and will esteem him more than myself as a geometer. In the same way, if, being a duke and a peer, you are not satisfied that I stand bareheaded before you, and should wish also that I had esteem for you, I would beg you to show me the qualities that deserve my esteem. If you did this, then it would be yours, and I could not refuse it to you justly; but if you did not do this, you would be unjust to demand it of me, and assuredly, you will not succeed in this, were you the greatest prince in the world.

THIRD DISCOURSE

I wish to make known to you, Sir, your true condition; for of all things in the world, it is that of which people of your status are most ignorant. What is it, according to you, to be a great nobleman? It is to be master of several objects of human desire, and thus to be able to satisfy the needs and desires of many. It is these needs and desires that draw them to you, and that make them submit to you: without that, they would not even look at you; but they hope, by those services and that deference that they give to you, to obtain from you, some portion of those goods that they desire and which they see that you have at your disposal.

God is surrounded by people full of charity, who ask Him for the goods of charity which are in His power: thus He is properly king of charity.

Similarly you are surrounded by a small number of persons, over whom you reign in your way. These people are full of desire. They ask you for the things desired: it is desire that binds them to you. You are then properly a king of desire. Your kingdom is of slight extent; but you are equal in that to the greatest kings on earth; they are like you kings of desire. It is desire that constitutes their strength, that is to say the possession of things that the greediness of men covets.

But in knowing your natural condition, make use of the means that it gives you, and do not pretend to rule by another basis than that which makes you king. It is not your strength and your natural power that subjects all these people to you. Do not pretend then to dominate them by force, or to treat them with harshness. Satisfy their just desires; Alleviate their needs; make it your pleasure to be beneficent; put forth to them as much as you can; and you will be acting as the true king of desire.

What I am telling you does not go very far; and if you remain there, you will not prevent yourself from being lost; but at least you will lose yourself as a virtuous man. There are people who damn themselves so foolishly through avarice, through brutality, through debauchery, through violence, through excesses, through blasphemy! The way that I open to you is doubtless more virtuous; but in truth it is always a great folly to damn oneself; and that is why one should not remain at this point. One should have contempt for desire and its kingdom and aspire to that kingdom of charity where all the subjects breathe only charity, and wish only the goods of charity. Others than I will tell you of the road to it: it suffices for me to have turned you from those brutish lives in which I see that several people of your esteem allow themselves to be carried away for want of knowing the true state of this condition.

Conversation with M. de Saci (1655)[1]

M. Pascal also came to live at Port-Royal-des-Champs at that time. I am not going to stop to state who that man was who is admired not only by all of France, but all of Europe as well. His mind, always lively, always active, possessed a range, an elevation, a firmness, a penetration, and a clarity beyond anything that can be imagined. There were no men competent in mathematics who did not give him precedence. Witness the story of the famous roulette, which was at that time the talk of all the learned people. It is known that he seemed to make copper come alive, and to make bronze have a mind. He made some small wheels, destitute of reason, on which were the first ten digits, give reason to the most rational people, and he made deaf machines speak in some sort of way, in order to resolve by playing, problems about numbers that held back the most learned people; which cost him so much time and mental effort that, in order to develop this machine to the point at which all the world admired it, and which I have seen with my own eyes, he allowed himself to be disconcerted by it for more than three years. That admirable man, finally being touched by God, submitted that so lofty mind to the gentle yoke of Jesus Christ, and that so noble and so great heart embraced penitence with humility. He came to Paris to throw himself into the arms of M. Singlin,[2] resolved to do all that he should command.

M. Singlin believed when he saw this great genius that it would be well to send him to Port-Royal-des-Champs, where M. Arnauld would lead him in what pertained to the higher sciences, and where M. de Saci would teach him to despise them. He came therefore to live at Port-Royal. Out of courtesy, M. de Saci could not avoid seeing him, especially since M. Singlin

[1]Isaac Le Maistre de Saci, 1613–1684, nephew of Antoine Arnauld, was a Jansenist priest who worked on translating the Bible. He was imprisoned in the Bastille from 1666 to 1668 during the persecution of the Jansenists. This discussion with Pascal took place in January 1655.

[2]Antoine Singlin, 1607–1664, was a Jansenist priest who was ordained by St. Vincent de Paul and who was the confessor to St. Cyran and to Port-Royal. He became the Superior there. In 1654 he made M. de Saci Pascal's director.

had requested him to do so. But the holy light that he found in Scripture and in the Fathers, made him hope that he would not be dazzled by all of M. Pascal's brilliance, which however charmed and carried everyone away.

He found in fact all that he [Pascal] said quite correct. He admitted with pleasure the strength of his mind and of his conversation. But there was nothing new in it. All the great things that M. Pascal said to him, he had seen previously in St. Augustine; and to do justice to everyone, he said, "M. Pascal is most estimable in that, not having read the Church Fathers, he had himself, by means of the penetration of his mind, found the same truths that they had found. He finds them surprising, he said, because he has not seen them anywhere else. But for us, we are used to seeing them on all sides in our books." Thus, this wise clergyman, finding that the ancients had not less light than the moderns, adhered to the former, and esteemed M. Pascal highly in that he agreed with St. Augustine in all matters.

M. de Saci's usual manner in talking with people was to adapt his conversation to those to whom he was speaking. If he met M. Champaigne, for example, he spoke with him about painting.[3] If he met M. Hamon, he discussed medicine with him. If he met the surgeon of the place, he asked him about surgery. Those who cultivated the vine, or trees, or grain, told him all that was noteworthy about them. Everything served him as a means for quickly passing to God, and for leading others there too. He therefore believed it was his duty to deal with M. Pascal within his domain, and to speak with him about the philosophical readings which occupied him the most. He got him onto this subject in the first discussions they had together. M. Pascal told him that the works that were most familiar to him were those of Epictetus and Montaigne, and he had the highest praise for those two minds. M. de Saci, who had always thought it a duty to read little of these authors, begged M. Pascal to tell all about them.

"Epictetus," he told him, "is one of the world's philosophers who has best understood man's duties. He insists, ahead of everything else, that man regard God as his principal object, that he be convinced that He governs everything justly; that he submit himself to Him gladly, and that he follow Him voluntarily with regard to all things, since He does nothing except with a superior wisdom. This attitude will thus put a stop to all complaints and murmurs, and will prepare man's mind to accept peaceably all of the most troublesome events. Never say, says he, 'I have lost that.' Say instead, 'I have given it back. My son is dead. I have given him back. My wife is dead. I have given her back.' So with regard to goods and everything else. 'But he who takes it from me is a wicked man,' you say. Why are you troubled by the fact that he who has lent it to you asks for it back again? While he lets you use it, take care of it like a good that belongs

---

[3]Phillippe de Champaigne (1602–1674), the famous painter; Jean Hamon, (1618–1687), the learned doctor of Port-Royal.

to someone else, in the way that a man making a trip acts in a hotel. You ought not, says he, desire that things be done as you would wish; but you ought to wish that they be done as they are done. Remember, he also says, that you are here as an actor, and that you play the role in the play that the producer gives to you. If he gives you a short role, play the short one. If he gives you a long one, play the long one. If he wants you to pretend to be a tramp, you ought to do it with all the simplicity that you can employ, and so with the rest. It is your job to play the role well which is given to you. But choosing it is another's business. Have before your eyes every day death and the evils which seem most unbearable, and you will never think of anything lower, and you desire nothing to excess.

"He also points out in thousands of ways what man ought to do. He insists that he be humble, that he hide his good resolutions, especially in the beginning, and that he achieve them secretly. Nothing destroys them more than revealing them. He does not weary of repeating that all of man's study and desire ought to be to find out God's will and to follow it.

"There, Monsieur," said Pascal to M. de Saci, "is the wisdom of that great mind who so well knew man's duties. I dare to say that he would have deserved to be adored, if he had known his impotence as well, since it would be necessary to be God to teach men both one and the other. Also, since he was made of earth and ashes, after having so well understood what ought to be done, here is how he destroys himself in the presumption concerning what can be done. He says that God has given man the means of taking care of all of his obligations; that these means are within our power; that happiness must be sought by things which are within our power, since God has given them to us for this purpose; that it is necessary to find out what there is in us that is free; that goods, life, esteem are not in our power, and do not lead therefore to God; but that the mind cannot be forced to believe that it knows to be false, nor can the will be forced to love that which will make it unhappy; that these two powers are free, and that it through them that we can make ourselves perfect; that man through these powers can know God perfectly, can love Him, obey Him, please Him, cure himself of all vices, acquire all virtues, thus making himself holy and the companion of God. These principles of a diabolically proud man lead to other errors, such as: that the soul is part of the Divine Substance; that pain and death are not evils; that one can commit suicide when one is so persecuted that he believes that God is calling him; and so on.

"As for Montaigne, concerning whom you also wish, Monsieur, that I talk to you, having been born in a Christian state, he professed the Catholic religion, and there was nothing odd about this. But since he wished to discover what morality reason ought to prescribe independent of the light of faith, he based his principle upon that supposition; and thus by considering man as destitute of all revelation, he discoursed in this manner. He places all things in a universal and so general doubt that this very doubt carries itself away, that is to say, whether he does doubt, and doubting even this last claim, his uncertainty revolves around itself in a perpetual circle, with no resting place; opposing itself equally to those who are sure that all is uncertain and to those who are sure that it all is not so, because he does not want to be sure about anything. It is in this doubt that doubts of itself and in this ignorance which is ignorant of itself, and which he calls his master form, that the essence of his view is to be found, which he could not . express by any positive terms. For, if he asserts that he doubts, he belies himself by affirming at least that he doubts; which being formally contrary to his intention, could only be employed by interrogation; so that, not wanting to state 'I do not know,' he says, 'What do I know?', which he employed in his emblem, placing it under some balance, which weighing the contradictories, are in perfect equilibrium. This is to say that he is a pure Pyrrhonian skeptic. All of his statements and all of his *Essays* proceed on this principle; and it is the thing he claims actually to establish, although he does not always indicate his intention. In his works he insensibly destroys all that passes as the most certain among men, not in order to establish the contrary with certitude of which he alone is the enemy, but solely in order to show that since the appearances are equal on the one side and the other, one does not know where to rest his belief.

"In this frame of mind he makes fun of all convictions. For example, he fights against those who have thought of establishing in France a great remedy against lawsuits by the populace and the alleged justice of the laws. As if one could ever sever the roots of doubts from which lawsuits are born, and as if there might be dikes that could arrest the torrent of uncertainty, and could capture conjectures! At this point, when he says that it would be as good to submit one's cause to the first passerby as to some judges armed with many ordinances, he does not contend that the order of the state ought to be changed. He is not so ambitious. He does not contend that his advice is better than others, and he does not believe that any is good. It is only in order to prove the vanity of the most accepted opinions; showing that the exclusion of all laws would rather decrease the number of quarrels, whereas the multitude of laws serves only to increase it, since difficulties augment proportionally to the weighing of them; since obscurities are multiplied by commentaries; and since the surest way to understand the meaning of a discourse is not by examining it, and by taking it as it appears at first. As soon as it is examined a little, all clarity vanishes. Also he judges all human actions and historical events randomly, sometimes in one way, sometimes in another, freely following his first impression, and without constraining his thoughts according to rules of reasoning, which have only false measures. He delights in showing, by his own example, the contrarities of the same mind. In this wholly free spirit, it is completely the same to him, whether or not he wins in dispute, having always, by victory or defeat, a means of showing the feebleness of opinions; being armed with so great advantage by this universal doubt, that he is strengthened in it equally by triumph and by loss.

"It is from this position, completely floating and wavering, that he fights with an invincible resolution against the heretics of his time concerning their claims to be the only ones who know the true meaning of Scripture; and it is also from this position that he attacks most vigorously the horrible impiety of those who dare to assert that there is no God. He takes them on especially in the *Apology for Raimond Sebond*, and finding them voluntarily deprived of all revelation, and abandoned to their own natural lights, all faith set aside, he questions them concerning by what authority they undertake to judge about this supreme Being who is infinite according to His own definition, they who actually do not know any of the things of nature! He asks them what principles they rest upon. He presses them to exhibit them. He examines all those that they can set forth, and goes so far into them, by the talent at which he excels, that he shows the vanity of all those that are accepted as the most natural and the surest ones. He asks if the soul knows anything: if it knows itself: if it is a substance or an accident, body or spirit; what is each of these things, and if there be anything which falls in neither one nor the other of the categories; if it knows its own body; what is matter; if it (the soul) can distinguish among the innumerable variety of bodies when they are produced out of it (matter); how it (the soul) can reason, if it is material; and how can it be joined to a particular body and feel its passions, if it is spiritual; when did it come into existence; with the body or before it; if it (the soul) will terminate with it (the body) or not; if it is never mistaken; if it knows when it errs, seeing that the essence of the mistake consists in not recognizing it as such; if in its darkness, it does not believe as firmly that two plus three equals six, as it afterwards knows that the answer is five; if animals reason, think, speak; and who can determine what time is, what space or extension are, what motion consists in, what constitutes unity, which are all things that surround us, and are completely inexplicable; what is health, sickness, life, death, good, evil, justice, sin, of which we speak all the time; if we have within us principles of truth, and if those that we believe, and call axioms or common notions, because they are common to all men, conform to the essential truth. And since we only know by faith alone that a completely good Being has truly given these to us in creating us to know the truth, who can know without this light, whether, having been formed by chance, they are not uncertain, or whether, having been formed by a false (or deceitful) and wicked being; he has only given to us falsely (or deceitfully) in order to seduce us; thereby showing that God and truth are inseparable, and if the one is or is not, if it is certain or uncertain, the other is necessarily the same. Who knows then if common sense, that we consider (or take) as the judge of truth, possesses this character from that which has created it? Further, who knows what is truth, and how we can be sure of possessing it without knowing (or being acquainted with) it? Who knows even what is being which cannot be defined, since there is nothing more general, and which could only be explained by employing the word itself at the outset, by saying "*It is* being . . . "? And since we do not know what are soul, body, time, space, motion, truth, good, nor even being, nor can we explain the ideas we form (or frame) of them, then how can we be sure that they are the same in all men, in view of the fact that we have no other sign of this than the uniformity of the consequences (or results). Which is not always an indication of that of the sources? For they (the sources) can be very different and yet lead to the same conclusions, everyone knowing that truth is often derived from falsity.

"Finally he examines the sciences very profoundly; geometry, concerning which he points out the uncertainty in the axioms, and in the terms that are not defined in the discipline, like 'extension,' 'motion,' etc; physics in many more ways; medicine in an infinity of ways; history, politics, ethics, jurisprudence and the rest, in such manner that we remain convinced that we are not thinking better at the moment than in some dream from which we will only awaken at death, and during which we possess as few principles of the truth as during natural sleep. It is thus that he so forcefully and cruelly reprimands reason bereft of faith, by making her doubt whether she is rational, and whether animals are or are not, or to a greater or less degree, he makes her descend from the excellence she has attributed to herself, and places her by grace on the same level with beasts, without allowing her to leave this state until she has been instructed by her Creator Himself concerning her status, of which she is ignorant, threatening her if she grumbles at being placed lowest of all, which is as easy as the opposite; and giving her, however, only the power to act in order to take note of her feebleness with a sincere humility, instead of ascending by a foolish insolence."

M. de Saci believing himself to be living in a new land and to be listening to a new language, said to himself the words of St. Augustine: "O God of truth! Are those who know these subtleties of reasoning more pleasing to you because of this?" He pitied this philosopher who pricked and tore himself on all sides with the thorns that he created, as St. Augustine said of himself when he was in that state. Then after a quite long reflection, he said to Pascal:

"I am grateful to you, sir. I am sure that if I had read Montaigne for a long time, I would not know him as well as I do as a result of this conversation I have just had with you. This man ought to wish to be known only by the accounts you give of his writings; and he might say, along with St. Augustine, *Ibi me vide, attende.* I certainly believe that this man had ability, but I do not know whether you attribute a bit more of it to him than he had by that logical chain that you make of his principles. You can judge that having spent my life as I have done, I have received little advice to read this author, all of whose works have none of what we ought to chiefly to seek in our readings, according to St. Augustine's rule, because his words do not seem to issue from a basic source of humility and piety. The philosophers of yesteryear, who are called Academic Skeptics, should be pardoned for casting all in doubt. But why did Montaigne need to enliven the mind by reviving a doctrine which now appears to be foolishness to Christians? For it can be said of Montaigne according to him (St. Augustine), 'In all that he says, he sets faith aside. Thus we who have faith, ought to set aside in the same way all that he says.' I do not blame at all the mind of that author, it being a great gift of God. But he could have made better use of it, making a sacrifice of it to God rather than to the devil. Of what value is a blessing, when it is used so badly? *Quid proderat* etc.? This holy teacher said of himself before his conversion. You are fortunate, sir, in having raised yourself above these people who are called learned, immersed in the drunkenness of knowledge, but whose hearts are devoid of truth. God has diffused other sweets and attractions in your heart than those that you found in Montaigne. He has recalled you from that dangerous pleasure, a *iucundidate pestifere* St. Augustine says, that of thanking God for having been forgiven for the sins committed while enjoying vanity too well. St. Augustine is much more to be believed in this, since he formerly held these views. And, as you say of Montaigne, that he combatted the heretics of his age by this universal doubt, it was also by this same doubt of the Academic Skeptics that St. Augustine gave up the Manichean heresy. When he had found God, he renounced these vanities that he termed sacrilegious, and did what he reports about some others. He realized with what wisdom St. Paul warned us not to allow ourselves to be seduced by these views. For he admits that there is a certain charm in them that delights. Sometimes one believes true things solely because they are eloquently stated. These are the dangerous meats, he says, but they are served in lovely dishes. But these meats, instead of nourishing the heart, empty it. It is then like the people who sleep and who think they are eating while they are asleep. These imaginary meats leave them also as empty as they were.''

M. de Saci told Pascal several similar things, whereupon Pascal said to him that if he had complimented him for knowing Montaigne well and for being able to exposit him clearly, he could tell him without flattery that he knew St. Augustine much better, and knew how to exposit him more cogently, though little to poor Montaigne's advantage. He acknowledged being highly edified by the solidity of everything that had just been presented to him. However, being still completely full of his author, he could not restrain himself, and said:

"I acknowledge, sir, that I cannot, without joy, see in this author proud reason wounded so invincibly by its own weapons, and this so bloody revolt of man against man, which throws him down into bestiality away from God's company, to which he had raised himself by the maxims (of his feeble reason). And I should have loved the minister of so great a vengeance with all my heart, if, being a disciple of the Church by faith, he had followed the rules of morality by leading men, whom he had so usefully humiliated, into not provoking by new crimes He who alone can save them from the crimes of which Montaigne has convinced them they are not even able to be aware.

"But, instead he acts like a pagan in this. From this principle, he says that without faith all is uncertain, and considering how much the true and the good are sought without there being any progress towards tranquility, he concludes that men should leave the concern about this to others; and should remain therefore at rest, gliding lightly over subjects for fear of drowning by plunging into them; and should accept the true and the good according to the first appearance, without weighing them, because they are so far from being solid that as soon as one grasps them, they escape through one's fingers leaving them empty. That is why he accepts the testimony of the senses and the common notions, since he would have to do violence to himself to deny them, and since he does not know if he would gain by so doing, not being able to tell where truth lies. Thus he flees from pain and death, because his instinct so pushes him, and because he does not wish to resist them for that reason, but without concluding that these are genuine evils thereby not relying too much on these natural emotions of fear, in view of the fact that others of pleasure are felt that are considered wrong, even though nature tells us otherwise. Thus there is nothing extravagant in his conduct. He acts like other men; and all that they do in the foolish belief that they are pursuing the true good, he does according to another principle, which is that since the probabilities are similar on one side and the other, example and convenience are the counterweights which influence him.

"He therefore follows his country's mores, because custom sways him. He mounts his horse like someone who would not be a philosopher, since he does it, but without believing that this is right; not knowing whether this animal, on the contrary is the one to make use of him. He also does some violence to himself in order to avoid certain vices, and he even keeps faithful in his marriage, because of the penalties that follow from a disorderly life. But if the difficulties he accepts exceed those that he avoids, he remains peaceful, the rule of his actions being always convenience and tranquility. He therefore completely casts away that stoical virtue that is portrayed with a stern express, a fierce look, bristling looks, brow sweaty and wrinkled, with a pained and taut stance, far from men, in a mournful silence, and alone atop a rock. This he says is a phantom which is capable of scaring children, and which accomplishes nothing with its continual travail other than to seek for the repose that it never attains. His own way of life is simple, unconstrained, pleasant, lively, one might say playful. It pursues whatever pleases it, and toys nonchalantly with good or bad things, lying indolently in the bosom of peaceful idleness, which points out to men who seek happiness so painfully, that it is to be found only where she is, and that ignorance and lack of curiosity are two soft pillows for a well constructed head, as he himself says.

"I cannot hide from you, sir, that in reading this author and in comparing him with Epictetus, I have found that they were certainly the two greatest defenders of the two most famous sects of the world, and the only ones in agreement with reason, since one can only follow one of these two routes, that is: either that there is a God, and then the supreme good is within Him, or that His Being is uncertain, and that then the true good also is, since he is not capable of it.

"I have taken an extreme pleasure in observing in these diverse reasonings the extent to which both men have attained some conformity with the genuine wisdom that they tried to know. For it is pleasing to find in nature her desire to paint God in all her works, in which we see some trace of Him, because they are images of Him. How much more is it just to consider in the productions of the mind the efforts made to imitate the essential truth, even while fleeing from it, and to observe the extent to which they attain it, and to which they wander from it, as I have tried to do in this study!

"It is true, sir, that you have just admirably made me see the slight use that Christians can make of these philosophical studies. I shall not stop, nevertheless, with your permission, from still further telling you my thoughts, ready nevertheless to renounce all the illumination that does not come from you: in which I will have the advantage either of having encountered the truth by good fortune, or of receiving it from you with certainty. It seems to me that the source of the errors of these two sects consists in that of not having known that man's present state differs from that of his creation: so that one of them, noticing several traces of man's original greatness, and being ignorant of his corruption, has treated his nature as sound and without need of rehabilitation, which leads him to the height of pride. On the other hand, the other sect, being aware of man's present misery and not knowing of his original dignity, treats his nature as necessarily weak and irreparable, which thrusts him into despair of attaining genuine good, and from this into extreme indolence. Thus these two states have to be known together in order to see the whole truth. By being known separately, they necessarily lead to one of these two vices, pride or laziness, in which all men certainly are before grace, since if they do not remain in their disorderly lives by indolence, they emerge from them by vanity, so true is what you have just told me from St. Augustine, and which I find widely to be the case. For in fact, homage is paid to them (the two vices) in many ways.

"It is then as a result of this imperfect understanding that it happens that the one, knowing man's duties, but unaware of his impotence, loses itself in presumption, and that the other, knowing his impotence and not his duty, falls into indolence; from which it seems that since the one leads to truth, the other to error, an alliance of the two should result in a perfect ethic. But instead of this peace, only war and general destruction would result from putting them together: for the one establishing certitude, the other doubt, the one the greatness of man, the other his weakness, the two of them together destroy the truth as well as falsehoods. So that they cannot subsist alone because of their defects, nor can they unite because of their opposition, and thus they destroy and annihilate each other in order to give way to the truth of the Gospel. It is this that harmonizes contrarities by a wholly divine skill, and uniting all that is true, and chasing away all that is false, makes of them a truly celestial wisdom in which the opposites are harmonized which were incompatible according to human views. And the reason for this is that these worldly philosophers locate these contraries in the same subject: for one of them attributed greatness to nature and the other of them, weakness to this same nature, which could not subsist. Faith instead teaches us to place them in different subjects: all that there is that is weak belonging to nature, all that there is that is strong belonging to grace. That is the astonishing and new union that God alone could teach, and that He alone could produce, and which is only a copy and an effect of the ineffable union of two natures in the sole person of a Man-God.

"I beg your pardon, sir," M. Pascal said to M. de Saci, "for declaiming in this manner before you concerning Theology, instead of keeping to philosophy, which alone was my subject. I was led into it imperceptibly, and it is difficult not to enter into it no matter what truth one deals with, because it is the heart of all truth, which is clear here since it so obviously includes all those which are found in these opinions. Thus I do not see how any of them (these sects) could refuse to follow it. For if they are full of the idea of man's greatness, what have they imagined that does not give way to the promises of the Gospel, which are nothing but the worthy price of the death of God? And if they are happy in observing nature's infirmity, their ideas are not equal to those of the real weakness of sin, of which the same death has been the remedy. Thus all find there more than they hoped for; and what is wonderful, they are there united, they who could not get together in an infinitely lower degree."

M. de Saci could not restrain himself from telling M. Pascal that he was surprised at how well he was able to put things; but he asserted at the same time that everyone did not possess the secret as he (Pascal) did of making such wise and elevated reflections on what they read. He told him that he was like those skillful doctors who, by a clever way of preparing the most deadly poisons, know how to extract the best remedies from them. He added that, although he fully realized, on the basis of what he had just told him, that these readings were useful to him (Pascal), he could not believe that they would be advantageous to many people whose intellects lagged a bit, and who would not have enough elevation to read these authors and to judge them, and to know how to draw pearls from amidst a dunghill, *aurum ex stercore*, one of the Fathers said. Which could much better be said of those philosophers whose dunghill, by their foul fumes, could darken the wavering faith of those who read them. This is why he would always advise such persons not to expose themselves lightly to these readings, from fear of becoming lost along with those philosophers, and of becoming the prey of devils and the food of worms, according to the words of the Bible, as these philosophers have been."

"Concerning the usefulness of these readings," M. Pascal said, "I will tell you my views very simply. I find in Epictetus an incomparable skill for disturbing the repose of those who seek it in external things, and in forcing them to realize that they are truly slaves and miserable blind men; that it is impossible that they will find anything but the error and pain that they are fleeing from unless they give themselves unconditionally to God alone. Montaigne is incomparable for confounding the pride of those who, outside of faith, dress themselves in a genuine justice; for disabusing those who cling to their own opinions, and who think they find unshakable truths in the sciences; and for so well convincing reason of its lack of understanding and its wanderings, that it is difficult, when good use is made of her principles, to be tempted to find repugnancies in the mysteries: for the mind is so worn out by them that it is very far from wishing to judge whether the Incarnation or the mystery of the Eucharist are possible; which ordinary men discuss only too often.

"But if Epictetus fights against laziness, he leads to pride, so that he can be extremely harmful to those who are convinced of the corruption of the most perfect justice which is not based on faith. And Montaigne is absolutely pernicious to those who have some inclination to impiety and vices. That is why these readings ought to be regulated with much care, discretion and regard for the condition and the morals of those to whom they are recommended. It seems to me that only in joining them together, could they not succeed very badly, in that one opposes the evil of the other: not that they could bestow virtue, but only disturb the vices: the soul finding itself struggling with these contraries, one of which chases away pride, and the other, laziness, and not being able to find repose in any of these vices by her (the soul's) reasonings, nor as well to flee from all of them."

It was thus that these two persons of such fine intellects finally agreed on the subject of reading these philosophers, and met at the same end, which they reached however by a somewhat different way: M. de Saci getting there at once by means of a clear view of Christianity, and M. Pascal only getting there after many detours by attaching himself to the principles of these philosophers.

At the time M. de Saci and all of Port-Royal-des-Champs were thus completely occupied with the joy brought about by the conversion and the sight of M. Pascal, and they marveled at the all powerful force of grace, which by a mercy of which there are few examples, had so profoundly humbled this mind who was himself so great.

The Provincial Letters, 1656–1657*

Letter I

Disputes in the Sorbonne, and the invention of proximate power—a term employed by the Jesuits to procure the censure of M. Arnauld

Paris, January 23, 1656

SIR,—We were entirely mistaken. It was only yesterday that I was undeceived. Until that time I had labored under the impression that the disputes in the Sorbonne were vastly important, and deeply affected the interests of religion. The frequent convocations of an assembly so illustrious as that of the Theological Faculty of Paris, attended by so many extraordinary and unprecedented circumstances, led one to form such high expectations, that it was impossible to help coming to the conclusion that the subject was most extraordinary. You will be greatly surprised, however, when you learn from the following account, the issue of this grand demonstration, which, having made myself perfectly master of the subject, I shall be able to tell you in very few words.

Two questions, then, were brought under examination; the one a question of fact, the other a question of right.

The question of fact consisted in ascertaining whether M. Arnauld[1] was guilty of presumption, for having asserted in his second letter that he had carefully perused the book of Jansenius, and that he had not discovered the propositions condemned by the late pope; but that, nevertheless, as he condemned these propositions wherever they might occur, he condemned them in Jansenius,[2] if they were really contained in that work.

The question here was, if he could, without presumption, entertain a doubt that these propositions were in Jansenius, after the bishops had declared that they were.

The matter having been brought before the Sorbonne, seventy-one

---

*Translated by Thomas M'Crie
[1]Antoine Arnauld, 1612–1694, leading Jansenist philosopher and theologian.
[2]Jansenius, Cornelius Jansen, 1585–1638, Bishop of Ypres and leader of the Jansenists; author of *Augustinus*.

doctors undertook his defense, maintaining that the only reply he could possibly give to the demands made upon him in so many publications, calling on him to say if he held that these propositions were in that book, was, that he had not been able to find them, but that if they were in the book, he condemned them in the book.

Some even went a step farther, and protested that, after all the search they had made into the book, they had never stumbled upon these propositions, and that they had, on the contrary, found sentiments entirely at variance with them. They then earnestly begged that, if any doctor present had discovered them, he would have the goodness to point them out; adding, that what was so easy could not reasonably be refused, as this would be the surest way to silence the whole of them, M. Arnauld included; but this proposal has been uniformly declined. So much for the one side.

On the other side are eighty secular doctors, and some forty mendicant friars, who have condemned M. Arnauld's proposition, without choosing to examine whether he has spoken truly or falsely—who, in fact, have declared, that they have nothing to do with the veracity of his proposition, but simply with its temerity.

Besides these, there were fifteen who were not in favor of the censure, and who are called Neutrals.

Such was the issue of the question of fact, regarding which, I must say, I give myself very little concern. It does not affect my conscience in the least whether M. Arnauld is presumptuous, or the reverse; and should I be tempted, from curiosity, to ascertain whether these propositions are contained in Jansenius, his book is neither so very rare nor so very large as to hinder me from reading it over from beginning to end, for my own satisfaction, without consulting the Sorbonne on the matter.

Were it not, however, for the dread of being presumptuous myself, I really think that I would be disposed to adopt the opinion which has been formed by the most of my acquaintances, who, though they have believed hitherto on common report that the propositions were in Jansenius, begin now to suspect the contrary, owing to this strange refusal to point them out—a refusal, the more extraordinary to me, as I have not yet met with a single individual who can say that he has discovered them in that work. I am afraid, therefore, that this censure will do more harm than good, and that the impression which it will leave on the minds of all who know its history will be just the reverse of the conclusion that has been come to. The truth is, the world has become skeptical of late, and will not believe things till it sees them. But, as I said before, this point is of very little moment, as it has no concern with religion.

The question of right, from its affecting the faith, appears much more important, and, accordingly, I took particular pains in examining it. You will be relieved, however, to find that it is of as little consequence as the former.

The point of dispute here, was an assertion of M. Arnauld's in the same letter, to the effect, "that the grace without which we can do nothing, was wanting to St. Peter at his fall." You and I supposed that the controversy here would turn upon the great principles of grace; such as, whether grace is given to all men? Or, if it is efficacious of itself? But we were quite mistaken. You must know I have become a great theologian within this short time; and now for the proofs of it!

To ascertain the matter with certainty, I repaired to my neighbor, M. N—, doctor of Navarre, who, as you are aware, is one of the keenest opponents of the Jansenists, and my curiosity having made me almost as keen as himself, I asked him if they would not formally decide at once that "grace is given to all men," and thus set the question at rest. But he gave me a sore rebuff, and told me that that was not the point; that there were some of his party who held that grace was not given to all; that the examiners themselves had declared, in a full assembly of the Sorbonne, that that opinion was *problematical*; and that he himself held the same sentiment, which he confirmed by quoting to me what he called that celebrated passage of St. Augustine: "We know that grace is not given to all men."

I apologized for having misapprehended his sentiment, and requested him to say if they would not at least condemn that other opinion of the Jansenists which is making so much noise, "That grace is efficacious of itself, and invincibly determines our will to what is good." But in this second query I was equally unfortunate. "You know nothing about the matter," he said, "that is not a heresy — it is an orthodox opinion; all the Thomists maintain it; and I myself have defended it in my Sorbonic thesis."

I did not venture again to propose my doubts, and yet I was as far as ever from understanding where the difficulty lay; so, at last, in order to get at it, I begged him to tell me where, then, lay the heresy of M. Arnauld's proposition. "It lies here," said he, "that he does not acknowledge that the righteous have the power of obeying the commandments of God, in the manner in which we understand it."

On receiving this piece of information, I took my leave of him; and, quite proud at having discovered the knot of the question, I sought M.N—, who is gradually getting better, and was sufficiently recovered to conduct me to the house of his brother-in-law, who is a Jansenist, if ever there was one, but a very good man notwithstanding. Thinking to insure myself a better reception, I pretended to be very high on what I took to be his side, and said: "Is it possible that the Sorbonne has introduced into the Church such an error as this, 'that all the righteous have always the power of obeying the commandments of God?'"

"What say you?" replied the doctor. "Call you that an error — a sentiment so Catholic that none but Lutherans and Calvinists impugn it?"

"Indeed!" said I, surprised in my turn. "So you are not of their opinion?"

"No," he replied; "we anathematize it as heretical and impious."

Confounded by this reply, I soon discovered that I had overacted the Jansenist, as I had formerly overdone the Molinist.[3] But not being sure if I had rightly understood him, I requested him to tell me frankly if he held "that the righteous have always a real power to observe the divine precepts?" Upon this the good man got warm (but it was with a holy zeal), and protested that he would not disguise his sentiments on any consideration —that such was, indeed, his belief, and that he and all his party would defend it to the death, as the pure doctrine of St. Thomas, and of St. Augustine their master.

This was spoken so seriously as to leave me no room for doubt; and under this impression I returned to my first doctor, and said to him, with an air of great satisfaction, that I was sure there would be peace in the Sorbonne very soon; that the Jansenists were quite at one with them in reference to the power of the righteous to obey the commandments of God; that I could pledge my word for them, and could make them seal it with their blood.

"Hold there" said he. "One must be a theologian to see the point of this question. The difference between us is so subtle, that it is with some difficulty we can discern it ourselves — you will find it rather too much for your powers of comprehension. Content yourself, then, with knowing that it is very true the Jansenists will tell you that all the righteous have always the power of obeying the commandments; that is not the point in dispute between us; but mark you, they will not tell you that that power is *proximate*. That is the point."

This was a new and unknown word to me. Up to this moment I had managed to understand matters, but that term involved me in obscurity; and I verily believe that it has been invented for no other purpose than to mystify. I requested him to give me an explanation of it, but he made a mystery of it, and sent me back, without any further satisfaction, to demand of the Jansenists if they would admit this *proximate power*. Having charged my memory with the phrase (as to my understanding, that was out of the question), I hastened with all possible expedition, fearing that I might forget it, to my Jansenist friend, and accosted him, immediately after our first salutations, with: "Tell me, pray, if you admit the *proximate power?*" He smiled, and replied, coldly: "Tell me yourself in what sense you understand it, and I may then inform you what I think of it." As my knowledge did not extend quite so far, I was at a loss what reply to make; and yet, rather than lose the object of my visit, I said at random: "Why, I understand it in the sense of the Molinists." "To which of the Molinists do

---

[3]Named after Father Louis Molina 1535–1600, Spanish Jesuit.

you refer me?" replied he, with the utmost coolness. I referred him to the whole of them together, as forming one body, and animated by one spirit.

"You know very little about the matter," returned he. "So far are they from being united in sentiment, that some of them are diametrically opposed to each other. But, being all united in the design to ruin M. Arnauld, they have resolved to agree on this term *proximate*, which both parties might use indiscriminately, though they understand it diversely, that thus, by a similarity of language, and an apparent conformity, they may form a large body, and get up a majority to crush him with the greater certainty."

This reply filled me with amazement; but without imbibing these impressions of the malicious designs of the Molinists, which I am unwilling to believe on his word, and with which I have no concern, I set myself simply to ascertain the various senses which they give to that mysterious word *proximate*. "I would enlighten you on the subject with all my heart," he said; "but you would discover in it such a mass of contrariety and contradiction, that you would hardly believe me. You would suspect me. To make sure of the matter, you had better learn it from some of themselves; and I shall give you some of their addresses. You have only to make a separate visit to one called M. le Moine[4] and to Father Nicolai."[5]

"I have no acquaintance with any of these persons," said I.

"Let me see, then," he replied, "if you know any of those whom I shall name to you; they all agree in sentiment with M. le Moine."

I happened, in fact, to know some of them.

"Well, let us see if you are acquainted with any of the Dominicans whom they call the 'New Thomists,' for they are all the same with Father Nicolai."

I knew some of them also whom he named; and, resolved to profit by this counsel, and to investigate the matter, I took my leave of him, and went immediately to one of the disciples of M. le Moine. I begged him to inform me what it was to have the *proximate power* of doing a thing.

"It is easy to tell you that," he replied; "it is merely to have all that is necessary for doing it in such a manner that nothing is wanting to performance."

"And so," said I, "to have the proximate power of crossing a river, for example, is to have a boat, boatmen, oars, and all the rest, so that nothing is wanting?"

"Exactly so," said the monk.

"And to have the proximate power of *seeing*," continued I, "must be to have good eyes and the light of day; for a person with good sight in the dark would not have the proximate power of seeing, according to you, as he would want the light, without which one cannot see?"

[4]Father Pierre Le Moine, 1602–1672.
[5]Father Jean Nicolai, 1594–1673, Dominican, author of an edition of St. Thomas Aquinas.

"Precisely," said he.

"And consequently," returned I, "when you say that all the righteous have the proximate power of observing the commandments of God, you mean that they have always all the grace necessary for observing them, so that nothing is wanting to them on the part of God."

"Stay there," he replied; "they have always all that is necessary for observing the commandments, or at least for asking it of God."

"I understand you," said I; "they have all that is necessary for praying to God to assist them, without requiring any new grace from God to enable them to pray."

"You have it now," he rejoined.

"But is it not necessary that they have an efficacious grace, in order to pray to God?"

"No," said he; "not according to M. le Moine."

To lose no time, I went to the Jacobins, and requested an interview with some whom I knew to be New Thomists, and I begged them to tell me what "proximate power" was. "Is it not," said I, "that power to which nothing is wanting in order to act?"

"No," said they.

"Indeed! fathers," said I; "if anything is wanting to that power, do you call it proximate? Would you say, for instance, that a man in the night time, and without any light, had the proximate power of seeing?"

"Yes, indeed, he would have it, in our opinion, if he is not blind."

"I grant that," said I; "but M. le Moine understands it in a different manner."

"Very true," they replied, "but so it is that we understand it."

"I have no objections to that," I said, "for I never quarrel about a name, provided I am apprised of the sense in which it is understood. But I perceive from this, that when you speak of the righteous having always the proximate power of praying to God, you understand that they require another supply for praying, without which they will never pray."

"Most excellent!" exclaimed the good fathers, embracing me, "exactly the thing; for they must have, besides, an efficacious grace bestowed upon all, and which determines their wills to pray; and it is heresy to deny the necessity of that efficacious grace in order to pray."

"Most excellent!" cried I, in return; "but, according to you, the Jansenists are Catholics, and M. le Moine a heretic; for the Jansenists maintain that, while the righteous have power to pray, they require nevertheless an efficacious grace; and this is what you approve. M. le Moine, again, maintains that the righteous may pray without efficacious grace; and this is what you condemn."

"Ay," said they; "but M. le Moine calls that power *proximate power*."

"How now! fathers," I exclaimed; "this is merely playing with words, to say that you are agreed as to the common terms which you employ, while you differ with them as to the sense of these terms."

The fathers made no reply; and at this juncture, who should come in but my old friend, the disciple of M. le Moine! I regarded this at the time as an extraordinary piece of good fortune; but I have discovered since then that such meetings are not rare — that, in fact, they are constantly mixing in each other's society.

"I know a man," said I, addressing myself to M. le Moine's disciple, "who holds that all the righteous have always the power of praying to God, but that, notwithstanding this, they will never pray without an efficacious grace which determines them, and which God does not always give to all the righteous. Is he a heretic?"

"Stay," said the doctor; "you might take me by surprise. Let us go cautiously to work. *Distinguo.* If he calls that power *proximate power*, he will be a Thomist, and therefore a Catholic; if not, he will be a Jansenist, and therefore a heretic."

"He calls it neither proximate nor non-proximate," said I.

"Then he is a heretic," quoth he; "I refer you to these good fathers if he is not."

I did not appeal to them as judges, for they had already nodded assent; but I said to them: "He refuses to admit that word *proximate*, because he can meet with nobody who will explain it to him."

Upon this one of the fathers was on the point of offering his definition of the term, when he was interrupted by M. le Moine's disciple, who said to him: "Do you mean, then, to renew our broils? Have we not agreed not to explain that word *proximate*, but to use it on both sides without saying what it signifies?" To this the Jacobin gave his assent.

I was thus let into the whole secret of their plot; and rising to take my leave of them, I remarked: "Indeed, fathers, I am much afraid this is nothing better than pure chicanery; and whatever may be the result of your convocations, I venture to predict that, though the censure should pass, peace will not be established. For though it should be decided that the syllables of that word *proximate* should be pronounced, who does not see that, the meaning not being explained, each of you will be disposed to claim the victory? The Jacobins will contend that the word is to be understood in their sense; M. le Moine will insist that it must be taken in his; and thus there will be more wrangling about the explanation of the word than about its introduction. For, after all, there would be no great danger in adopting it without any sense, seeing it is through the sense only that it can do any harm. But it would be unworthy of the Sorbonne and of theology to employ equivocal and captious terms without giving any explanation of them. In short, fathers, tell me, I entreat you, for the last time, what is necessary to be believed in order to be a good Catholic?"

"You must say," they all vociferated simultaneously, "that all the righteous have the *proximate power*, abstracting from it all sense — from the sense of the Thomists and the sense of other divines."

"That is to say," I replied, in taking leave of them, "that I must pronounce that word to avoid being the heretic of a name. For, pray, is this a Scripture word?" "No," said they. "Is it a word of the Fathers, the Councils, or the Popes?" "No." "Is the word, then, used by St. Thomas?" "No." "What necessity, therefore, is there for using it since it has neither the authority of others nor any sense of itself?" "You are an opinionative fellow," said they, "but you shall say it, or you shall be a heretic, and M. Arnauld into the bargain; for we are the majority, and should it be necessary, we can bring a sufficient number of Cordeliers into the field to carry the day."

On hearing this solid argument, I took my leave of them, to write you the foregoing account of my interview, from which you will perceive that the following points remain undisputed and uncondemned by either party. *First*, That grace is not given to all men. *Second*, That all the righteous have always the power of obeying the divine commandments. *Third*, That they require, nevertheless, in order to obey them, and even to pray, an efficacious grace, which invincibly determines their will. *Fourth*, That this efficacious grace is not always granted to all the righteous, and that it depends on the pure mercy of God. So that, after all, the truth is safe, and nothing runs any risk but that word without the sense, *proximate.*

Happy the people who are ignorant of its existence! — happy those who lived before it was born! — for I see no help for it, unless the gentlemen of the Academy, by an act of absolute authority, banish that barbarous term, which causes so many divisions, from beyond the precincts of the Sorbonne. Unless this be done, the censure appears certain; but I can easily see that it will do no other harm than diminish the credit of the Sorbonne, and deprive it of that authority which is so necessary to it on other occasions.

Meanwhile, I leave you at perfect liberty to hold by the word *proximate* or not, just as you please; for I love you too much to persecute you under that pretext. If this account is not displeasing to you, I shall continue to apprise you of all that happens. — I am, &c.

Letter IV

On actual grace and sins of ignorance

Paris, February 25, 1656

SIR, — Nothing can come up to the Jesuits. I have seen Jacobins, doctors, and all sorts of people in my day, but such an interview as I have just had was wanting to complete my knowledge of mankind. Other men are merely copies of them. As things are always found best at the fountainhead, I paid

a visit to one of the ablest among them, in company with my trusty
Jansenist — the same who accompanied me to the Dominicans. Being
particularly anxious to learn something of a dispute which they have with
the Jansenists about what they call *actual grace*, I said to the worthy father
that I would be much obliged to him if he would instruct me on this
point — that I did not even know what the term meant, and would thank
him to explain it. "With all my heart," the Jesuit replied; "for I dearly love
inquisitive people. Actual grace, according to our definition, 'is an inspiration of God, whereby He makes us to know His will, and excites within us a
desire to perform it.'"

"And where," said I, "lies your difference with the Jansenists on this
subject?"

"The difference lies here," he replied; "we hold that God bestows actual
grace *on all men in every case of temptation*; for we maintain, that unless a
person have, whenever tempted, actual grace to keep him from sinning, his
sin, whatever it may be, can never be imputed to him. The Jansenists, on
the other hand, affirm that sins, though committed without actual grace,
are, nevertheless, imputed; but they are a pack of fools." I got a glimpse of
his meaning; but, to obtain from him a fuller explanation, I observed: "My
dear father, it is that phrase *actual grace* that puzzles me; I am quite a
stranger to it, and if you would have the goodness to tell me the same thing
over again, without employing that term, you would infinitely oblige me."

"Very good," returned the father; "that is to say, you want me to
substitute the definition in place of the thing defined; that makes no
alteration of the sense; I have no objections. We maintain it, then, as an
undeniable principle, *that an action cannot be imputed as a sin, unless God
bestow on us, before committing it, the knowledge of the evil that is in the action,
and an inspiration inciting us to avoid it.* Do you understand me now?"

Astonished at such a declaration, according to which, no sins of surprise,
nor any of those committed in entire forgetfulness of God, could be
imputed, I turned round to my friend the Jansenist, and easily discovered
from his looks that he was of a different way of thinking. But as he did not
utter a word, I said to the monk, "I would fain wish, my dear father, to
think that what you have now said is true, and that you have good proofs for
it."

"Proofs, say you!" he instantly exclaimed: "I shall furnish you with these
very soon, and the very best sort too; let me alone for that."

So saying, he went in search of his books, and I took this opportunity of
asking my friend if there was any other person who talked in this manner?
"Is this so strange to you?" he replied. "You may depend upon it that
neither the fathers, nor the popes, nor councils, nor Scripture, nor any book
of devotion, employ such language; but if you wish casuists and modern
schoolmen, he will bring you a goodly number of them on his side." "O!

but I care not a fig about these authors, if they are contrary to tradition," I said. "You are right," he replied.

As he spoke, the good father entered the room, laden with books; and presenting to me the first that came to hand. "Read that," he said; "this is 'The Summary of Sins,' by Father Bauny[1] — the fifth edition too, you see, which shows that it is a good book."

"It is a pity, however," whispered the Jansenist in my ear, "that this same book has been condemned at Rome, and by the bishops of France."

"Look at page 906," said the father. I did so, and read as follows: "In order to sin and become culpable in the sight of God, it is necessary to know that the thing we wish to do is not good, or at least to doubt that it is — to fear or to judge that God takes no pleasure in the action which we contemplate, but forbids it; and in spite of this, to commit the deed, leap the fence, and transgress."

"This is a good commencement," I remarked. "And yet," said he, "mark how far envy will carry some people. It was on that very passage that M. Hallier, before he became one of our friends, bantered Father Bauny, by applying to him these words: 'Behold the man that taketh away the sins of the world'"

"Certainly," said I, "according to Father Bauny, we may be said to behold a redemption of an entirely new description."

"Would you have a more authentic witness on the point?" added he. "Here is the book of Father Annat. It is the last that he wrote against M. Arnauld. Turn up to page 34, where there is a dog's ear, and read the lines which I have marked with pencil — they ought to be written in letters of gold." I then read these words: "He that has no thought of God, nor of his sins, nor any apprehension (that is, as he explained it, any knowledge) of his obligation to exercise the acts of love to God or contrition, has no actual grace for exercising those acts; but it is equally true that he is guilty of no sin in omitting them, and that, if he is damned, it will not be as a punishment for that omission." And a few lines below, he adds: "The same thing may be said of a culpable commission."

"You see," said the monk, "how he speaks of sins of *omission* and of *commission*. Nothing escapes him. What say you to that?"

"Say!" I exclaimed. "I am delighted! What a charming train of consequences do I discover flowing from this doctrine! I can see the whole results already; and such mysteries present themselves before me! Why, I see more people, beyond all comparison, justified by this ignorance and forgetfulness of God, than by grace and the sacraments! But, my dear father, are you not inspiring me with a delusive joy? Are you sure there is nothing here

---

[1] Father Étienne Bauny, 1564–1649.

like that *sufficiency which suffices not?* I am terribly afraid of the *Distinguo*; —
I was taken in with that once already! Are you quite in earnest?"

"How now!" cried the monk, beginning to get angry, "here is no matter
for jesting. I assure you there is no such thing as equivocation here."

"I am not making a jest of it," said I; "but that is what I really dread,
from pure anxiety to find it true."

"Well then," he said, "to assure yourself still more of it, here are the
writings of M. le Moine, who taught the doctrine in a full meeting of the
Sorbonne. He learned it from us, to be sure; but he has the merit of having
cleared it up most admirably. O how circumstantially he goes to work! He
shows that, in order to make out an action to be a *sin*, all these things must
have passed through the mind. Read, and weigh every word." — I then read
what I now give you in a translation from the original Latin: "1. On the one
hand, God sheds abroad on the soul some measure of love, which gives it a
bias toward the thing commanded; and on the other, a rebellious concupiscence solicits it in the opposite direction. 2. God inspires the soul with a
knowledge of its own weakness. 3. God reveals the knowledge of the
physician who can heal it. 4. God inspires it with a desire to be healed. 5.
God inspires a desire to pray and solicit his assistance."

"And unless all these things occur and pass through the soul," added the
monk, "the action is not properly a sin, and cannot be imputed, as M. le
Moine shows in the same place and in what follows. Would you wish to
have other authorities for this? Here they are."

"All modern ones, however," whispered my Jansenist friend.

"So I perceive," said I to him aside; and then, turning to the monk: "O
my dear sir," cried I, "what a blessing this will be to some persons of my
acquaintance! I must positively introduce them to you. You have never,
perhaps, met with people who had fewer sins to account for all your life.
For, in the first place, they never think of God at all; their vices have got
the better of their reason; they have never known either their weakness or
the physician who can cure it; they have never thought of 'desiring the
health of their soul,' and still less of 'praying to God to bestow it'; so that,
according to M. le Moine, they are still in the state of baptismal innocence.
They have 'never had a thought of loving God or of being contrite for their
sins'; so that, according to Father Annat, they have never committed sin
through the want of charity and penitence. Their life is spent in a perpetual
round of all sorts of pleasures, in the course of which they have not been
interrupted by the slightest remorse. These excesses had led me to imagine
that their perdition was inevitable; but you, father, inform me that these
same excesses secure their salvation. Blessings on you, my good father, for
this way of justifying people! Others prescribe painful austerities for healing the soul; but you show that souls which may be thought desperately
distempered are in quite good health. What an excellent device for being
happy both in this world and in the next! I had always supposed that the

less a man thought of God, the more he sinned; but, from what I see now, if one could only succeed in bringing himself not to think upon God at all, everything would be pure with him in all time coming. Away with your half-and-half sinners, who retain some sneaking affection for virtue! They will be damned every one of them, these semi-sinners. But commend me to your arrant sinners — hardened, unalloyed, out-and-out, thorough-bred sinners. Hell is no place for them; they have cheated the devil, purely by virtue of their devotion to his service!"

The good father, who saw very well the connection between these consequences and his principle, dexterously evaded them; and maintaining his temper, either from good nature or policy, he merely replied: "To let you understand how we avoid these inconveniences, you must know that, while we affirm that these reprobates to whom you refer would be without sin if they had no thoughts of conversion and no desires to devote themselves to God, we maintain that they all actually *have* such thoughts and desires, and that God never permitted a man to sin without giving him previously a view of the evil which he contemplated, and a desire, either to avoid the offense, or at all events to implore his aid to enable him to avoid it; and none but Jansenists will assert the contrary."

"Strange! father," returned I; "is this, then, the heresy of the Jansenists, to deny that every time a man commits a sin, he is troubled with a remorse of conscience, in spite of which, he 'leaps the fence and transgresses,' as Father Bauny has it? It is rather too good a joke to be made a heretic for that. I can easily believe that a man may be damned for not having good thoughts; but it never would have entered my head to imagine that any man could be subjected to that doom for not believing that all mankind must have good thoughts! But, father, I hold myself bound in conscience to disabuse you, and to inform you that there are thousands of people who have no such desires — who sin without regret — who sin with delight — who make a boast of sinning. And who ought to know better about these things than yourself? You cannot have failed to have confessed some of those to whom I allude; for it is among persons of high rank that they are most generally to be met with. But mark, father, the dangerous consequences of your maxim. Do you not perceive what effect it may have on those libertines who like nothing better than to find out matter of doubt in religion? What a handle do you give them, when you assure them, as an article of faith, that on every occasion when they commit a sin, they feel an inward presentiment of the evil, and a desire to avoid it? Is it not obvious that, feeling convinced by their own experience of the falsity of your doctrine on this point, which you say is a matter of faith, they will extend the inference drawn from this to all the other points? They will argue that, since you are not trustworthy in one article, you are to be suspected in them all; and thus you shut them up to conclude, either that religion is false, or that you must know very little about it."

Here my friend the Jansenist, following up my remarks, said to him: "You would do well, father, if you wish to preserve your doctrine, not to explain so precisely as you have done to us, what you mean by *actual* grace. For, how could you, without forfeiting all credit in the estimation of men, openly declare that *nobody sins without having previously the knowledge of his weakness, and of a physician, or the desire of a cure, and of asking it of God?* Will it be believed, on your word, that those who are immersed in avarice, impurity, blasphemy, duelling, revenge, robbery and sacrilege, have really a desire to embrace chastity, humility, and the other Christian virtues? Can it be conceived that those philosophers who boasted so loudly of the powers of nature, knew its infirmity and its physician? Will you maintain that those who held it as a settled maxim that 'it is not God that bestows virtue, and that no one ever asked it from him,' would think of asking it for themselves? Who can believe that the Epicureans, who denied a divine providence, ever felt any inclination to pray to God? — men who said that 'it would be an insult to invoke the Deity in our necessities, as if he were capable of wasting a thought on beings like us?' In a word, how can it be imagined that idolaters and atheists, every time they are tempted to the commission of sin, in other words, infinitely often during their lives, have a desire to pray to the true God, of whom they are ignorant, that he would bestow on them virtues of which they have no conception?"

"Yes," said the worthy monk, in a resolute tone, "we will affirm it: and sooner than allow that any one sins without having the consciousness that he is doing evil, and the desire of the opposite virtue, we will maintain that the whole world, reprobates and infidels included, have these inspirations and desires in every case of temptation. You cannot show me, from the Scripture at least, that this is not the truth."

On this remark I struck in, by exclaiming: "What! father, must we have recourse to the Scripture to demonstrate a thing so clear as this? This is not a point of faith, nor even of reason. It is a matter of fact: we see it — we know it — we feel it."

But the Jansenist, keeping the monk to his own terms, addressed him as follows: "If you are willing, father, to stand or fall by Scripture, I am ready to meet you there; only you must promise to yield to its authority; and since it is written that 'God has not revealed his judgments to the Heathen, but left them to wander in their own ways,' you must not say that God has enlightened those whom the Sacred Writings assure us 'he has left in darkness and in the shadow of death.' Is it not enough to show the erroneousness of your principle, to find that St. Paul calls himself 'the chief of sinners,' for a sin which he committed 'ignorantly, and with zeal?' Is it not enough, to and from the Gospel, that those who crucified Jesus Christ had need of the pardon which he asked for them, although they knew not the malice of their action, and would never have committed it, according to St. Paul, if they had known it? Is it not enough that Jesus Christ apprises us that there will be persecutors of the Church, who, while making every effort to ruin her, will 'think that they are doing God service'; teaching us that this sin, which in the judgment of the apostle, is the greatest of all sins, may be committed by persons who, so far from knowing that they were sinning, would think that they sinned by not committing it? In fine, is it not enough that Jesus Christ himself has taught us that there are two kinds of sinners, the one of whom sin with 'knowledge of their Master's will,' and the other without knowledge; and that both of them will be 'chastised,' although, indeed, in a different manner?"

Sorely pressed by so many testimonies from Scripture, to which he had appealed, the worthy monk began to give way; and, leaving the wicked to sin without inspiration, he said: "You will not deny that *good men*, at least, never sin unless God give them" — "You are flinching," said I, interrupting him; "you are flinching now, my good father; you abandon the general principle, and finding that it will not hold good in regard to the wicked, you would compound the matter, by making it apply at least to the righteous. But in this point of view the application of it is, I conceive, so circumscribed, that it will hardly apply to anybody, and it is scarcely worth while to dispute the point."

My friend, however, who was so ready on the whole question, that I am inclined to think he had studied it all that very morning, replied: "This, father, is the last entrenchment to which those of your party who are willing to reason at all are sure to retreat; but you are far from being safe even here. The example of the saints is not a whit more in your favor. Who doubts that they often fall into sins of surprise, without being conscious of them? Do we not learn from the saints themselves how often concupiscence lays hidden snares for them; and how generally it happens, as St. Augustine complains of himself in his Confessions, that, with all their discretion, they 'give to pleasure what they mean only to give to necessity?'

"How usual is it to see the more zealous friends of truth betrayed by the heat of controversy into sallies of bitter passion for their personal interests, while their consciences, at the time, bear them no other testimony than that they are acting in this manner purely for the interests of truth, and they do not discover their mistake till long afterwards!

"What, again, shall we say of those who, as we learn from examples in ecclesiastical history, eagerly involve themselves in affairs which are really bad, because they believe them to be really good; and yet this does not hinder the fathers from condemning such persons as having sinned on these occasions?

"And were this not the case, how could the saints have their secret faults? How could it be true that God alone knows the magnitude and the number of our offenses; that no one knows whether he is worthy of hatred or love; and that the best of saints, though unconscious of any culpability, ought always, as St. Paul says of himself, to remain in 'fear and trembling?'

"You perceive, then, father, that this knowledge of the evil, and love of the opposite virtue, which you imagine to be essential to constitute sin, are equally disproved by the examples of the righteous and of the wicked. In the case of the wicked, their passion for vice sufficiently testifies that they have no desire for virtue; and in regard to the righteous, the love which they bear to virtue plainly shows that they are not always conscious of those sins which, as the Scripture teaches, they are daily committing.

"So true is it, indeed, that the righteous often sin through ignorance, that the greatest saints rarely sin otherwise. For how can it be supposed that souls so pure, who avoid with so much care and zeal the least things that can be displeasing to God as soon as they discover them, and who yet sin many times every day, could possibly have, every time before they fell into sin, 'the knowledge of their infirmity on that occasion, and of their physician, and the desire of their souls' health, and of praying to God for assistance,' and that, in spite of these inspirations, these devoted souls 'nevertheless transgress,' and commit the sin?

"You must conclude then, father, that neither sinners nor yet saints have always that knowledge, or those desires and inspirations every time they offend; that is, to use your own terms, they have not always actual grace. Say no longer, with your modern authors, that it is impossible for those to sin who do not know righteousness; but rather join with St. Augustine and the ancient fathers in saying that it is impossible *not* to sin, when we do not know righteousness.

The good father, though thus driven from both of his positions, did not lose courage, but after ruminating a little, "Ha!" he exclaimed, "I shall convince you immediately." And again taking up Father Bauny, he pointed to the same place he had before quoted, exclaiming, "Look now—see the ground on which he establishes his opinion! I was sure he would not be deficient in good proofs. Read what he quotes from Aristotle, and you will see that after so express an authority, you must either burn the books of this prince of philosophers or adopt our opinion. Hear, then, the principles which support Father Bauny: Aristotle states first, *'that an action cannot be imputed as blameworthy, if it be involuntary.'*"

"I grant that," said my friend.

"This is the first time you have agreed together," said I. "Take my advice, father, and proceed no further."

"That would be doing nothing," he replied; "we must know what are the conditions necessary to constitute an action voluntary."

"I am much afraid," returned I, "that you will get at loggerheads on that point."

"No fear of that," said he; "this is sure ground—Aristotle is on my side. Hear, now, what Father Bauny says: 'In order that an action be voluntary, it must proceed from a man who perceives, knows, and comprehends what is good and what is evil in it. That is a voluntary action, as we commonly say with the philosopher' (that is Aristotle, you know, said the monk, squeezing my hand); which is done by a person knowing the particulars of the action; so that when the will is led inconsiderately, and without mature reflection, to embrace or reject, to do or omit to do anything, before the understanding has been able to see whether it would be right or wrong, such an action is neither good nor evil; because previous to this mental inquisition, view, and reflection on the good or bad qualities of the matter in question, the act by which it is done is not voluntary.' Are you satisfied now?" said the father.

"It appears," returned I, "that Aristotle agrees with Father Bauny; but that does not prevent me from feeling surprised at this statement. What, sir! is it not enough to make an action voluntary that the man knows what he is doing, and does it just because he chooses to do it? Must we suppose, besides this, that he 'perceives, knows, and comprehends what is good and evil in the action?" Why, on this supposition there would be hardly such a thing in nature as voluntary actions, for no one scarcely thinks about all this. How many oaths in gambling — how many excesses in debauchery — how many riotous extravagances in the carnival, must, on this principle, be excluded from the list of voluntary actions, and consequently neither good nor bad, because not accompanied by those 'mental reflections on the good and evil qualities' of the action? But is it possible, father, that Aristotle held such a sentiment? I have always understood that he was a sensible man."

"I shall soon convince you of that," said the Jansenist, and requesting a sight of Aristotle's Ethics, he opened it at the beginning of the third book, from which Father Bauny had taken the passage quoted, and said to the monk: "I excuse you, my dear sir, for having believed, on the word of Father Bauny, that Aristotle held such a sentiment; but you would have changed your mind had you read him for yourself. It is true that he teaches, that 'in order to make an action voluntary, we must know the particulars of that action.' But what else does he mean by that, than the *particular circumstances* of the action? The examples which he adduces clearly show this to be his meaning, for they are exclusively confined to cases in which the persons were ignorant of some of the circumstances; such as that of 'a person who, wishing to exhibit a machine, discharges a dart which wounds a bystander; and that of Merope, who killed her own son instead of her enemy,' and such like.

"Thus you see what is the kind of ignorance that renders actions involuntary; namely, that of the particular circumstances, which is termed by divines, as you must know, *ignorance of the fact*. But with respect to *ignorance of the right* — ignorance of the good or evil in an action — which is the only point in question, let us see if Aristotle agrees with Father Bauny. Here are the words of the philosopher: 'All wicked men are ignorant of what they ought to do, and what they ought to avoid; and it is this very ignorance which makes them wicked and vicious. Accordingly, a man cannot be said to act involuntarily merely because he is ignorant of what it is proper for him to do in order to fulfil his duty. This ignorance in the choice of good and evil does not make the action involuntary; it only makes it vicious. The same thing may be affirmed of the man who is ignorant generally of the rules of his duty; such ignorance is worthy of blame, not of excuse. And consequently, the ignorance which renders actions involuntary and excusable is simply that which relates to the fact and its particular circumstances. In this case the person is excused and forgiven, being considered as having acted contrary to his inclination.'

"After this, father, will you maintain that Aristotle is of your opinion? And who can help being astonished to find that a Pagan philosopher had more enlightened views than your doctors, in a matter so deeply affecting morals, and the direction of conscience, too, as the knowledge of those conditions which render actions voluntary or involuntary, and which, accordingly, charge or discharge them as sinful? Look for no more support, then, father, from the prince of philosophers, and no longer oppose yourselves to the prince of theologians, who has thus decided the point in the first book of his Retractations, chapter xv.: 'Those who sin through ignorance, though they sin without meaning to sin, commit the deed only because they *will* commit it. And, therefore, even this sin of ignorance cannot be committed except by the will of him who commits it, though by a will which incites him to the action merely, and not to the sin; and yet the action itself is nevertheless sinful, for it is enough to constitute it such that he has done what he was bound not to do.'"

The Jesuit seemed to be confounded more with the passage from Aristotle, I thought, than that from St. Augustine; but while he was thinking on what he could reply, a messenger came to inform him that Madame la Maréchale of—, and Madame the Marchioness of—, requested his attendance. So taking a hasty leave of us, he said: "I shall speak about it to our fathers. They will find an answer to it, I warrant you; we have got some long heads among us."

We understood him perfectly well; and on our being left alone, I expressed to my friend my astonishment at the subversion which this doctrine threatened to the whole system of morals. To this he replied that he was quite astonished at my astonishment. "Are you not yet aware," he said, "that they have gone to far greater excess in morals than in any other matter?" He gave me some strange illustrations of this, promising me more at some future time. The information which I may receive on this point, will, I hope, furnish the topic of my next communication.—I am, &c.

Letter V

Design of the Jesuits in establishing a new system of morals—two sorts of casuists among them, a great many lax, and some severe ones—reason of this difference—explanation of the doctrine of probability—a multitude of modern and unknown authors substituted in the place of the holy fathers.

Paris, March 20, 1656

SIR, — According to my promise, I now send you the first outlines of the morals taught by those good fathers the Jesuits — "those men distinguished for learning and sagacity, who are all under the guidance of divine wisdom — a surer guide than all philosophy." You imagine, perhaps, that I am in jest, but I am perfectly serious; or rather, they are so when they speak thus of themselves in their book entitled "The Image of the First Century." I am only copying their own words, and may now give you the rest of the eulogy: "They are a society of men, or rather let us call them angels, predicted by Isaiah in these words, 'Go, ye swift and ready angels.'" The prediction is as clear as day, is it not? "They have the spirit of eagles; they are a flock of phœnixes (a late author having demonstrated that there are a great many of these birds); they have changed the face of Christendom!" Of course, we must believe all this, since they have said it; and in one sense you will find the account amply verified by the sequel of this communication, in which I propose to treat of their maxims.

Determined to obtain the best possible information, I did not trust to the representations of our friend the Jansenist, but sought an interview with some of themselves. I found, however, that he told me nothing but the bare truth, and I am persuaded he is an honest man. Of this you may judge from the following account of these conferences.

In the conversation I had with the Jansenist, he told me so many strange things about these fathers, that I could with difficulty believe them, till he pointed them out to me in their writings; after which he left me nothing more to say in their defense, than that these might be the sentiments of some individuals only, which it was not fair to impute to the whole fraternity. And, indeed, I assured him that I knew some of them who were as severe as those whom he quoted to me were lax. This led him to explain to me the spirit of the Society, which is not known to every one; and you will perhaps have no objections to learning something about it.

"You imagine," he began, "that it would tell considerably in their favor to show that some of their fathers are as friendly to Evangelical maxims as others are opposed to them; and you would conclude from that circumstance, that these loose opinions do not belong to the whole Society. That I grant you; for had such been the case, they would not have suffered persons among them holding sentiments so diametrically opposed to licentiousness. But as it is equally true that there are among them those who hold these licentious doctrines, you are bound also to conclude that the Spirit of the Society is not that of Christian severity; for had such been the case, they would not have suffered persons among them holding sentiments so diametrically opposed to that severity."

"And what, then," I asked, "can be the design of the whole as a body? Perhaps they have no fixed principle, and every one is left to speak out at random whatever he thinks."

"That cannot be," returned my friend; "such an immense body could not subsist in such a haphazard sort of way, or without a soul to govern and regulate its movements; besides, it is one of their express regulations, that none shall print a page without the approval of their superiors."

"But," said I, "how can these same superiors give their consent to maxims so contradictory?"

"That is what you have yet to learn," he replied. "Know, then, that their object is not the corruption of manners — that is not their design. But as little is it their sole aim to reform them — that would be bad policy. Their idea is briefly this: They have such a good opinion of themselves as to believe that it is useful, and in some sort essentially necessary to the good of religion, that their influence should extend everywhere, and that they should govern all consciences. And the Evangelical or severe maxims being best fitted for managing some sorts of people, they avail themselves of these when they find them favorable to their purpose. But as these maxims do not suit the views of the great bulk of the people, they waive them in the case of such persons, in order to keep on good terms with all the world. Accordingly, having to deal with persons of all classes and of all different nations, they find it necessary to have casuists assorted to match this diversity.

"On this principle, you will easily see that if they had none but the looser sort of casuists, they would defeat their main design, which is to embrace all; for those that are truly pious are fond of a stricter discipline. But as there are not many of that stamp, they do not require many severe directors to guide them. They have a few for the select few; while whole multitudes of lax casuists are provided for the multitudes that prefer laxity.

"It is in virtue of this 'obliging and accommodating, conduct,' as Father Petau[1] calls it, that they may be said to stretch out a helping hand to all mankind. Should any person present himself before them, for example, fully resolved to make restitution of some ill-gotten gains, do not suppose that they would dissuade him from it. By no means; on the contrary, they would applaud and confirm him in such a holy resolution. But suppose another should come who wishes to be absolved without restitution, and it will be a particularly hard case indeed, if they cannot furnish him with means of evading the duty, of one kind or another, the lawfulness of which they will be ready to guarantee.

"By this policy they keep all their friends, and defend themselves against all their foes; for, when charged with extreme laxity, they have nothing more to do than produce their austere directors, with some books which

[1]Father Denys Petau, 1583–1652, leading theologian.

they have written on the severity of the Christian code of morals; and simple people, or those who never look below the surface of things, are quite satisfied with these proofs of the falsity of the accusation.

"Thus are they prepared for all sorts of persons, and so ready are they to suit the supply to the demand, that when they happen to be in any part of the world where the doctrine of a crucified God is accounted foolishness, they suppress the offense of the cross, and preach only a glorious and not a suffering Jesus Christ. This plan they followed in the Indies and in China, where they permitted Christians to practice idolatry itself, with the aid of the following ingenious contrivance:—they made their converts conceal under their clothes an image of Jesus Christ, to which they taught them to transfer mentally those adorations which they rendered ostensibly to the idol of Cachinchoam and Keum-fucum . . . To such a length did this practice go, that the Congregation *De Propaganda* were obliged expressly to forbid the Jesuits, on pain of excommunication, to permit the worship of idols on any pretext whatever, or to conceal the mystery of the cross from their catechumens; strictly enjoining them to admit none to baptism who were not thus instructed, and ordering them to expose the image of the crucifix in their churches . . .

"Such is the manner in which they have spread themselves over the whole earth, aided by *the doctrine of probable opinions*, which is at once the source and the basis of all this licentiousness. You must get some of themselves to explain this doctrine to you. They make no secret of it, any more than of what you have already learned; with this difference only, that they conceal their carnal and worldly policy under the garb of divine and Christian prudence; as if the faith, and tradition, its ally, were not always one and the same at all times and in all places; as if it were the part of the rule to bend in conformity to the subject which it was meant to regulate; and as if souls, to be purified from their pollutions, had only to corrupt the law of the Lord, in place of 'the law of the Lord, which is clean and pure, converting the soul which lieth in sin,' and bringing it into conformity with its salutary lessons!

"Go and see some of these worthy fathers, I beseech you, and I am confident that you will soon discover, in the laxity of their moral system, the explanation of their doctrine about grace. You will then see the Christian virtues exhibited in such a strange aspect, so completely stripped of the charity which is the life and soul of them—you will see so many crimes palliated and irregularities tolerated, that you will no longer be surprised at their maintaining that 'all men have always enough of grace' to lead a pious life, in the sense in which they understand piety. Their morality being entirely Pagan, nature is quite competent to its observance. When we maintain the necessity of efficacious grace, we assign it another sort of virtue for its object. Its office is not to cure one vice by means of another; it is not merely to induce men to practise the external duties of religion: it aims at a virtue higher than that propounded by Pharisees, or the greatest sages of Heathenism. The law and reason are 'sufficient graces' for these purposes. But to disenthral the soul from the love of the world — to tear it from what it holds most dear — to make it die to itself — to lift it up and bind it wholly, only, and forever, to God — can be the work of none but an all-powerful hand. And it would be as absurd to affirm that we have the full power of achieving such objects, as it would be to allege that those virtues, devoid of the love of God, which these fathers confound with the virtues of Christianity, are beyond our power."

Such was the strain of my friend's discourse, which was delivered with much feeling; for he takes these sad disorders very much to heart. For my own part, I began to entertain a high admiration for these fathers, simply on account of the ingenuity of their policy; and following his advice, I waited on a good casuist of the Society, one of my old acquaintances, with whom I now resolved purposely to renew my former intimacy. Having my instructions how to manage them, I had no great difficulty in getting him afloat. Retaining his old attachment, he received me immediately with a profusion of kindness; and after talking over some indifferent matters, I took occasion from the present season, to learn something from him about fasting, and thus slip insensibly into the main subject. I told him, therefore, that I had difficulty in supporting the fast. He exhorted me to do violence to my inclinations; but as I continued to murmur, he took pity on me, and began to search out some ground for a dispensation. In fact he suggested a number of excuses for me, none of which happened to suit my case, till at length he bethought himself of asking me, whether I did not find it difficult to sleep without taking supper. "Yes, my good father," said I; "and for that reason I am obliged often to take a refreshment at mid-day, and supper at night."

"I am extremely happy," he replied, "to have found out a way of relieving you without sin: go in peace — you are under no obligation to fast. However, I would not have you depend on my word: step this way to the library."

On going thither with him he took up a book, exclaiming, with great rapture, "Here is the authority for you: and, by my conscience, such an authority! It is ESCOBAR!"[2]

"Who is Escobar?" I inquired.

"What! not know Escobar!" cried the monk; "the member of our Society who compiled this Moral Theology from twenty-four of our fathers, and on this founds an analogy, in his preface, between his book and 'that in the Apocalypse which was sealed with seven seals,' and states that 'Jesus presents it thus sealed to the four living creatures, Suarez,[3] Vasquez,[4]

---

[2]Father Antonio Escobar, 1589–1669, leading Spanish Jesuit writer.
[3]Father Francisco Suarez, 1648–1617, leading Spanish Jesuit.
[4]Father Gabriel Vasquez, 1551–1604, important Spanish Jesuit theologian.

Molina, and Valencia,[5] in presence of the four-and-twenty Jesuits who represent the four-and-twenty elders.''

He read me, in fact, the whole of that allegory, which he pronounced to be admirably appropriate, and which conveyed to my mind a sublime idea of the excellence of the work. At length, having sought out the passage on fasting, "Oh, here it is!" he said; "treatise 1, example 13, no. 67: 'If a man cannot sleep without taking supper, is he bound to fast? Answer: *By no means!*' Will that not satisfy you?"

"Not exactly," replied I; "for I might sustain the fast by taking my refreshment in the morning, and supping at night."

"Listen, then, to what follows; they have provided for all that: 'And what is to be said, if the person might make a shift with a refreshment in the morning and supping at night?'"

"That's my case exactly."

"'Answer: Still he is not obliged to fast; because no person is obliged to change the order of his meals.'"

"A most excellent reason!" I exclaimed.

"But tell me, pray," continued the monk, "do you take much wine?"

"No, my dear father," I answered; "I cannot endure it."

"I merely put the question," returned he, "to apprise you that you might, without breaking the fast, take a glass or so in the morning, or whenever you felt inclined for a drop; and that is always something in the way of supporting nature. Here is the decision at the same place, no. 57: 'May one, without breaking the fast, drink wine at any hour he pleases, and even in a large quantity? Yes, he may: and a dram of hippocrass too.' I had no recollection of the hippocrass," said the monk; "I must take a note of that in my memorandum-book."

"He must be a nice man, this Escobar," observed I.

"Oh! everybody likes him," rejoined the father; "he has such delightful questions! Only observe this one in the same place, no. 38: 'If a man doubt whether he is twenty-one years old, is he obliged to fast? No. But suppose I were to be twenty-one to-night an hour after midnight, and to-morrow were the fast, would I be obliged to fast to-morrow? No; for you were at liberty to eat as much as you pleased for an hour after midnight, not being till then fully twenty-one; and therefore having a right to break the fast day, you are not obliged to keep it.'"

"Well, that is vastly entertaining!" cried I.

"Oh," rejoined the father, "it is impossible to tear one's self away from the book: I spend whole days and nights in reading it; in fact, I do nothing else."

The worthy monk, perceiving that I was interested, was quite delighted, and went on with his quotations. "Now," said he, "for a taste of Filiutius,[6]

[5]Father Gregory Valencia, 1551–1663, Jesuit teacher in Italy and Germany.
[6]Father Vincent Filiutius, 1566–1622.

one of the four-and-twenty Jesuits: 'Is a man who has exhausted himself any way—by profligacy, for example—obliged to fast? By no means. But if he has exhausted himself expressly to procure a dispensation from fasting, will he be held obliged? He will not, even though he should have had that design.' There now! would you have believed that?"

"Indeed, good father, I do not believe it yet," said I. "What! is it no sin for a man not to fast when he has it in his power? And is it allowable to court occasions of committing sin, or rather, are we not bound to shun them? That would be easy enough, surely."

"Not always so," he replied; "that is just as it may happen."

"Happen, how?" cried I.

"Oh!" rejoined the monk, "so you think that if a person experience some inconvenience in avoiding the occasions of sin, he is still bound to do so? Not so thinks Father Bauny. 'Absolution,' says he, 'is not to be refused to such as continue in the proximate occasions of sin, if they are so situated that they cannot give them up without becoming the common talk of the world, or subjecting themselves to personal inconvenience.'"

"I am glad to hear it, father," I remarked; "and now that we are not obliged to avoid the occasions of sin, nothing more remains but to say that we may deliberately court them."

"Even that is occasionally permitted," added he; "the celebrated casuist Basil Ponce[7] has said so, and Father Bauny quotes his sentiment with approbation, in his Treatise on Penance, as follows: 'We may seek an occasion of sin directly and designedly—*primo et per se*—when our own or our neighbor's spiritual or temporal advantage induces us to do so.'"

"Truly," said I, "it appears to be all a dream to me, when I hear grave divines talking in this manner! Come now, my dear father, tell me con-scientiously, do *you* hold such a sentiment as that?"

"No, indeed," said he, "I do not."

"You are speaking, then, against your conscience," continued I.

"Not at all," he replied; "I was speaking on that point not according to my own conscience, but according to that of Ponce and Father Bauny, and them you may follow with the utmost safety, for I assure you that they are able men."

"What, father! because they have put down these three lines in their books, will it therefore become allowable to court the occasions of sin? I always thought that we were bound to take the Scripture and the tradition of the Church as our only rule, and not your casuists."

"Goodness!" cried the monk, "I declare you put me in mind of these Jansenists. Think you that Father Bauny and Basil Ponce are not able to render their opinion *probable*?"

"Probable won't do for me," said I; "I must have certainty."

[7]Father Basil Ponce, c.1629, a Spanish Augustinian.

"I can easily see," replied the good father, "that you know nothing about our doctrine of *probable opinions*. If you did, you would speak in another strain. Ah! my dear sir, I must really give you some instructions on this point; without knowing this, positively you can understand nothing at all. It is the foundation—the very A, B, C, of our whole moral philosophy."

Glad to see him come to the point to which I had been drawing him on, I expressed my satisfaction, and requested him to explain what was meant by a probable opinion?

"That," he replied, "our authors will answer better than I can do. The generality of them, and among others, our four-and-twenty elders, describe it thus: 'An opinion is called probable, when it is founded upon reasons of some consideration. Hence it may sometimes happen that a single *very grave doctor* may render an opinion probable.' The reason is added: 'For a man particularly given to study would not adhere to an opinion unless he was drawn to it by a good and sufficient reason.'"

"So it would appear," I observed, with a smile, "that a single doctor may turn consciences round about and upside down as he pleases, and yet always land them in a safe position."

"You must not laugh at it, sir," returned the monk; "nor need you attempt to combat the doctrine. The Jansenists tried this; but they might have saved themselves the trouble—it is too firmly established. Hear Sanchez,[8] one of the most famous of our fathers: 'You may doubt, perhaps, whether the authority of a single good and learned doctor renders an opinion probable. I answer, that it does; and this is confirmed by Angelus, Sylvester, Navarre, Emanuel Sa,[9] &c. It is proved thus: A probable opinion is one that has a considerable foundation. Now the authority of a learned and pious man is entitled to very great consideration; because (mark the reason), if the testimony of such a man has great influence in convincing us that such and such an event occurred, say at Rome, for example, why should it not have the same weight in the case of a question in morals?'"

"An odd comparison this," interrupted I, "between the concerns of the world and those of conscience!"

"Have a little patience," rejoined the monk; "Sanchez answers that in the very next sentence: 'Nor can I assent to the qualification made here by some writers, namely, that the authority of such a doctor, though sufficient in matters of human right, is not so in those of divine right. It is of vast weight in both cases.'"

"Well, father," said I, frankly, "I really cannot admire that rule. Who can assure me, considering the freedom your doctors claim to examine everything by reason, that what appears safe to one may seem so to all the rest? The diversity of judgments is so great"—

[8]Father Tommaso Sanchez, 1550–1610.
[9]Father Emmanuel Sa, 1530–1596, a Portuguese Jesuit.

"You don't understand it," said he, interrupting me; "no doubt they are often of different sentiments, but what signifies that? — each renders his own opinion probable and safe. We all know well enough that they are far from being of the same mind; what is more, there is hardly an instance in which they ever agree. There are very few questions, indeed, in which you do not find the one saying yes, and the other saying no. Still, in all these cases, each of the contrary opinions is probable. And hence Diana[10] says on a certain subject: 'Ponce and Sanchez hold opposite views of it; but, as they are both learned men, each renders his own opinion probable.'"

"But, father," I remarked, "a person must be sadly embarrassed in choosing between them!" — "Not at all," he rejoined; "he has only to follow the opinion which suits him best." — "What! if the other is more probable?" "It does not signify." — "And if the other is the safer?" "It does not signify," repeated the monk; "this is made quite plain by Emanuel Sa, of our Society, in his Aphorisms: 'A person may do what he considers allowable according to a probable opinion, though the contrary may be the safer one. The opinion of a single grave doctor is all that is requisite."

"And if an opinion be at once the less probable and the less safe, is it allowable to follow it," I asked, "even in the way of rejecting one which we believe to be more probable and safe?"

"Once more, I say yes," replied the monk. "Hear what Filiutius, that great Jesuit of Rome, says: 'It is allowable to follow the less probable opinion, even though it be the less safe one. That is the common judgment of modern authors.' Is not that quite clear?"

"Well, reverend father," said I, "you have given *us* elbow-room, at all events! Thanks to your probable opinions, we have got liberty of conscience with a witness! And are you casuists allowed the same latitude in giving your responses?"

"Oh, yes," said he, "we answer just as we please; or rather, I should say, just as it may please those who ask our advice. Here are our rules, taken from Fathers Layman,[11] Vasquez, Sanchez, and the four-and-twenty worthies, in the words of Layman: 'A doctor, on being consulted, may give an advice, not only probable according to his own opinion, but contrary to his opinion, provided this judgment happens to be more favorable or more agreeable to the person that consults him. Nay, I go further, and say, that there would be nothing unreasonable in his giving those who consult him a judgment held to be probable by some learned person, even though he should be satisfied in his own mind that it is absolutely false.'"

"Well, seriously, father," I said, "your doctrine is a most uncommonly comfortable one! Only think of being allowed to answer yes or no, just as

[10]Father Antonio Diana, 1586–1663.
[11]Father Paul Layman, 1575–1635, an Austrian Jesuit.

you please! It is impossible to prize such a privilege too highly. I see now the advantage of the contrary opinions of your doctors. One of them always serves your turn, and the other never gives you any annoyance. If you do not find your account on the one side, you fall back on the other, and always land in perfect safety."

"That is quite true," he replied.

"I understand you," resumed I; "but a practical difficulty has just occurred to me, which is this, that supposing a person to have consulted one of your doctors, and obtained from him a pretty liberal opinion, there is some danger of his getting into a scrape by meeting a confessor who takes a different view of the matter, and refuses him absolution unless he recant the sentiment of the casuist. Have you not provided for such a case as that, father?"

"Can you doubt it?" he replied. "We have bound them, sir, to absolve their penitents who act according to probable opinions, under the pain of mortal sin, to secure their compliance. 'When the penitent,' says Father Bauny, 'follows a probable opinion, the confessor is bound to absolve him, though his opinion should differ from that of his penitent.'"

"But he does not say it would be a mortal sin not to absolve him," said I.

"How hasty you are!" rejoined the monk; "listen to what follows; he has expressly decided that, 'to refuse absolution to a penitent who acts according to a probable opinion, is a sin which is in its nature mortal.' And to settle that point, he cites the most illustrious of our fathers — Suarez, Vasquez, and Sanchez."

"My dear sir," said I, "that is a most prudent regulation. I see nothing to fear now. No confessor can dare to be refractory after this. Indeed, I was not aware that you had the power of issuing your orders on pain of damnation. I thought that your skill had been confined to the taking away of sins; I had no idea that it extended to the introduction of new ones. But from what I now see, you are omnipotent."

"That is not a correct way of speaking," rejoined the father. "We do not introduce sins; we only pay attention to them. I have had occasion to remark, two or three times during our conversation, that you are no great scholastic."

"Be that as it may, father, you have at least answered my difficulty. But I have another to suggest. How do you manage when the Fathers of the Church happen to differ from any of your casuists?"

"You really know very little of the subject," he replied. "The Fathers were good enough for the morality of their own times; but they lived too far back for that of the present age, which is no longer regulated by them, but by the modern casuists. On this Father Cellot,[12] following the famous

---

[12]Father Louis Cellot, 1588–1658, French Jesuit leader.

Reginald,[13] remarks: 'In questions of morals, the modern casuists are to be preferred to the ancient fathers, though those lived nearer to the times of the apostles.' And following out this maxim, Diana thus decides: 'Are beneficiaries bound to restore their revenue when guilty of mal-appropriation of it? The ancients would say yes, but the moderns say no; let us, therefore, adhere to the latter opinion, which relieves from the obligation of restitution.'"

"Delightful words these, and most comfortable they must be to a great many people!" I observed.

"We leave the fathers," resumed the monk, "to those who deal with positive divinity. As for us, who are the directors of conscience, we read very little of them, and quote only the modern casuists. There is Diana, for instance, a most voluminous writer; he has prefixed to his works a list of his authorities, which amount to two hundred and ninety-six, and the most ancient of them is only about eighty years old."

"It would appear, then," I remarked, "that all these have come into the world since the date of your Society?"

"Thereabouts," he replied.

"That is to say, dear father, on your advent, St. Augustine, St. Chrysostom, St. Ambrose, St. Jerome, and all the rest, in so far as morals are concerned, disappeared from the stage. Would you be so kind as let me know the names, at least, of those modern authors who have succeeded them?"

"A most able and renowned class of men they are," replied the monk. "Their names are, Villalobos, Conink, Llamas, Achokier, Dealkozer, Dellacruz, Veracruz, Ugolin, Tambourin, Fernandez, Martinez, Suarez, Henriquez, Vasquez, Lopez, Gomez, Sanchez, De Vechis, De Grassis, De Grassalis, De Pitigianis, De Graphæis, Squilanti, Bizozeri, Barcola, De Bobadilla, Simanacha, Perez de Lara, Aldretta, Lorca, De Scarcia, Quaranta, Scophra, Pedrezza, Cabrezza, Bisbe, Dias, De Clavasio, Villagut, Adam à Manden, Iribarne, Binsfeld, Volfangi à Vorberg, Vosthery, Strevesdorf."[14]

"O my dear father!" cried I, quite alarmed, "were all these people Christians?"

"How! Christians!" returned the casuist; "did I not tell you that these are the only writers by whom we now govern Christendom?"

Deeply affected as I was by this announcement, I concealed my emotion from the monk, and only asked him if all these authors were Jesuits?

"No," said he; "but that is of little consequence; they have said a number of good things for all that. It is true the greater part of these same good things are extracted or copied from our authors, but we do not stand

[13]Father Valère Reginald, 1543–1623, a French Jesuit.
[14]These were all moral casuists of the sixteenth and seventeenth centuries.

on ceremony with them on that score, more especially as they are in the constant habit of quoting our authors with applause. When Diana, for example, who does not belong to our Society, speaks of Vasquez, he calls him 'that phœnix of genius'; and he declares more than once, 'that Vasquez alone is to him worth all the rest of men put together.' Accordingly, our fathers often make use of this good Diana; and if you understand our doctrine of probability, you will see that this is no small help in its way. In fact, we are anxious that others besides the Jesuits would render their opinions probable, to prevent people from ascribing them all to us; for you will observe, that when any author, whoever he may be, advances a probable opinion, we are entitled, by the doctrine of probability, to adopt it if we please; and yet, if the author does not belong to our fraternity, we are not responsible for its soundness."

"I understand all that," said I. "It is easy to see that all are welcome that come your way, except the ancient fathers; you are masters of the field, and have only to walk the course. But I foresee three or four serious difficulties and powerful barriers which will oppose your career."

"And what are these?" cried the monk, looking quite alarmed.

"They are the Holy Scriptures," I replied, "the popes, and the councils, whom you cannot gainsay, and who are all in the way of the Gospel."

"Is that all?" he exclaimed; "I declare you put me in a fright. Do you imagine that we would overlook such an obvious scruple as that, or that we have not provided against it? A good idea, forsooth, to suppose that we would contradict Scripture, popes, and councils! I must convince you of your mistake; for I should be sorry you should go away with an impression that we are deficient in our respect to these authorities. You have doubtless taken up this notion from some of the opinions of our fathers, which are apparently at variance with their decisions, though in reality they are not. But to illustrate the harmony between them would require more leisure than we have at present; and as I would not like you to retain a bad impression of us, if you agree to meet with me to-morrow, I shall clear it all up then."

Thus ended our interview, and thus shall end my present communication, which has been long enough, besides, for one letter. I am sure you will be satisfied with it, in the prospect of what is forthcoming. — I am, &c.

Letter VI

Various artifices of the Jesuits to elude the authority of the Gospel, of councils, and of the popes — some consequences which result from their doctrine of probability — their relaxation in favor of beneficiaries, priests, monks, and domestics — story of John D'Alba

Paris, April 10, 1656

Sɪʀ, — I mentioned, at the close of my last letter, that my good friend the Jesuit had promised to show me how the casuists reconcile the contrarieties between their opinions and the decisions of the popes, the councils, and the Scripture. This promise he fulfilled at our last interview, of which I shall now give you an account.

"One of the methods," resumed the monk, "in which we reconcile these apparent contradictions, is by the interpretation of some phrase. Thus, Pope Gregory XIV, decided that assassins are not worthy to enjoy the benefit of sanctuary in churches, and ought to be dragged out of them; and yet our four-and-twenty elders affirm that 'the penalty of this bull is not incurred by all those that kill in treachery.' This may appear to you a contradiction; but we get over this by interpreting the word *assassin* as follows: 'Are assassins unworthy of sanctuary in churches? Yes, by the bull of Gregory XIV they are. But by the word *assassins* we understand those that have received money to murder one; and accordingly, such as kill without taking any reward for the deed, but merely *to oblige their friends*, do not come under the category of assassins.' "

"Take another instance: It is said in the Gospel, 'Give alms of your superfluity.' Several casuists, however, have contrived to discharge the wealthiest from the obligation of alms-giving. This may appear another paradox, but the matter is easily put to rights by giving such an interpretation to the word *superfluity* that it will seldom or never happen that any one is troubled with such an article. This feat has been accomplished by the learned Vasquez, in his Treatise on Alms, c. 4: 'What men of the world lay up to improve their circumstances, or those of their relatives, cannot be termed superfluity; and accordingly, such a thing as superfluity is seldom to be found among men of the world, not even excepting kings.' Diana, too, who generally founds on our fathers, having quoted these words of Vasquez, justly concludes, 'that as to the question whether the rich are bound to give alms of their superfluity, even though the affirmative were true, it will seldom or never happen to be obligatory in practice.' "

"I see very well how that follows from the doctrine of Vasquez," said I. "But how would you answer this objection, that, in working out one's salvation, it would be as safe, according to Vasquez, to give no alms, provided one can muster as much ambition as to have no superfluity; as it is safe, according to the Gospel, to have no ambition at all, in order to have some superfluity for the purpose of alms-giving?"

"Why," returned he, "the answer would be, that both of these ways are safe according to the Gospel; the one according to the Gospel in its more literal and obvious sense, and the other according to the same Gospel as interpreted by Vasquez. There you see the utility of interpretations. When the terms are so clear, however," he continued, "as not to admit of an interpretation, we have recourse to the observation of favorable circumstances. A single example will illustrate this. The popes have denounced excommunication on monks who lay aside their canonicals; our casuists, notwithstanding, put it as a question, 'On what occasions may a monk lay aside his religious habits without incurring excommunication?' They mention a number of cases in which they may, and among others the following: 'If he has laid it aside for an infamous purpose, such as to pick pockets or to go *incognito* into haunts of profligacy, meaning shortly after to resume it.' It is evident the bulls have no reference to cases of that description."

I could hardly believe that, and begged the father to show me the passage in the original. He did so, and under the chapter headed "Practice according to the School of the Society of Jesus" . . . He showed me the same thing in Diana . . . "And why, father," I asked, "are they discharged from excommunication on such occasions?"

"Don't you understand it?" he replied. "Only think what a scandal it would be, were a monk surprised in such a predicament with his canonicals on! . . .

"I know nothing about all that," said I.

"Then it is a sign you have not read much of Escobar," returned the monk.

"I got him only yesterday, father," said I; "and I had no small difficulty, too, in procuring a copy. I don't know how it is, but everybody of late has been in search of him."

"The passage to which I referred," returned the monk, "may be found in treatise 1, example 8, no. 102. Consult it at your leisure when you go home."

I did so that very night; but it is so shockingly bad, that I dare not transcribe it.

The good father then went on to say: "You now understand what use we make of favorable circumstances. Sometimes, however, obstinate cases will occur, which will not admit of this mode of adjustment; so much so, indeed, that you would almost suppose they involved flat contradictions. For example, three popes have decided that monks who are bound by a particular vow to a Lenten life, cannot be absolved from it even though they should become bishops. And yet Diana avers that notwithstanding this decision they *are* absolved."

"And how does he reconcile that?" said I.

"By the most subtle of all the modern methods, and by the nicest possible application of probability," replied the monk. "You may recollect you were told the other day, that the affirmative and negative of most opinions have each, according to our doctors, some probability — enough, at least, to be followed with a safe conscience. Not that the *pro* and *con* are both true in the same sense — that is impossible — but only they are both probable, and therefore safe, as a matter of course. On this principle our worthy friend Diana remarks: 'To the decision of these three popes, which is contrary to my opinion, I answer, that they spoke in this way by adhering to the affirmative side — which, in fact, even in my judgment, is probable; but it does not follow from this that the negative may not have its probability too.' And in the same treatise, speaking of another subject on which he again differs from a pope, he says: 'The pope, I grant, has said it as the head of the Church; but his decision does not extend beyond the sphere of the probability of his own opinion.' Now you perceive this is not doing any harm to the opinions of the popes; such a thing would never be tolerated at Rome, where Diana is in high repute. For he does not say that what the popes have decided is not probable; but leaving their opinion within the sphere of probability, he merely says that the contrary is also probable."

"That is very respectful," said I.

"Yes," added the monk, "and rather more ingenious than the reply made by Father Bauny, when his books were censured at Rome; for when pushed very hard on this point by M. Hallier, he made bold to write: 'What has the censure of Rome to do with that of France?' You now see how, either by the interpretation of terms, by the observation of favorable circumstances, or by the aid of the double probability of *pro* and *con*, we always contrive to reconcile those seeming contradictions which occasioned you so much surprise, without ever touching on the decisions of Scripture, councils, or popes."

"Reverend father," said I, "how happy the world is in having such men as you for its masters! And what blessings are these probabilities! I never knew the reason why you took such pains to establish that a single doctor, *if a grave one*, might render an opinion probable, and that the contrary might be so too, and that one may choose any side one pleases, even though he does not believe it to be the right side, and all with such a safe conscience, that the confessor who should refuse him absolution on the faith of the casuists would be in a state of damnation. But I see now that a single casuist may make new rules of morality at his discretion, and dispose, according to his fancy, of everything pertaining to the regulation of manners."

"What you have now said," rejoined the father, "would require to be modified a little. Pay attention now, while I explain our method, and you will observe the progress of a new opinion, from its birth to its maturity. First, the grave doctor who invented it exhibits it to the world, casting it abroad like seed, that it may take root. In this state it is very feeble; it requires time gradually to ripen. This accounts for Diana, who has introduced a great many of these opinions, saying: 'I advance this opinion; but as it is new, I give it time to come to maturity' . . . Thus in a few years it becomes insensibly consolidated; and after a considerable time it is sanctioned by the tacit approbation of the Church, according to the grand maxim of Father Bauny, 'that if an opinion has been advanced by some casuist, and has not been impugned by the Church, it is a sign that she approves of it.' And, in fact, on this principle he authenticates one of his own principles in his sixth treatise, p. 312.''

"Indeed, father!" cried I, "why, on this principle the Church would approve of all the abuses which she tolerates, and all the errors in all the books which she does not censure!"

"Dispute the point with Father Bauny," he replied. "I am merely quoting his words, and you begin to quarrel with *me*. There is no disputing with facts, sir. Well, as I was saying, when time has thus matured an opinion, it thenceforth becomes completely probable and safe. Hence the learned Caramuel,[2] in dedicating his Fundamental Theology to Diana, declares that this great Diana has rendered many opinions probable which were not so before, and that, therefore, in following them, persons do not sin now, though they would have sinned formerly."

"Truly, father," I observed, "it must be worth one's while living in the neighborhood of your doctors. Why, of two individuals who do the same actions, he that knows nothing about their doctrine sins, while he that knows it does no sin. It seems, then, that their doctrine possesses at once an edifying and a justifying virtue! The law of God, according to St. Paul, made transgressors; but this law of yours makes nearly all of us innocent. I beseech you, my dear sir, let me know all about it. I will not leave you till you have told me all the maxims which your casuists have established."

"Alas!" the monk exclaimed, "our main object, no doubt, should have been to establish no other maxims than those of the Gospel in all their strictness: and it is easy to see, from the Rules for the regulation of our manners, that if we tolerate some degree of relaxation in others, it is rather out of complaisance than through design. The truth is, sir, we are forced to it. Men have arrived at such a pitch of corruption nowadays, that unable to make them come to us, we must even go to them, otherwise they would cast us off altogether; and what is worse, they would become perfect castaways. It is to retain such characters as these that our casuists have taken under consideration the vices to which people of various conditions are most addicted, with the view of laying down maxims which, while they cannot be said to violate the truth, are so gentle that he must be a very impracticable subject indeed who is not pleased with them. The grand project of our Society, for the good of religion, is never to repulse any one, let him be what he may, and so avoid driving people to despair.

"They have got maxims, therefore, for all sorts of persons; for beneficiaries, for priests, for monks; for gentlemen, for servants; for rich men, for commercial men; for people in embarrassed or indigent circumstances; for devout women, and women that are not devout; for married people, and irregular people. In short, nothing has escaped their foresight."

---

[2]Father Juan de Lobkowitz Caramuel, 1606–1682, Spanish Cistercian moral theorist.

"In other words," said I, "they have got maxims for the clergy, the nobility, and the commons. Well, I am quite impatient to hear them."

"Let us commence," resumed the father, "with the beneficiaries. You are aware of the traffic with benefices that is now carried on, and that were the matter referred to St. Thomas and the ancients who have written on it, there might chance to be some simoniacs in the Church. This rendered it highly necessary for our fathers to exercise their prudence in finding out a palliative. With what success they have done so will appear from the following words of Valencia, who is one of Escobar's 'four living creatures.' At the end of a long discourse, in which he suggests various expedients, he propounds the following at page 2039, vol. iii., which, to my mind, is the best: 'If a person gives a temporal in exchange for a spiritual good'—that is, if he gives money for a benefice—'and gives the money as the price of the benefice, it is manifest simony. But if he gives it merely as the motive which inclines the will of the patron to confer on him the living, it is not simony, even though the person who confers it considers and expects the money as the principal object.' Tanner[3] who is also a member of our Society, affirms the same thing, vol. iii., p. 1519, although he 'grants that St. Thomas is opposed to it; for he expressly teaches that it is always simony to give a spiritual for a temporal good, if the temporal is the end in view.' By this means we prevent an immense number of simoniacal transactions; for who would be so desperately wicked as to refuse, when giving money for a benefice, to take the simple precaution of so directing his intentions as to give it as *a motive* to induce the beneficiary to part with it, instead of giving it as *the price* of the benefice? No man, surely, can be so far left to himself as that would come to."

"I agree with you there," I replied; "all men, I should think, have *sufficient grace* to make a bargain of that sort."

"There can be no doubt of it," returned the monk. "Such, then, is the way in which we soften matters in regard to the beneficiaries. And now for the priests—we have maxims pretty favorable to them also. Take the following, for example, from our four-and-twenty elders: 'Can a priest, who has received money to say a mass, take an additional sum upon the same mass? Yes, says Filiutius, he may, by applying that part of the sacrifice which belongs to himself as a priest to the person who paid him last; provided he does not take a sum equivalent to a whole mass, but only a part, such as the third of a mass.'"

"Surely, father," said I, "this must be one of those cases in which the *pro* and the *con* have both their share of probability. What you have now stated cannot fail, of course, to be probable, having the authority of such men as Filiutius and Escobar; and yet, leaving that within the sphere of probability, it strikes me that the contrary opinion might be made out to be probable

---

[3]Father Adam Tanner, 1572–1632, Austrian Jesuit, chancellor of the University of Prague.

too, and might be supported by such reasons as the following: That, while the Church allows priests who are in poor circumstances to take money for their masses, seeing it is but right that those who serve at the altar should live by the altar, she never intended that they should barter the sacrifice for money, and still less, that they should deprive themselves of those benefits which they ought themselves, in the first place, to draw from it; to which I might add, that, according to St. Paul, the priests are to offer sacrifice first for themselves, and then for the people; and that accordingly, while permitted to participate with others in the benefit of the sacrifice, they are not at liberty to forego their share, by transferring it to another for a third of a mass, or, in other words, for the matter of fourpence or fivepence. Verily, father, little as I pretend to be a *grave* man, I might contrive to make this opinion probable."

"It would cost you no great pains to do that," replied the monk; "it is visibly probable already. The difficulty lies in discovering probability in the converse of opinions manifestly good; and this is a feat which none but great men can achieve. Father Bauny shines in this department. It is really delightful to see that learned casuist examining with characteristic ingenuity and subtlety, the negative and affirmative of the same question, and proving both of them to be right! Thus in the matter of priests, he says in one place: 'No law can be made to oblige the curates to say mass every day; for such a law would unquestionably expose them to the danger of saying it sometimes in mortal sin.' And yet in another part of the same treatise, he says, 'that priests who have received money for saying mass every day ought to say it every day, and that they cannot excuse themselves on the ground that they are not always in a fit state for the service; because it is in their power at all times to do penance, and if they neglect this they have themselves to blame for it, and not the person who made them say mass.' And to relieve their minds from all scruples on the subject, he thus resolves the question: 'May a priest say mass on the same day in which he has committed a mortal sin of the worst kind, in the way of confessing himself beforehand?' Villalobos[4] says no, because of his impurity; but Sancius[5] says, He may without any sin; and I hold his opinion to be safe, and one which may be followed in practice."

"Follow this opinion in practice!" cried I. "Will any priest who has fallen into such irregularities, have the assurance on the same day to approach the altar, on the mere word of Father Bauny? Is he not bound to submit to the ancient laws of the Church, which debarred from the sacrifice forever, or at least for a long time, priests who had committed sins of that description — instead of following the modern opinions of casuists, who would admit him to it on the very day that witnessed his fall?"

[4]Francisco de Villalobos, 1480–1539.
[5]Francisco Sanchez, 1523–1601.

"You have a very short memory," returned the monk. "Did I not inform you a little ago that, according to our fathers Cellot and Reginald, 'in matters of morality we are to follow, not the ancient fathers, but the modern casuists?'"

"I remember it perfectly," said I; "but we have something more here: we have the laws of the Church."

"True," he replied; "but this shows you do not know another capital maxim of our fathers, 'that the laws of the Church lose their authority when they have gone into desuetude as Filiutius says. We know the present exigencies of the Church much better than the ancients could do. Were we to be so strict in excluding priests from the altar, you can understand there would not be such a great number of masses. Now a multitude of masses brings such a revenue of glory to God and of good to souls, that I may venture to say, with Father Cellot, that there would not be too many priests, 'though not only all men and women, were that possible, but even inanimate bodies, and even brute beasts were transformed into priests to celebrate mass.'"

I was so astounded at the extravagance of this imagination, that I could not utter a word, and allowed him to go on with his discourse. "Enough, however, about priests; I am afraid of getting tedious: let us come to the *monks*. The grand difficulty with them is the obedience they owe to their superiors; now observe the palliative which our fathers apply in this case. Castro Palao[6] of our Society has said: 'Beyond all dispute, a monk who has a probable opinion of his own, is not bound to obey his superior, though the opinion of the latter is the more probable. For the monk is at liberty to adopt the opinion which is more agreeable to himself as Sanchez says. And though the order of his superior be just, that does not oblige you to obey him, for it is not just at all points or in every respect but only probably so; and consequently, you are only probably bound to obey him, and probably not bound.'"

"Certainly, father," said I, "it is impossible too highly to estimate this precious fruit of the double probability."

"It is of great use indeed," he replied; "but we must be brief. Let me only give you the following specimen of our famous Molina in favor of monks who are expelled from their convents for irregularities. Escobar quotes him thus: 'Molina asserts that a monk expelled from his monastery is not obliged to reform in order to get back again, and that he is no longer bound by his vow of obedience.'"

"Well, father," cried I, "this is all very comfortable for the clergy. Your casuists, I perceive, have been very indulgent to them, and no wonder — they were legislating, so to speak, for themselves. I am afraid people of

[6]Father Ferdinand de Castro Palao, S.J., 1581–1633, rector of the College of Medina.

other conditions are not so liberally treated. Every one for himself in this world."

"There you do us wrong," returned the monk; "they could not have been kinder to themselves than we have been to them. We treat all, from the highest to the lowest, with an even-handed charity, sir. And to prove this, you tempt me to tell you our maxims for servants. In reference to this class, we have taken into consideration the difficulty they must experience, when they are men of conscience, in serving profligate masters. For if they refuse to perform all the errands in which they are employed, they lose their places; and if they yield obedience, they have their scruples. To relieve them from these, our four-and-twenty fathers have specified the services which they may render with a safe conscience; such as 'carrying letters and presents, opening doors and windows, helping their master to reach the window, holding the ladder which he is mounting. All this,' say they, 'is allowable and indifferent; it is true that, as to holding the ladder, they must be threatened, more than usually, with being punished for refusing; for it is doing an injury to the master of a house to enter it by the window.' You perceive the judiciousness of that observation, of course?"

"I expected nothing less," said I, "from a book edited by four-and-twenty Jesuits."

"But," added the monk, "Father Bauny has gone beyond this; he has taught valets how to perform these sorts of offices for their masters quite innocently, by making them direct their intention, not to the sins to which they are necessary, but to the gain which is to accrue from them. In his Summary of Sins, p. 710, first edition, he thus states the matter: 'Let confessors observe,' says he, 'that they cannot absolve valets who perform base errands, if they consent to the sins of their masters; but the reverse holds true, if they have done the thing merely from a regard to their temporal emolument.' And that, I should conceive, is no difficult matter to do; for why should they insist on consenting to sins of which they taste nothing but the trouble? The same Father Bauny has established a prime maxim in favor of those who are not content with their wages: 'May servants who are dissatisfied with their wages, use means to raise them by laying their hands on as much of the property of their masters as they may consider necessary to make the said wages equivalent to their trouble? They may, in certain circumstances; as when they are so poor that, in looking for a situation, they have been obliged to accept the offer made to them, and when other servants of the same class are gaining more than they, elsewhere.'"

"Ha, father!" cried I, "that is John d'Alba's passage, I declare."

"What John d'Alba?" inquired the father: "what do you mean?"

"Strange, father!" returned I: "do you not remember what happened in this city in the year 1647? Where in the world were you living at that time?"

"I was teaching cases of conscience in one of our colleges far from Paris," he replied.

"I see you don't know the story, father: I must tell it you. I heard it related the other day by a man of honor, whom I met in company. He told us that this John d'Alba, who was in the service of your fathers in the College of Clermont, in the Rue St. Jacques, being dissatisfied with his wages, had purloined something to make himself amends; and that your fathers, on discovering the theft, had thrown him into prison on the charge of larceny. The case was reported to the court, if I recollect right, on the 16th of April, 1647; for he was very minute in his statements, and indeed they would hardly have been credible otherwise. The poor fellow, on being questioned, confessed to having taken some pewter plates, but maintained that for all that he had not *stolen* them; pleading in his defense this very doctrine of Father Bauny, which he produced before the judges, along with a pamphlet by one of your fathers, under whom he had studied cases of conscience, and who had taught him the same thing. Whereupon M. de Montrouge, one of the most respected members of the court, said, in giving his opinion, 'that he did not see how, on the ground of the writings of these fathers — writings containing a doctrine so illegal, pernicious, and contrary to all laws, natural, divine, and human, and calculated to ruin all families, and sanction all sorts of household robbery — they could discharge the accused. But his opinion was, that this too faithful disciple should be whipped before the college gate, by the hand of the common hangman; and that, at the same time, this functionary should burn the writings of these fathers which treated of larceny, with certification that they were prohibited from teaching such doctrine in future, upon pain of death.'

"The result of this judgment, which was heartily approved of, was waited for with much curiosity, when some incident occurred which made them delay procedure. But in the meantime the prisoner disappeared, nobody knew how, and nothing more was heard about the affair; so that John d'Alba got off, pewter plates and all. Such was the account he gave us, to which he added, that the judgment of M. de Montrouge was entered on the records of the court, where any one may consult it. We were highly amused at the story."

"What are you trifling about now?" cried the monk. "What does all that signify? I was explaining the maxims of our casuists, and was just going to speak of those relating to gentlemen, when you interrupt me with impertinent stories."

"It was only something put in by the way, father," I observed: "and besides, I was anxious to apprise you of an important circumstance, which I find you have overlooked in establishing your doctrine of probability."

"Ay, indeed!" exclaimed the monk, "what defect can this be, that has escaped the notice of so many ingenious men?"

"You have certainly," continued I, "contrived to place your disciples in perfect safety so far as God and the conscience are concerned; for they are quite safe in that quarter, according to you, by following in the wake of a grave doctor. You have also secured them on the part of the confessors, by obliging priests, on the pain of mortal sin, to absolve all who follow a probable opinion. But you have neglected to secure them on the part of the judges; so that, in following your probabilities, they are in danger of coming into contact with the whip and the gallows. This is a sad oversight."

"You are right," said the monk; "I am glad you mentioned it. But the reason is, we have no such power over magistrates as over the confessors, who are obliged to refer to us in cases of conscience, in which we are the sovereign judges."

"So I understand," returned I; "but if, on the one hand, you are the judges of the confessors, are you not, on the other hand, the confessors of the judges? Your power is very extensive. Oblige them, on pain of being debarred from the sacraments, to acquit all criminals who act on a probable opinion; otherwise it may happen, to the great contempt and scandal of probability, that those whom you render innocent in theory may be whipped or hanged in practice. Without something of this kind, how can you expect to get disciples?"

"The matter deserves consideration," said he; "it will never do to neglect it. I shall suggest it to our father Provincial. You might, however, have reserved this advice to some other time, without interrupting the account I was about to give you of the maxims which we have established in favor of gentlemen; and I shall not give you any more information, except on condition that you do not tell me any more stories."

This is all you shall have from me at present; for it would require more than the limits of one letter to acquaint you with all that I learned in a single conversation. — Meanwhile I am, &c.

Letter VII

Method of directing the intention adopted by the casuists — permission to kill in defense of honor and property, extended even to priests and monks — curious question raised by Caramuel, as to whether Jesuits may be allowed to kill Jansenists

Paris, April 25, 1656

SIR, — Having succeeded in pacifying the good father, who had been rather disconcerted by the story of John d'Alba, he resumed the conversation, on my assuring him that I would avoid all such interruptions in future, and spoke of the maxims of his casuists with regard to gentlemen, nearly in the following terms: —

"You know," he said, "that the ruling passion of persons in that rank of life is 'the point of honor,' which is perpetually driving them into acts of violence apparently quite at variance with Christian piety; so that, in fact, they would be almost all of them excluded from our confessionals, had not our fathers relaxed a little from the strictness of religion, to accommodate themselves to the weakness of humanity. Anxious to keep on good terms both with the Gospel, by doing their duty to God, and with the men of the world, by showing charity to their neighbor, they needed all the wisdom they possessed to devise expedients for so nicely adjusting matters as to permit these gentlemen to adopt the methods usually resorted to for vindicating their honor, without wounding their consciences, and thus reconcile two things apparently so opposite to each other as piety and the point of honor. But, sir, in proportion to the utility of the design, was the difficulty of the execution. You cannot fail, I should think, to realize the magnitude and arduousness of such an enterprise?"

"It astonishes me, certainly," said I, rather coldly.

"It astonishes you, forsooth!" cried the monk. "I can well believe that; many besides you might be astonished at it. Why, don't you know that, on the one hand, the Gospel commands us 'not to render evil for evil, but to leave vengeance to God'; and that, on the other hand, the laws of the world forbid our enduring an affront without demanding satisfaction from the offender, and that often at the expense of his life? You have never, I am sure, met with anything, to all appearance, more diametrically opposed than these two codes of morals; and yet, when told that our fathers have reconciled them, you have nothing more to say than simply that this astonishes you!"

"I did not sufficiently explain myself, father. I should certainly have considered the thing perfectly impracticable, if I had not known, from what I have seen of your fathers, that they are capable of doing with ease what is impossible to other men. This led me to anticipate that they must have discovered some method for meeting the difficulty — a method which I admire even before knowing it, and which I pray you to explain to me."

"Since that is your view of the matter," replied the monk, "I cannot refuse you. Know, then, that this marvellous principle is our grand method of *directing the intention* — the importance of which, in our moral system, is such, that I might almost venture to compare it with the doctrine of probability. You have had some glimpses of it in passing, from certain maxims which I mentioned to you. For example, when I was showing you how servants might execute certain troublesome jobs with a safe conscience, did you not remark that it was simply by diverting their intention from the evil to which they were accessary, to the profit which they might reap from the transaction? Now that is what we call *directing the intention*. You saw, too, that were it not for a similar divergence of the mind, those who give money for benefices might be downright simoniacs. But I will now show you this grand method in all its glory, as it applies to the subject of homicide — a crime which it justifies in a thousand instances; in order that, from this startling result, you may form an idea of all that it is calculated to effect."

"I foresee already," said I, "that, according to this mode, everything will be permitted; it will stick at nothing."

"You always fly from the one extreme to the other," replied the monk: "prithee avoid that habit. For just to show you that we are far from permitting everything, let me tell you that we never suffer such a thing as a formal intention to sin, with the sole design of sinning; and if any person whatever should persist in having no other end but evil in the evil that he does, we break with him at once: such conduct is diabolical. This holds true, without exception of age, sex, or rank. But when the person is not of such a wretched disposition as this, we try to put in practice our method of *directing the intention*, which simply consists in his proposing to himself, as the end of his actions, some allowable object. Not that we do not endeavor, as far as we can, to dissuade men from doing things forbidden; but when we cannot prevent the action, we at least purify the motive, and thus correct the viciousness of the means by the goodness of the end. Such is the way in which our fathers have contrived to permit those acts of violence to which men usually resort in vindication of their honor. They have no more to do than to turn off their intention from the desire of vengeance, which is criminal, and direct it to a desire to defend their honor, which, according to us, is quite warrantable. And in this way our doctors discharge all their duty towards God and towards man. By permitting the action, they gratify the world; and by purifying the intention, they give satisfaction to the Gospel. This is a secret, sir, which was entirely unknown to the ancients; the world is indebted for the discovery entirely to our doctors. You understand it now, I hope?"

"Perfectly well," was my reply. "To men you grant the outward material effect of the action; and to God you give the inward and spiritual movement of the intention; and by this equitable partition, you form an alliance between the laws of God and the laws of men. But, my dear sir, to be frank with you, I can hardly trust your premises, and I suspect that your authors will tell another tale."

"You do me injustice," rejoined the monk; "I advance nothing but what I am ready to prove, and that by such a rich array of passages, that altogether their number, their authority, and their reasonings, will fill you with admiration. To show you, for example, the alliance which our fathers have formed between the maxims of the Gospel and those of the world, by thus regulating the intention, let me refer you to Reginald: 'Private persons are forbidden to avenge themselves; for St. Paul says to the Romans (ch. 12th), "Recompense to no man evil for evil"; and Ecclesiasticus says (ch. 28th), "He that taketh vengeance shall draw on himself the vengeance of

God, and his sins will not be forgotten." Besides all that is said in the Gospel about forgiving offenses, as in the 6th and 18th chapters of St. Matthew.'"

"Well, father, if after that he says anything contrary to the Scripture, it will not be from lack of scriptural knowledge, at any rate. Pray, how does he conclude?"

"You shall hear," he said. "From all this it appears that a military man may demand satisfaction on the spot from the person who has injured him — not, indeed, with the intention of rendering evil for evil, but with that of preserving his honor. See you how carefully they guard against the intention of rendering evil for evil, because the Scripture condemns it? This is what they will tolerate on no account. Thus Lessius[1] observes, that 'if a man has received a blow on the face, he must on no account have an intention to avenge himself; but he may lawfully have an intention to avert infamy, and may, with that view, repel the insult immediately, even at the point of the sword.' So far are we from permitting any one to cherish the design of taking vengeance on his enemies, that our fathers will not allow any even to *wish their death* — by a movement of hatred. 'If your enemy is disposed to injure you,' says Escobar, 'you have no right to wish his death, by a movement of hatred; though you may, with a view to save yourself from harm.' So legitimate, indeed, is this wish, with such an intention, that our great Hurtado de Mendoza[2] says, that 'we may *pray God* to visit with speedy death those who are bent on persecuting us, if there is no other way of escaping from it.'"

"May it please your reverence," said I, "the Church has forgotten to insert a petition to that effect among her prayers."

"They have not put in everything into the prayers that one may lawfully ask of God," answered the monk. "Besides, in the present case the thing was impossible, for this same opinion is of more recent standing than the Breviary. You are not a good chronologist, friend. But, not to wander from the point, let me request your attention to the following passage, cited by Diana from Gaspar Hurtado,[3] one of Escobar's four-and-twenty fathers: 'An incumbent may, without any mortal sin, desire the decease of a life-renter on his benefice, and a son that of his father, and rejoice when it happens; provided always it is for the sake of the profit that is to accrue from the event, and not from personal aversion.'"

"Good!" cried I. "That is certainly a very happy hit; and I can easily see that the doctrine admits of a wide application."

"In short," said he, "Sanchez (mark, now, what great names I am quoting to you!) Sanchez, sir, goes a step further; for he shows how, simply

---

[1]Father Leonard Lessius (Leys), 1554–1623, Belgian Jesuit theologian.
[2]Father Pedro Hurtado de Mendoza, 1578–1651, Spanish theologian.
[3]Father Gaspar Hurtado, 1607–1647, rector of the University of Alcala.

by managing the intention rightly, a person may not only receive a challenge, but give one. And our Escobar follows him."

"Prove that, father," said I, "and I shall give up the point: but I will not believe that he has written it, unless I see it in print."

"Read it yourself, then," he replied: and, to be sure, I read the following extract from the Moral Theology of Sanchez: "It is perfectly reasonable to hold that a man may fight a duel to save his life, his honor, or any considerable portion of his property, when it is apparent that there is a design to deprive him of these unjustly, by law-suits and chicanery, and when there is no other way of preserving them. Navarre justly observes, that in such cases, it is lawful either to accept or to send a challenge. The same author adds, that there is nothing to prevent one from dispatching one's adversary in a private way. Indeed, in the circumstances referred to, it is advisable to avoid employing the method of the duel, if it is possible to settle the affair by privately killing our enemy; for, by this means, we escape at once from exposing our life in the combat, and from participating in the sin which our opponent would have committed by fighting the duel!"

"A most pious assassination!" said I. "Still, however, pious though it be, it is assassination, if a man is permitted to kill his enemy in a treacherous manner."

"Did I say that he might kill him treacherously?" cried the monk. "God forbid! I said he might kill him *privately*, and you conclude that he may kill him *treacherously* as if that were the same thing!"

Letter IX

False worship of the Virgin introduced by the Jesuits — devotion made easy — their maxims on ambition, envy, gluttony, equivocation, and mental reservations — female dress — gaming — hearing Mass

Paris, July 3, 1656

SIR, — I shall use as little ceremony with you as the worthy monk did with me, when I saw him last. The moment he perceived me, he came forward with his eyes fixed on a book which he held in his hand, and accosted me thus: "Would you not be infinitely obliged to any one who should open to you the gates of paradise? Would you not give millions of gold to have a key by which you might gain admittance whenever you thought proper? You need not be at such expense; here is one — here are a hundred for much less money."

At first I was at a loss to know whether the good father was reading, or talking to me, but he soon put the matter beyond doubt by adding:

"These, sir, are the opening words of a fine book, written by Father Barry[1] of our Society; for I never give you anything of my own."

"What book is it?" asked I.

"Here is its title," he replied: "*Paradise opened to Philagio, in a Hundred Devotions to the Mother of God, easily practised.*"

"Indeed, father! and is each of these easy devotions a sufficient passport to heaven?"

"It is," returned he. "Listen to what follows: 'The devotions to the Mother of God, which you will find in this book, are so many celestial keys, which will open wide to you the gates of paradise, provided you practise them'; and accordingly, he says at the conclusion, 'that he is satisfied if you practise only one of them.'"

"Pray, then, father, do teach me one of the easiest of them."

"They are all easy," he replied, "for example—Saluting the Holy Virgin when you happen to meet her image—saying the little chaplet of the pleasures of the Virgin—fervently pronouncing the name of Mary—commissioning the angels to bow to her for us—wishing to build her as many churches as all the monarchs on earth have done—bidding her good morrow every morning, and good night in the evening—saying the *Ave Maria* every day, in honor of the heart of Mary'—which last devotion, he says, possesses the additional virtue of securing us the heart of the Virgin."

"But, father," said I, "only provided we give her our own in return, I presume?"

"That," he replied, "is not absolutely necessary, when a person is too much attached to the world. Hear Father Barry: 'Heart for heart would, no doubt, be highly proper; but yours is rather too much attached to the world, too much bound up in the creature, so that I dare not advise you to offer, at present, that *poor little slave* which you call your heart.' And so he contents himself with the *Ave Maria* which he had prescribed."

"Why, this is extremely easy work," said I, "and I should really think that nobody will be damned after that."

"Alas!" said the monk, "I see you have no idea of the hardness of some people's hearts. There are some, sir, who would never engage to repeat, every day, even these simple words, *Good day, Good evening*, just because such a practice would require some exertion of memory. And, accordingly, it became necessary for Father Barry to furnish them with expedients still easier, such as wearing a chaplet night and day on the arm, in the form of a bracelet, or carrying about one's person a rosary, or an image of the Virgin. 'And, tell me now,' as Father Barry says, 'if I have not provided you with easy devotions to obtain the good graces of Mary?'"

"Extremely easy indeed, father," I observed.

"Yes," he said, "it is as much as could possibly be done, and I think

---

[1] Father Paul de Barry, 1585-1661, French Jesuit.

should be quite satisfactory. For he must be a wretched creature indeed, who would not spare a single moment in all his lifetime to put a chaplet on his arm, or a rosary in his pocket, and thus secure his salvation; and that, too, with so much certainty that none who have tried the experiment have ever found it to fail, in whatever way they may have lived; though, let me add, we exhort people not to omit holy living. Let me refer you to the example of this, given at p. 34; it is that of a female who, while she practised daily the devotion of saluting the images of the Virgin, spent all her days in mortal sin, and yet was saved after all, by the merit of that single devotion."

"And how so?" cried I.

"Our Saviour," he replied, "raised her up again, for the very purpose of showing it. So certain it is, that none can perish who practise any one of these devotions."

"My dear sir," I observed, "I am fully aware that the devotions to the Virgin are a powerful means of salvation, and that the least of them, if flowing from the exercise of faith and charity, as in the case of the saints who have practised them, are of great merit; but to make persons believe that, by practising these without reforming their wicked lives, they will be converted by them at the hour of death, or that God will raise them up again, does appear calculated rather to keep sinners going on in their evil courses, by deluding them with false peace and foolhardy confidence, than to draw them off from sin by that genuine conversion which grace alone can effect."

"What does it matter," replied the monk, "by what road we enter paradise, provided we do enter it? as our famous Father Binet, formerly our Provincial, remarks on a similar subject, in his excellent book, On the Mark of Predestination. 'Be it by hook or by crook,' as he says, 'what need we care, if we reach at last the celestial city.'"

"Granted," said I; "but the great question is, if we will get there at all."

"The Virgin will be answerable for that," returned he; "so says Father Barry in the concluding lines of his book: 'If, at the hour of death, the enemy should happen to put in some claim upon you, and occasion disturbance in the little commonwealth of your thoughts, you have only to say that Mary will answer for you, and that he must make his application to her.'"

"But, father, it might be possible to puzzle you, were one disposed to push the question a little further. Who, for example, has assured us that the Virgin will be answerable in this case?"

"Father Barry will be answerable for her," he replied. "'As for the profit and happiness to be derived from these devotions,' he says, 'I will be answerable for that; I will stand bail for the good Mother.'"

"But, father, who is to be answerable for Father Barry?"

"How!" cried the monk; "for Father Barry? is he not a member of our

Society; and do you need to be told that our Society is answerable for all the books of its members? It is highly necessary and important for you to know about this. There is an order in our Society, by which all booksellers are prohibited from printing any work of our fathers without the approbation of our divines and the permission of our superiors. This regulation was passed by Henry III., 10th May 1583, and confirmed by Henry IV., 20th December 1603, and by Louis XIII., 14th February 1612; so that the whole of our body stands responsible for the publications of each of the brethren. This is a feature quite peculiar to our community. And, in consequence of this, not a single work emanates from us which does not breathe the spirit of the Society. That, sir, is a piece of information quite *apropos*."

"My good father," said I, "you oblige me very much, and I only regret that I did not know this sooner, as it will induce me to pay considerably more attention to your authors."

"I would have told you sooner," he replied, "had an opportunity offered; I hope, however, you will profit by the information in future, and, in the meantime, let us prosecute our subject. The methods of securing salvation which I have mentioned are, in my opinion, very easy, very sure, and sufficiently numerous; but it was the anxious wish of our doctors that people should not stop short at this first step, where they only do what is absolutely necessary for salvation, and nothing more. Aspiring, as they do without ceasing, after the greater glory of God, they sought to elevate men to a higher pitch of piety; and as men of the world are generally deterred from devotion by the strange ideas they have been led to form of it by some people, we have deemed it of the highest importance to remove this obstacle which meets us at the threshold. In this department Father Le Moine has acquired much fame, by his work entitled Devotion Made Easy,[2] composed for this very purpose. The picture which he draws of devotion in this work is perfectly charming. None ever understood the subject before him. Only hear what he says in the beginning of his work: 'Virtue has never as yet been seen aright; no portrait of her, hitherto produced, has borne the least verisimilitude. It is by no means surprising that so few have attempted to scale her rocky eminence. She has been held up as a cross-tempered dame, whose only delight is in solitude; she has been associated with toil and sorrow; and, in short, represented as the foe of sports and diversions, which are, in fact, the flowers of joy and the seasoning of life.'"

"But, father, I am sure, I have heard at least, that there have been great saints who led extremely austere lives."

"No doubt of that," he replied; "but still, to use the language of the doctor, 'there have always been a number of genteel saints, and well-bred devotees'; and this difference in their manners, mark you, arises entirely

[2] *Devotion aisée*, 1652.

from a difference of humors. 'I am far from denying,' says my author, 'that there are devout persons to be met with, pale and melancholy in their temperament, fond of silence and retirement, with phlegm instead of blood in their veins, and with faces of clay; but there are many others of a happier complexion, and who possess that sweet and warm humor, that genial and rectified blood, which is the true stuff that joy is made of.'

"You see," resumed the monk, "that the love of silence and retirement is not common to all devout people; and that, as I was saying, this is the effect rather of their complexion than their piety. Those austere manners to which you refer, are, in fact, properly the character of a savage and barbarian, and, accordingly, you will find them ranked by Father Le Moine among the ridiculous and brutal manners of a moping idiot. The following is the description he has drawn of one of these in the seventh book of his Moral Pictures: 'He has no eyes for the beauties of art or nature. Were he to indulge in anything that gave him pleasure, he would consider himself oppressed with a grievous load. On festival days, he retires to hold fellowship with the dead. He delights in a grotto rather than a palace, and prefers the stump of a tree to a throne. As to injuries and affronts, he is as insensible to them as if he had the eyes and ears of a statue. Honor and glory are idols with whom he has no acquaintance, and to whom he has no incense to offer. To him a beautiful woman is no better than a spectre; and those imperial and commanding looks — those charming tyrants who hold so many slaves in willing and chainless servitude — have no more influence over his optics than the sun over those of owls,' &c."

"Reverend sir," said I, "had you not told me that Father Le Moine was the author of that description, I declare I would have guessed it to be the production of some profane fellow, who had drawn it expressly with the view of turning the saints into ridicule. For if that is not the picture of a man entirely denied to those feelings which the Gospel obliges us to renounce, I confess that I know nothing of the matter."

"You may now perceive, then, the extent of your ignorance," he replied; "for these are the features of a feeble, uncultivated mind, 'destitute of those virtuous and natural affections which it ought to possess,' as Father Le Moine says at the close of that description. Such is his way of teaching 'Christian virtue and philosophy,' as he announces in his advertisement; and, in truth, it cannot be denied that this method of treating devotion is much more agreeable to the taste of the world than the old way in which they went to work before our times."

P. S. — Since writing the above, I have seen "Paradise Opened by a Hundred Devotions Easily Practised," by Father Barry; and also the "Mark of Predestination," by Father Binet,[3] both of them pieces well worth the seeing.

[3]Father Etienne Binet, 1569–1639, Jesuit Provincial of France.

Letter XIII
To the Reverend Fathers of the Society of Jesus

The doctrine of Lessius on homicide the same with that of Valentia—
how easy it is to pass from speculation to practice—why the Jesuits
have recourse to this distinction, and how little it serves for their
vindication

September 30, 1656

REVEREND FATHERS,—I have just seen your last production, in which
you have continued your list of Impostures up to the twentieth, and
intimate that you mean to conclude with this the first part of your accusations against me, and to proceed to the second, in which you are to adopt a
new mode of defence, by showing that there are other casuists besides
those of your Society who are as lax as yourselves. I now see the precise
number of charges to which I have to reply; and as the fourth, to which we
have now come, relates to homicide, it may be proper, in answering it, to
include the 11th, 13th, 14th, 15th, 16th, 17th, and 18th, which refer to the
same subject.

In the present letter, therefore, my object shall be to vindicate the
correctness of my quotations from the charges of falsity which you bring
against me. But as you have ventured, in your pamphlets, to assert that
"the sentiments of your authors on murder are agreeable to the decisions of
popes and ecclesiastical laws," you will compel me, in my next letter, to
confute a statement at once so unfounded and so injurious to the Church. It
is of some importance to show that she is innocent of your corruptions, in
order that heretics may be prevented from taking advantage of your aberra-
tions, to draw conclusions tending to her dishonor. And thus, viewing on
the one hand your pernicious maxims, and on the other the canons of the
Church which have uniformly condemned them, people will see, at one
glance, what they should shun and what they should follow.

Your fourth charge turns on a maxim relating to murder, which you say I
have falsely ascribed to Lessius. It is as follows: "That if a man has received
a buffet, he may immediately pursue his enemy, and even return the blow
with the sword, not to avenge himself, but to retrieve his honor." This, you
say, is the opinion of the casuist Vittoria.[1] But this is nothing to the point.
There is no inconsistency in saying that it is at once the opinion of Vittoria
and of Lessius; for Lessius himself says that it is also held by Navarre and
Henriquez,[2] who teach identically the same doctrine. The only question,
then, is, if Lessius holds this view as well as his brother casuists. You

[1] Father Francisco Vittoria, 1480–1549, the father of Spanish Scholasticism.
[2] Father Henrico Henriquez, 1520–1600, one of the first Jesuits.

maintain "that Lessius quotes this opinion solely for the purpose of refuting it, and that I therefore attribute to him a sentiment which he produces only to overthrow—the basest and most disgraceful act of which a writer can be guilty." Now I maintain, fathers, that he quotes the opinion solely for the purpose of supporting it. Here is a question of fact, which it will be very easy to settle. Let us see, then, how you prove your allegation, and you will see afterwards how I prove mine.

To show that Lessius is not of that opinion, you tell us that he condemns the practice of it; and in proof of this, you quote one passage of his (l. 2, c. 9, n. 92), in which he says, in so many words, "I condemn the practice of it." I grant that, on looking for these words, at number 92, to which you refer, they will be found there. But what will people say, fathers, when they discover, at the same time, that he is treating in that place of a question totally different from that of which we are speaking, and that the opinion of which he there says that he condemns the practice, has no connection with that now in dispute, but is quite distinct? And yet to be convinced that this is the fact, we have only to open the book to which you refer, and there we find the whole subject in its connection as follows: At number 79 he treats the question, "If it is lawful to kill for a buffet?" and at number 80 he finishes this matter without a single word of condemnation. Having disposed of this question, he opens a new one at art. 81, namely, "If it is lawful to kill for slanders?" and it is when speaking of *this* question that he employs the words you have quoted—"I condemn the practice of it."

Is it not shameful, fathers, that you should venture to produce these words to make it be believed that Lessius condemns the opinion that it is lawful to kill for a buffet? and that, on the ground of this single proof, you should chuckle over it, as you have done, by saying: "Many persons of honor in Paris have already discovered this notorious falsehood by consulting Lessius, and have thus ascertained the degree of credit due to that slanderer?" Indeed! and is it thus that you abuse the confidence which those persons of honor repose in you? To show them that Lessius does not hold a certain opinion, you open the book to them at a place where he is condemning another opinion; and these persons not having begun to mistrust your good faith, and never thinking of examining whether the author speaks in that place of the subject in dispute, you impose on their credulity. I make no doubt, fathers, that to shelter yourselves from the guilt of such a scandalous lie, you had recourse to your doctrine of equivocations; and that, having read the passage *in a loud voice*, you would say, *in a lower key*, that the author was speaking there of something else. But I am not so sure whether this saving clause, which is quite enough to satisfy your consciences, will be a very satisfactory answer to the just complaint of those "honorable persons," when they shall discover that you have hoodwinked them in this style.

Take care, then, fathers, to prevent them by all means from seeing my letters; for this is the only method now left to you to preserve your credit for a short time longer. This is not the way in which I deal with your writings: I send them to all my friends: I wish everybody to see them. And I verily believe that both of us are in the right for our own interests; for after having published with such parade this fourth Imposture, were it once discovered that you have made it up by foisting in one passage for another, you would be instantly denounced. It will be easily seen, that if you could have found what you wanted in the passage where Lessius treated of this matter, you would not have searched for it elsewhere, and that you had recourse to such a trick only because you could find nothing in that passage favorable to your purpose.

You would have us believe that we may find in Lessius what you assert, "that he does *not* allow that this opinion (that a man may be lawfully killed for a buffet) is probable in theory;" whereas Lessius distinctly declares, at number 80: "This opinion, that a man may kill for a buffet, *is* probable in theory." Is not this, word for word, the reverse of your assertion? And can we sufficiently admire the hardihood with which you have advanced, in set phrase, the very reverse of a matter of fact! To your conclusion, from a fabricated passage, that Lessius was *not* of that opinion, we have only to place Lessius himself, who, in the genuine passage, declares that he *is* of that opinion.

Again, you would have Lessius to say "that he condemns the practice of it;" and, as I have just observed, there is not in the original a single word of condemnation; all that he says is: "It appears that it ought not to be EASILY permitted in practice. Is that, fathers, the language of a man who *condemns* a maxim? Would you say that adultery and incest ought not to be *easily permitted* in practice? Must we not, on the contrary, conclude, that as Lessius says no more than that the practice ought not to be easily permitted, his opinion is, that it may be permitted sometimes, though rarely? And, as if he had been anxious to apprise everybody when it might be permitted, and to relieve those who have received affronts from being troubled with unreasonable scruples, from not knowing on what occasions they might lawfully kill in practice, he has been at pains to inform them what they ought to avoid in order to practise the doctrine with a safe conscience. Mark his words: "It seems," says he, "that it ought not to be easily permitted, *because* of the danger that persons may act in this manner out of hatred or revenge, or with excess, or that this may occasion too many murders." From this it appears that murder is freely permitted by Lessius, if one avoids the inconveniences referred to — in other words, if one can act without hatred or revenge, and in circumstances that may not open the door to a great many murders. To illustrate the matter, I may give you an example of recent occurrence — the case of the buffet of Compiègne. You will grant that the person who received the blow on that occasion has shown by the way in which he has acted, that he was sufficiently master of the passions of hatred and revenge. It only remained for him, therefore, to see that he did not give occasion to too many murders; and you need hardly be told, fathers, it is such a rare spectacle to find Jesuits bestowing buffets on the officers of the royal household, that he had no great reason to fear that a murder committed on this occasion would be likely to draw many others in its train. You cannot, accordingly, deny that the Jesuit who figured on that occasion was *killable* with a safe conscience, and that the offended party might have converted him into a practical illustration of the doctrine of Lessius. And very likely, fathers, this might have been the result had he been educated in your school, and learnt from Escobar that the man who has received a buffet is held to be disgraced until he has taken the life of him who insulted him. But there is ground to believe, that the very different instructions which he received from a curate, who is no great favorite of yours, have contributed not a little in this case to save the life of a Jesuit.

Tell us no more, then, of inconveniences which may, in many instances, be so easily got over, and in the absence of which, according to Lessius, murder is permissible even in practice. This is frankly avowed by your authors, as quoted by Escobar, in his "Practice of Homicide, according to your Society." "Is it allowable," asks this casuist, "to kill him who has given me a buffet? Lessius says it is permissible in speculation, though not to be followed in practice on account of the risk of hatred, or of murders prejudicial to the State. Others, however, have judged that, BY AVOIDING THESE INCONVENIENCES, THIS IS PERMISSIBLE AND SAFE IN PRACTICE &c. See how your opinions mount up, by little and little, to the climax of probabilism! The present one you have at last elevated to this position, by permitting murder without any distinction between speculation and practice, in the following terms: "It is lawful, when one has received a buffet, to return the blow immediately with the sword, not to avenge one's self, but to preserve one's honor." Such is the decision of your fathers of Caen in 1644, embodied in their publications produced by the university before parliament, when they presented their third remonstrance against your doctrine of homicide, as shown in the book then emitted by them, on page 339.

Mark, then, fathers, that your own authors have themselves demolished this absurd distinction between speculative and practical murder—a distinction which the university treated with ridicule, and the invention of which is a secret of your policy, which it may now be worth while to explain. The knowledge of it, besides being necessary to the right understanding of your 15th, 16th, 17th, and 18th charges, is well calculated, in general, to open up, by little and little, the principles of that mysterious policy.

In attempting, as you have done, to decide cases of conscience in the most agreeable and accommodating manner, while you met with some questions in which religion alone was concerned—such as those of contrition, penance, love to God, and others only affecting the inner court of conscience — you encountered another class of cases in which evil society was interested as well as religion — such as those relating to usury, bankruptcy, homicide, and the like. And it is truly distressing to all that love the Church, to observe that, in a vast number of instances, in which you had only Religion to contend with, you have violated her laws without reservation, without distinction, and without compunction; because you knew that it is not here that God visibly administers his justice. But in those cases in which the State is interested as well as Religion, your apprehension of man's justice has induced you to divide your decisions into two shares. To the first of these you give the name of *speculation*; under which category crimes, considered in themselves, without regard to society, but merely to the law of God, you have permitted, without the least scruple, and in the way of trampling on the divine law which condemns them. The second you rank under the denomination of *practice*; and here, considering the injury which may be done to society, and the presence of magistrates who look after the public peace, you take care, in order to keep yourselves on the safe side of the law, not to approve always in practice the murders and other crimes which you have sanctioned in speculation. Thus, for example, on the question, "If it be lawful to kill for slanders?" your authors, Filiutius, Reginald, and others, reply: "This is permitted in speculation, but is not to be approved in *practice*, on account of the great number of murders which might ensue, and which might injure the State, if all slanderers were to be killed, *and also because one might be punished in a court of justice for having killed another for that matter.*" Such is the style in which your opinions begin to develop themselves, under the shelter of this distinction, in virtue of which, without doing any sensible injury to society, you only ruin religion. In acting thus, you consider yourselves quite safe. You suppose that, on the one hand, the influence you have in the Church will effectually shield from punishment your assaults on truth; and that, on the other, the precautions you have taken against too easily reducing your permissions to practice will save you on the part of the civil powers, who, not being judges in cases of conscience, are properly concerned only with the outward practice. Thus an opinion which would be condemned under the name of practice, comes out quite safe under the name of speculation. But this basis once established, it is not difficult to erect on it the rest of your maxims. There is an infinite distance between God's prohibition of murder, and your speculative permission of the crime; but between that permission and the practice the distance is very small indeed. It only remains to show, that what is allowable in speculation is also so in practice; and there can be no want of reasons for this. You have contrived to find them in far more difficult cases. Would you like to see, fathers, how this may be managed? I refer you to the reasoning of Escobar, who has distinctly decided the point in the first of the six volumes of his grand Moral Theology, of which I have already spoken — a work in which he shows quite another spirit from that which appears in his former compilation from your four-and-twenty elders. At that time he thought that there might be opinions probable in speculation, which might not be safe in practice; but he has now come to form an opposite judgment, and has, in this, his latest work, confirmed it. Such is the wonderful growth attained by the doctrine of probability in general, as well as by every probable opinion in particular, in the course of time. Attend, then, to what he says: "I cannot see how it can be that an action which seems allowable in speculation should not be so likewise in practice; because what may be done in practice depends on what is found to be lawful in speculation, and the things differ from each other only as cause and effect. Speculation is that which determines to action. WHENCE IT FOLLOWS THAT OPINIONS PROBABLE IN SPECULATION MAY BE FOLLOWED WITH A SAFE CONSCIENCE IN PRACTICE, and that even with more safety than those which have not been so well examined as matters of speculation."

Verily, fathers, your friend Escobar reasons uncommonly well sometimes; and, in point of fact, there is such a close connection between speculation and practice, that when the former has once taken root, you have no difficulty in permitting the latter, without any disguise. A good illustration of this we have in the permission "to kill for a buffet," which, from being a point of simple speculation, was boldly raised by Lessius into a practice "which ought not easily to be allowed;" from that promoted by Escobar to the character of "an easy practice;" and from thence elevated by your fathers of Caen, as we have seen, without any distinction between theory and practice, into a full permission. Thus you bring your opinions to their full growth very gradually. Were they presented all at once in their finished extravagance, they would beget horror; but this slow imperceptible progress gradually habituates men to the sight of them, and hides their offensiveness. And in this way the permission to murder, in itself so odious both to Church and State, creeps first into the Church, and then from the Church into the State.

A similar success has attended the opinion of "killing for slander," which has now reached the climax of a permission without any distinction. I should not have stopped to quote my authorities on this point from your writings, had it not been necessary in order to put down the effrontery with which you have asserted, twice over, in your fifteenth Imposture, "that there never was a Jesuit who permitted killing for slander." Before making this statement, fathers, you should have taken care to prevent it from coming under my notice, seeing that it is so easy for me to answer it. For not to mention that your fathers Reginald, Filiutius, and others, have permitted it in speculation, as I have already shown, and that the principle laid down by Escobar leads us safely on to the practice, I have to tell you that you have authors who have permitted it in so many words, and among others Father Hereau in his public lectures, on the conclusion of which the king put him under arrest in your house, for having taught, among other errors, that when a person who has slandered us in the presence of men of honor, continues to do so after being warned to desist, it is allowable to kill him, not publicly, indeed, for fear of scandal, but IN A PRIVATE WAY — *sed clam.*

I have had occasion already to mention Father Lamy, and you do not need to be informed that his doctrine on this subject was censured in 1649 by the University of Louvain. And yet two months have not elapsed since your Father Des Bois maintained this very censured doctrine of Father Lamy, and taught that "it was allowable for a monk to defend the honor which he acquired by his virtue, EVEN BY KILLING the person who assails his reputation — which has raised such a scandal in that town, that the whole of the curés united to impose silence on him, and to oblige him, by a canonical process, to retract his doctrine. The case is now pending in the Episcopal court.

What say you now, fathers? Why attempt, after that, to maintain that "no Jesuit ever held that it was lawful to kill for slander?" Is anything more necessary to convince you of this than the very opinions of your fathers which you quote, since they do not condemn murder in speculation, but only in practice, and that, too, "on account of the injury that might thereby accrue to the State?" And here I would just beg to ask, whether the whole matter in dispute between us is not simply and solely to ascertain if you have or have not subverted the law of God which condemns murder? The point in question is, not whether you have injured the commonwealth, but whether you have injured religion. What purpose, then, can it serve, in a dispute of this kind, to show that you have spared the State, when you make it apparent, at the same time, that you have destroyed the faith? Is this not evident from your saying that the meaning of Reginald, on the question of killing for slanders, is, "that a private individual has a right to employ that mode of defense, viewing it simply *in itself*?" I desire nothing beyond this concession to confute you. "A private individual," you say, "has a right to employ that mode of defense" (that is, killing for slanders), "viewing the thing in itself;" and, consequently, fathers, the law of God, which forbids us to kill, is nullified by that decision.

It serves no purpose to add, as you have done, "that such a mode is unlawful and criminal, even according to the law of God, on account of the murders and disorders which would follow in society, because the law of God obliges us to have regard to the good of society." This is to evade the question: for there are two laws to be observed — one forbidding us to kill, and another forbidding us to harm society. Reginald has not perhaps, broken the law which forbids us to do harm to society; but he has most certainly violated that which forbids us to kill. Now this is the only point with which we have to do. I might have shown, besides, that your other writers, who have permitted these murders in practice, have subverted the one law as well as the other. But, to proceed, we have seen that you *sometimes* forbid doing harm to the State; and you allege that your design in that is to fulfil the law of God, which obliges us to consult the interests of society. That may be true, though it is far from being certain, as you might do the same thing purely from fear of the civil magistrate. With your permission, then, we shall scrutinize the real secret of this movement.

Is it not certain, fathers, that if you had really any regard to God, and if the observance of his law had been the prime and principal object in your thoughts, this respect would have invariably predominated in all your leading decisions and would have engaged you at all times on the side of religion? But if it turns out, on the contrary, that you violate, in innumerable instances, the most sacred commands that God has laid upon men, and that, as in the instances before us, you annihilate the law of God, which forbids these actions as criminal in themselves, and that you only scruple to approve of them in practice, from bodily fear of the civil magistrate, do you not afford us ground to conclude that you have no respect to God in your apprehensions, and that if you yield an apparent obedience to his law, in so far as regards the obligation to do no harm to the State, this is not done out of any regard to the law itself, but to compass your own ends, as has ever been the way with politicians of no religion?

What, fathers! will you tell us that, looking simply to the law of God, which says, "Thou shalt not kill," we have a right to kill for slanders? And after having thus trampled on the eternal law of God, do you imagine that you atone for the scandal you have caused, and can persuade us of your reverence for him, by adding that you prohibit the practice for State reasons, and from dread of the civil arm? Is not this, on the contrary, to raise a fresh scandal? — I mean not by the respect which you testify for the magistrate; that is not my charge against you, and it is ridiculous in you to banter, as you have done, on this matter. I blame you, not for fearing the magistrate, but for fearing none but the magistrate. And I blame you for this, because it is making God less the enemy of vice than man. Had you said that to kill for slander was allowable according to men, but not according to God, that might have been something more endurable; but when you maintain, that what is too criminal to be tolerated among men, may yet be innocent and right in the eyes of that Being who is righteousness itself, what is this but to declare before the whole world, by a subversion of principle as shocking in itself as it is alien to the spirit of the saints, that while you can be braggarts before God, you are cowards before men?

Had you really been anxious to condemn these homicides, you would have allowed the commandment of God which forbids them to remain intact; and had you dared at once to permit them, you would have permitted them openly, in spite of the laws of God and men. But your object being to permit them imperceptibly, and to cheat the magistrate, who watches over the public safety, you have gone craftily to work. You separate

144 PASCAL

your maxims into two portions. On the one side, you hold out "that it is lawful in speculation to kill a man for slander;"—and nobody thinks of hindering you from taking a speculative view of matters. On the other side, you come out with this detached axiom, "that what is permitted in speculation is also permissible in practice;"—and what concern does society seem to have in this general and metaphysical-looking proposition? And thus these two principles, so little suspected, being embraced in their separate form, the vigilance of the magistrate is eluded; while it is only necessary to combine the two together, to draw from them the conclusion which you aim at—namely, that it is lawful in practice to put a man to death for a simple slander.

It is, indeed, fathers, one of the most subtle tricks of your policy, to scatter through your publications the maxims which you club together in your decisions. It is partly in this way that you establish your doctrine of probabilities, which I have frequently had occasion to explain. That general principle once established, you advance propositions harmless enough when viewed apart, but which, when taken in connection with that pernicious dogma, become positively horrible. An example of this, which demands an answer, may be found in the 11th page of your "Impostures," where you allege that "several famous theologians have decided that it is lawful to kill a man for a box on the ear." Now, it is certain, that if that had been said by a person who did not hold probabilism, there would be nothing to find fault with in it; it would in this case amount to no more than a harmless statement, and nothing could be elicited from it. But you, fathers, and all who hold that dangerous tenet, "that whatever has been approved by celebrated authors is probable and safe in conscience," when *you* add to this "that several celebrated authors are of opinion that it is lawful to kill a man for a box on the ear," what is this but to put a dagger into the hand of all Christians, for the purpose of plunging it into the heart of the first person that insults them, and to assure them that, having the judgment of so many grave authors on their side, they may do so with a perfectly safe conscience?

What monstrous species of language is this, which, in announcing that certain authors hold a detestable opinion, is at the same time giving a decision in favor of that opinion—which solemnly teaches whatever it simply tells! We have learnt, fathers, to understand this peculiar dialect of the Jesuitical school; and it is astonishing that you have the hardihood to speak it out so freely, for it betrays your sentiments somewhat too broadly. It convicts you of permitting murder for a buffet, as often as you repeat that many celebrated authors have maintained that opinion.

This charge, fathers, you will never be able to repel; nor will you be much helped out by those passages from Vasquez and Suarez that you adduce against me, in which they condemn the murders which their associates have approved. These testimonies, disjoined from the rest of your doctrine, may hoodwink those who know little about it; but we, who know better, put your principles and maxims together. You say, then, that Vasquez condemns murders; but what say you on the other side of the question, my reverend fathers? Why, "that the probability of one sentiment does not hinder the probability of the opposite sentiment; and that it is warrantable to follow the less probable and less safe opinion, giving up the more probable and more safe one." What follows from all this taken in connection, but that we have perfect freedom of conscience to adopt any one of these conflicting judgments which pleases us best? And what becomes of all the effect which you fondly anticipate from your quotations? It evaporates in smoke, for we have no more to do than to conjoin for your condemnation the maxims which you have disjoined for your exculpation. Why, then, produce those passages of your authors which I have not quoted, to qualify those which I have quoted, as if the one could excuse the other? What right does that give you to call me an "impostor?" Have I said that all your fathers are implicated in the same corruptions? Have I not, on the contrary, been at pains to show that your interest lay in having them of all different minds, in order to suit all your purposes? Do you wish to kill your man? — here is Lessius for you. Are you inclined to spare him? — here is Vasquez. Nobody need go away in ill humor — nobody without the authority of a grave doctor. Lessius will talk to you like a Heathen on homicide, and like a Christian, it may be, on charity. Vasquez, again, will descant like a Heathen on charity, and like a Christian on homicide. But by means of probabilism, which is held both by Vasquez and Lessius, and which renders all your opinions common property, they will lend their opinions to one another, and each will be held bound to absolve those who have acted according to opinions which each of them has condemned. It is this very variety, then, that confounds you. Uniformity, even in evil, would be better than this. Nothing is more contrary to the orders of St. Ignatius and the first generals of your Society, than this confused medley of all sorts of opinions, good and bad. I may, perhaps, enter on this topic at some future period; and it will astonish many to see how far you have degenerated from the original spirit of your institution, and that your own generals have foreseen that the corruption of your doctrine on morals might prove fatal, not only to your Society, but to the Church universal.

Meanwhile, I repeat that you can derive no advantage from the doctrine of Vasquez. It would be strange, indeed, if, out of all the Jesuits that have written on morals, one or two could not be found who may have hit upon a truth which has been confessed by all Christians. There is no glory in maintaining the truth, according to the Gospel, that it is unlawful to kill a man for smiting us on the face; but it is foul shame to deny it. So far, indeed, from justifying you, nothing tells more fatally against you than the fact that, having doctors among you who have told you the truth, you abide not in the truth, but love the darkness rather than the light. You have been taught by Vasquez that it is a Heathen, and not a Christian, opinion to hold that we may knock down a man for a blow on the cheek; and that it is subversive both of the Gospel and of the decalogue to say that we may kill for such a matter. The most profligate of men will acknowledge as much. And yet you have allowed Lessius, Escobar, and others, to decide, in the face of these well-known truths, and in spite of all the laws of God against manslaughter, that it is quite allowable to kill a man for a buffet!

What purpose, then, can it serve to set this passage of Vasquez over against the sentiment of Lessius, unless you mean to show that, in the opinion of Vasquez, Lessius is a "Heathen" and a "profligate?" and that, fathers, is more than I durst have said myself. What else can be deduced from it than that Lessius "subverts both the Gospel and the decalogue;" that, at the last day, Vasquez will condemn Lessius on this point, as Lessius will condemn Vasquez on another; and that all your fathers will rise up in judgment one against another, mutually condemning each other for their sad outrages on the law of Jesus Christ?

To this conclusion, then, reverend fathers, must we come at length, that as your probabilism renders the good opinions of some of your authors useless to the Church, and useful only to your policy, they merely serve to betray, by their contrariety, the duplicity of your hearts. This you have completely unfolded, by telling us, on the one hand, that Vasquez and Suarez are against homicide, and on the other hand, that many celebrated authors are for homicide; thus presenting two roads to our choice, and destroying the simplicity of the Spirit of God, who denounces his anathema on the deceitful and the double-hearted: "Woe be to the double hearts, and the sinner that goeth two ways!"

Letter XV
To The Reverend Fathers, The Jesuits

Showing that the Jesuits first exclude calumny from their catalogue of crimes, and then employ it in denouncing their opponents

November 25, 1656

REVEREND FATHERS, — As your scurrilities are daily increasing, and as you are employing them in the merciless abuse of all pious persons opposed to your errors, I feel myself obliged, for their sake and that of the Church, to bring out that grand secret of your policy, which I promised to disclose some time ago, in order that all may know, through means of your own maxims, what degree of credit is due to your calumnious accusations.

I am aware that those who are not very well acquainted with you, are at a great loss what to think on this subject, as they find themselves under the painful necessity, either of believing the incredible crimes with which you charge your opponents, or (what is equally incredible) of setting you down as slanderers. "Indeed!" they exclaim, "were these things not true, would clergymen publish them to the world — would they debauch their consciences and damn themselves by venting such libels?" Such is their way of reasoning, and thus it is that the palpable proof of your falsifications coming into collision with their opinion of your honesty, their minds hang in a state of suspense between the evidence of truth which they cannot gainsay, and the demands of charity which they would not violate. It follows, that since their high esteem for you is the only thing that prevents them from discrediting your calumnies, if we can succeed in convincing them that you have quite a different idea of calumny from that which they suppose you to have, and that you actually believe that in blackening and defaming your adversaries you are working out your own salvation, there can be little question that the weight of truth will determine them immediately to pay no regard to your accusations. This, fathers, will be the subject of the present letter.

My design is not simply to show that your writings are full of calumnies; I mean to go a step beyond this. It is quite possible for a person to say a number of false things believing them to be true; but the character of a liar implies the intention to tell lies. Now I undertake to prove, fathers, that it is your deliberate intention to tell lies, and that it is both knowingly and purposely that you load your opponents with crimes of which you know them to be innocent, because you believe that you may do so without falling from a state of grace. Though you doubtless know this point of your morality as well as I do, this need not prevent me from telling you about it; which I shall do, were it for no other purpose than to convince all men of its existence, by showing them that I can maintain it to your face, while you cannot have the assurance to disavow it, without confirming, by that very disavowment, the charge which I bring against you.

The doctrine to which I allude is so common in your schools, that you have maintained it not only in your books, but, such is your assurance, even in your public theses; as, for example, in those delivered at Louvain in the year 1645, where it occurs in the following terms: "What is it but a venial sin to calumnate and forge false accusations to ruin the credit of those who speak evil of us?" So settled is this point among you, that if any one dare to oppose it, you treat him as a blockhead and a hare-brained idiot. Such was the way in which you treated Father Quiroga, the German Capuchin, when he was so unfortunate as to impugn the doctrine. The poor man was instantly attacked by Dicastille,[1] one of your fraternity; and the following is a specimen of the manner in which he manages the dispute: "A certain

---

[1] Father Juan de Discatillus, S.J., 1585-1653, taught at Toledo and Vienna.

rueful-visaged, bare-footed, cowled friar whom I do not choose to name, had the boldness to denounce this opinion, among some women and ignorant people, and to allege that it was scandalous and pernicious against all good manners, hostile to the peace of states and societies, and, in short, contrary to the judgment not only of all Catholic doctors, but of all true Catholics. But in opposition to him I maintained, as I do still, that calumny, when employed against a calumniator, though it should be a falsehood, is not a mortal sin either against justice or charity: and to prove the point, I referred him to the whole body of our fathers, and to whole universities, exclusively composed of them, whom I had consulted on the subject; and among others the reverend Father John Gans, confessor to the emperor; the reverend Father Daniel Bastele, confessor to the archduke Leopold; Father Henri, who was preceptor to these two princes; all the public and ordinary professors of the university of Vienna" (wholly composed of Jesuits); "all the professors of the university of Gratz" (all Jesuits); "all the professors of the university of Prague" (where Jesuits are the masters); — "from all of whom I have in my possession approbations of my opinions, written and signed with their own hands; besides having on my side the reverend Father Panalossa, a Jesuit, preacher to the emperor and the king of Spain; Father Pilliceroli, a Jesuit, and many others, who had all judged this opinion to be probable before our dispute began." You perceive, fathers, that there are few of your opinions which you have been at more pains to establish than the present, as indeed there were few of them of which you stood more in need. For this reason, doubtless, you have authenticated it so well, that the casuists appeal to it as an indubitable principle. "There can be no doubt," says Caramuel, "that it is a probable opinion that we contract no mortal sin by calumniating another, in order to preserve our own reputation. For it is maintained by more than twenty grave doctors, by Gaspard Hurtado, and Dicastille, Jesuits, &c.; so that, were this doctrine not probable, it would be difficult to find any one such in the whole compass of theology."

Wretched indeed must that theology be, and rotten to the very core, which, unless it has been decided to be safe in conscience to defame our neighbor's character to preserve our own, can hardly boast of a safe decision on any other point! How natural is it, fathers, that those who hold this principle should occasionally put it in practice! The corrupt propensity of mankind leans so strongly in that direction of itself, that the obstacle of conscience once being removed, it would be folly to suppose that it will not burst forth with all its native impetuosity. If you desire an example of this, Caramuel will furnish you with one that occurs in the same passage: "This maxim of Father Dicastille," he says, "having been communicated by a German countess to the daughters of the empress, the belief thus impressed on their minds that calumny was only a venial sin, gave rise in the course of a few days to such an immense number of false and scandalous tales, that the whole court was thrown into a flame and filled with alarm. It is easy, indeed, to conceive what a fine use these ladies would make of the new light they had acquired. Matters proceeded to such a length, that it was found necessary to call in the assistance of a worthy Capuchin friar, a man of exemplary life, called Father Quiroga" (the very man whom Dicastille rails at so bitterly), "who assured them that the maxim was most pernicious, especially among women, and was at the greatest pains to prevail upon the empress to abolish the practice of it entirely." We have no reason, therefore, to be surprised at the bad effects of this doctrine; on the contrary, the wonder would be, if it had failed to produce them. Self-love is always ready enough to whisper in our ear, when we are attacked, that we suffer wrongfully; and more particularly in your case, fathers, whom vanity has blinded so egregiously as to make you believe that to wound the honor of your Society, is to wound that of the Church. There would have been good ground to look on it as something miraculous, if you had *not* reduced this maxim to practice. Those who do not know you are ready to say, How could these good fathers slander their enemies, when they cannot do so but at the expense of their own salvation? But if they knew you better, the question would be, How could these good fathers forego the advantage of decrying their enemies, when they have it in their power to do so without hazarding their salvation? Let none, therefore, henceforth be surprised to find the Jesuits calumniators; they can exercise this vocation with a safe conscience; there is no obstacle in heaven or on earth to prevent them. In virtue of the credit they have acquired in the world, they can practise defamation without dreading the justice of mortals; and, on the strength of their self-assumed authority in matters of conscience, they have invented maxims for enabling them to do it without any fear of the justice of God.

Contradictions

About ten or twelve years ago, you were accused of holding that maxim of Father Bauny, "that it is permissible to seek directly (*primo et per se*) a proximate occasion of sin, for the spiritual or temporal good of ourselves or our neighbor" (tr. 4, q. 14); as an example of which, he observes, "It is allowable to visit infamous places, for the purpose of converting abandoned females, even although the practice should be very likely to lead into sin, as in the case of one who has found from experience that he has frequently yielded to their temptations." What answer did your Father Caussin[1] give to this charge in the year 1644? "Just let any one look at the passage in Father Bauny," said he, "let him peruse the page, the margins, the preface,

---

[1] Father Nicolas Caussin, S.J., 1583–1651, confessor of King Louis XIII.

the appendix, in short, the whole book from beginning to end, and he will not discover the slightest vestige of such a sentence, which could only enter into the mind of a man totally devoid of conscience, and could hardly have been forged by any other but an instrument of Satan." Father Pintereau[2] talks in the same style: "That man must be lost to all conscience who would teach so detestable a doctrine; but he must be worse than a devil who attributes it to Father Bauny. Reader, there is not a single trace or vestige of it in the whole of his book." Who would not believe that persons talking in this tone have good reason to complain, and that Father Bauny has, in very deed, been misrepresented? Have you ever asserted anything against me in stronger terms? And, after such a solemn asseveration, that "there was not a single trace or vestige of it in the whole book," who would imagine that the passage is to be found, word for word, in the place referred to?

Truly, fathers, if this be the means of securing your reputation, so long as you remain unanswered, it is also, unfortunately, the means of destroying it forever, so soon as an answer makes its appearance. For so certain is it that you told a lie at the period before mentioned, that you make no scruple of acknowledging, in your apologies of the present day, that the maxim in question is to be found in the very place which had been quoted; and what is most extraordinary, the same maxim which, twelve years ago, was "detestable," has now become so innocent, that in your ninth Imposture (p. 10) you accuse me of "ignorance and malice, in quarrelling with Father Bauny for an opinion which has not been rejected in the School." What an advantage it is, fathers, to have to do with people that deal in contradictions! I need not the aid of any but yourselves to confute you; for I have only two things to show — first, That the maxim in dispute is a worthless one; and, secondly, That it belongs to Father Bauny; and I can prove both by your own confession. In 1644, you confessed that it was "detestable"; and, in 1656, you avow that it is Father Bauny's. This double acknowledgment completely justifies me, fathers; but it does more, it discovers the spirit of your policy. For, tell me, pray, what is the end you propose to yourselves in your writings? Is it to speak with honesty? No, fathers; that cannot be, since your defences destroy each other. Is it to follow the truth of the faith? As little can this be your end; since, according to your own showing, you authorize a "detestable" maxim. But, be it observed, that while you said the maxim was "detestable," you denied, at the same time, that it was the property of Father Bauny, and so he was innocent; and when you now acknowledge it to be his, you maintain, at the same time, that it is a good maxim, and so he is innocent still. The innocence of this monk, therefore, being the only thing common to your two answers, it is obvious that this was the sole end which you aimed at in putting them forth; and

[2]Father François Pinthereau, 1604–1664, rector of the Jesuit College of Caen.

that, when you say of one and the same maxim, that it is in a certain book, and that it is not; that it is a good maxim, and that it is a bad one; your sole object is to whitewash some one or other of your fraternity; judging in the matter, not according to the truth, which never changes, but according to your own interest, which is varying every hour. Can I say more than this? You perceive that it amounts to a demonstration; but it is far from being a singular instance and, to omit a multitude of examples of the same thing, I believe you will be contented with my quoting only one more. . . .

Letter XVI
To The Reverend Fathers, The Jesuits

Shameful calumnies of the Jesuits against pious clergymen and innocent nuns

December 4, 1656

REVEREND FATHERS, — I now come to consider the rest of your calumnies, and shall begin with those contained in your advertisements, which remain to be noticed. As all your other writings, however, are equally well stocked with slander, they will furnish me with abundant materials for entertaining you on this topic as long as I may judge expedient. In the first place, then, with regard to the fable which you have propagated in all your writings against the bishop of Ypres, I beg leave to say, in one word, that you have maliciously wrested the meaning of some ambiguous expressions in one of his letters, which being capable of a good sense, ought, according to the spirit of the Gospel, to have been taken in good part, and could only be taken otherwise according to the spirit of your Society. For example, when he says to a friend, "Give yourself no concern about your nephew; I will furnish him with what he requires from the money that lies in my hands," what reason have you to interpret this to mean, that he would take that money without restoring it, and not that he merely advanced it with the purpose of replacing it?

Letter XVII

January 23, 1657

It is evident, therefore, that as the Church, in condemning a book, assumes that the error which she condemns is contained in that book, it is a point of faith to hold that error as condemned; but it is not a point of faith to hold that the book, in fact, contains the error which the Church supposes it does.

Enough has been said, I think, to prove this; I shall, therefore, conclude my examples by referring to that of Pope Honorius, the history of which is so well known. At the commencement of the seventh century, the Church being troubled by the heresy of the Monothelites, that pope, with the view of terminating the controversy, passed a decree which seemed favorable to these heretics, at which many took offense. The affair, nevertheless, passed over without making much disturbance during his pontificate; but fifty years after, the Church being assembled in the sixth general council, in which Pope Agathon presided by his legates, this decree was impeached, and, after being read and examined, was condemned as containing the heresy of the Monothelites, and under that character burnt, in open court, along with the other writings of these heretics. Such was the respect paid to this decision, and such the unanimity with which it was received throughout the whole Church, that it was afterwards ratified by two other general councils, and likewise by two popes, Leon II. and Adrian II., the latter of whom lived two hundred years after it had passed; and this universal and harmonious agreement remained undisturbed for seven or eight centuries. Of late years, however, some authors, and among the rest Cardinal Bellarmine, without seeming to dread the imputation of heresy, have stoutly maintained, against all this array of popes and councils, that the writings of Honorious are free from the error which had been ascribed to them; "because," says the cardinal, "general councils being liable to err in questions of fact, we have the best grounds for asserting that the sixth council was mistaken with regard to the fact now under consideration; and that, misconceiving the sense of the Letters of Honorius, it has placed this pope most unjustly in the ranks of heretics." Observe, then, I pray you, father, that a man is not heretical for saying that Pope Honorius was not a heretic; even though a great many popes and councils, after examining his writings, should have declared that he was so.

I now come to the question before us, and shall allow you to state your case as favorably as you can. What will you then say, father, in order to stamp your opponents as heretics? That "Pope Innocent X. has declared that the error of the five propositions is to be found in Jansenius?" I grant you that; what inference do you draw from it? That "it is heretical to deny that the error of the five propositions is to be found in Jansenius"? How so, father? Have we not here a question of fact exactly similar to the preceding examples? The pope has declared that the error of the five propositions is contained in Jansenius, in the same way as his predecessors decided that the errors of the Nestorians and the Monothelites polluted the pages of Theodoret and Honorius. In the latter case, your writers hesitate not to say, that while they condemn the heresies, they do not allow that these authors actually maintained them; and, in like manner, your opponents now say, that they condemn the five propositions, but cannot admit that Jansenius has taught them. Truly, the two cases are as like as they could well be; and if there be any disparity between them, it is easy to see how far it must go in favor of the present question, by a comparison of many particular circumstances, which, as they are self-evident, I do not specify. How comes it to pass, then, that when placed in precisely the same predicament, your friends are Catholics and your opponents heretics? On what strange principle of exception do you deprive the latter of a liberty which you freely award to all the rest of the faithful? What answer will you make to this, father? Will you say, "The pope has confirmed his constitution by a brief." To this I would reply, that two general councils and two popes confirmed the condemnation of the letters of Honorius. But what argument do you found upon the language of that brief, in which all that the pope says is, that "he has condemned the doctrine of Jansenius in these five propositions"? What does that add to the constitution, or what more can you infer from it? Nothing, certainly, except that as the sixth council condemned the doctrine of Honorius, in the belief that it was the same with that of the Monothelites, so the pope has said that he has condemned the doctrine of Jansenius in these five propositions, because he was led to suppose it was the same with that of the five propositions. And how could he do otherwise than suppose it? Your Society published nothing else; and you yourself, father, who have asserted that the said propositions were in that author "word for word," happened to be in Rome (for I know all your motions) at the time when the censure was passed. Was he to distrust the sincerity or the competence of so many grave ministers of religion? And how could he help being convinced of the fact, after the assurance which you had given him that the propositions were in that author "word for word"? It is evident, therefore, that in the event of its being found that Jansenius has not supported these doctrines, it would be wrong to say as your writers have done in the cases before mentioned, that the pope has deceived himself in this point of fact, which it is painful and offensive to publish at any time; the proper phrase is, that you have deceived the pope, which, as you are now pretty well known, will create no scandal.

Determined, however, to have a heresy made out, let it cost what it may, you have attempted, by the following manœuvre, to shift the question from the point of fact, and make it bear upon a point of faith. "The pope," say you, "declares that he has condemned the doctrine of Jansenius in these five propositions; therefore it is essential to the faith to hold that the doctrine of Jansenius touching these five propositions is heretical, *let it be what it may*." Here is a strange point of faith, that a doctrine is heretical *be what it may*. What! if Jansenius should happen to maintain that "*we are capable of resisting internal grace*," and that "*it is false to say that Jesus Christ died for the elect only*," would this doctrine be condemned just because it is his doctrine? Will the proposition, that "*man has a freedom of will to do good or evil*," be true when found in the pope's constitution, and false when discovered in Jansenius? By what fatality must he be reduced to such a predicament, that truth, when admitted into his book, becomes heresy? You must confess, then, that he is only heretical on the supposition that he is friendly to the errors condemned, seeing that the constitution of the pope is the rule which we must apply to Jansenius, to judge if his character answer the description there given of him; and, accordingly, the question, *Is his doctrine heretical?* must be resolved by another question of fact. *Does it correspond to the natural sense of these propositions?* as it must necessarily be heretical if it does correspond to that sense, and must necessarily be orthodox if it be of an opposite character. For, in one word, since according to the pope and the bishops, "the propositions are condemned *in their proper and natural sense,*" they cannot possibly be condemned in the sense of Jansenius, except on the understanding that the sense of Jansenius is the same with the proper and natural sense of these propositions; and this I maintain to be purely a question of fact.

The question, then, still rests upon the point of fact, and cannot possibly be tortured into one affecting the faith. But though incapable of twisting it into a matter of heresy, you have it in your power to make it a pretext for persecution, and might, perhaps, succeed in this, were there not good reason to hope that nobody will be found so blindly devoted to your interests as to countenance such a disgraceful proceeding, or inclined to compel people, as you wish to do, to sign a declaration *that they condemn these propositions in the sense of Jansenius,* without explaining what the sense of Jansenius is. Few people are disposed to sign a blank confession of faith. Now this would really be to sign one of that description, leaving you to fill up the blank afterwards with whatsoever you pleased, as you would be at liberty to interpret according to your own taste the unexplained sense of Jansenius. Let it be explained, then, beforehand, otherwise we shall have, I fear, another version of your *proximate power,* without any sense at all. This mode of proceeding, you must be aware, does not take with the world. Men in general detest all ambiguity, especially in the matter of religion, where it is highly reasonable that one should know at least what one is asked to condemn. And how is it possible for doctors, who are persuaded that Jansenius can bear no other sense than that of efficacious grace, to consent to declare that they condemn his doctrine without explaining it, since, with their present convictions, which no means are used to alter, this would be neither more nor less than to condemn efficacious grace, which cannot be condemned without sin? Would it not, therefore, be a piece of monstrous tyranny to place them in such an unhappy dilemma, that they must either bring guilt upon their souls in the sight of God, by signing that condemnation against their consciences, or be denounced as heretics for refusing to sign it?

But there is a mystery under all this. You Jesuits cannot move a step without a stratagem. It remains for me to explain why you do not explain the sense of Jansenius. The sole purpose of my writing is to discover your designs, and, by discovering, to frustrate them. I must, therefore, inform those who are not already aware of the fact, that your great concern in this dispute being to uphold the *sufficient grace* of your Molina, you could not effect this without destroying the *efficacious grace* which stands directly opposed to it. Perceiving, however, that the latter was now sanctioned at Rome, and by all the learned in the Church, and unable to combat the doctrine on its own merits, you resolved to attack it in a clandestine way, under the name of the doctrine of Jansenius. You were resolved, accordingly, to get Jansenius condemned without explanation; and, to gain your purpose, gave out that his doctrine was not that of efficacious grace, so that every one might think he was at liberty to condemn the one without denying the other. Hence your efforts, in the present day, to impress this idea upon the minds of such as have no acquaintance with that author; an object which you yourself, father, have attempted, by means of the following ingenious syllogism: "The pope has condemned the doctrine of Jansenius; but the pope has not condemned efficacious grace: therefore, the doctrine of efficacious grace must be different from that of Jansenius." If this mode of reasoning were conclusive, it might be demonstrated in the same way that Honorius and all his defenders are heretics of the same kind. "The sixth council has condemned the doctrine of Honorius; but the council has not condemned the doctrine of the Church: therefore the doctrine of Honorius is different from that of the Church; and therefore, all who defend him are heretics." It is obvious that no conclusion can be drawn from this; for the pope has done no more than condemn the doctrine of the five propositions, which was represented to him as the doctrine of Jansenius.

But it matters not; you have no intention to make use of this logic for any length of time. Poor as it is, it will last sufficiently long to serve your present turn. All that you wish to effect by it, in the meantime, is to induce those who are unwilling to condemn efficacious grace to condemn Jansenius with less scruple. When this object has been accomplished, your argument will soon be forgotten, and their signatures remaining as an eternal testimony in condemnation of Jansenius, will furnish you with an occasion to make a direct attack upon efficacious grace, by another mode of reasoning much more solid than the former, which shall be forthcoming in proper time. "The doctrine of Jansenius," you will argue, "has been condemned by the universal subscriptions of the Church. Now this doctrine is manifestly that of efficacious grace" (and it will be easy for you to prove that); "therefore the doctrine of efficacious grace is condemned even by the confession of his defenders."

Behold your reason for proposing to sign the condemnation of a doctrine without giving an explanation of it! Behold the advantage you expect to gain from subscriptions thus procured! Should your opponents, however, refuse to subscribe, you have another trap laid for them. Having dexterously combined the question of faith with that of fact, and not allowing them to separate between them, nor to sign the one without the other, the consequence will be, that, because they could not subscribe the two together, you will publish it in all directions that they have refused the two together. And thus though, in point of fact, they simply decline acknowledging that Jansenius has maintained the propositions which they condemn, which cannot be called heresy, you will boldly assert that they have refused to condemn the propositions themselves, and that it is this that constitutes their heresy.

Such is the fruit which you expect to reap from their refusal, and which will be no less useful to you than what you might have gained from their consent. So that, in the event of these signatures being exacted, they will fall into your snares, whether they sign or not, and in both cases you will gain your point; such is your dexterity in uniformly putting matters into a train for our own advantage, whatever bias they may happen to take in their course!

How well I know you, father! and how grieved am I to see that God has abandoned you so far as to allow you such happy success in such an unhappy course! Your good fortune deserves commiseration, and can excite envy only in the breasts of those who know not what truly good fortune is. It is an act of charity to thwart the success you aim at in the whole of this proceeding, seeing that you can only reach it by the aid of falsehood, and by procuring credit to one of two lies — either that the Church has condemned efficacious grace, or that those who defend that doctrine maintain the five condemned errors.

The world must, therefore, be apprised of two facts: First, That, by your own confession, efficacious grace has not been condemned; and secondly, That nobody supports these errors. So that it may be known that those who may refuse to sign what you are so anxious to exact from them, refuse merely in consideration of the question of *fact*; and that, being quite ready to subscribe that of *faith*, they cannot be deemed heretical on that account; because, to repeat it once more, though it be matter of faith to believe these propositions to be heretical, it will never be matter of faith to hold that they are to be found in the pages of Jansenius. They are innocent of all error; that is enough. It may be that they interpret Jansenius too favorably; but it may be also that you do not interpret him favorably enough. I do not enter upon this question. All that I know is, that, according to your maxims, you believe that you may, without sin, publish him to be a heretic contrary to your own knowledge; whereas, according to their maxims, they cannot, without sin, declare him to be a Catholic, unless they are persuaded that he is one. They are, therefore, more honest than you, father; they have examined Jansenius more faithfully than you; they are no less intelligent than you; they are, therefore, no less credible witnesses than you. But come what may of this point of fact, there are certainly Catholics; for, in order to be so, it is not necessary to declare that another man is not a Catholic; it is enough, in all conscience, if a person, without charging error upon anybody else, succeed in discharging himself.

Reverend Father, — If you have found any difficulty in deciphering this letter, which is certainly not printed in the best possible type, blame nobody but yourself. Privileges are not so easily granted to me as they are to you. You can procure them even for the purpose of combating miracles; I cannot have them even to defend myself. The printing-houses are perpetually haunted. In such circumstances, you yourself would not advise me to write you any more letters, for it is really a sad annoyance to be obliged to have recourse to an Osnabruck impression.

Letter XVIII
To The Reverend Father Annat, Jesuit

Showing still more plainly, on the authority of Father Annat himself, that there is really no heresy in the Church, and that in questions of fact we must be guided by our senses, and not by authority even of the popes

March 24, 1657

REVEREND FATHER, — Long have you labored to discover some error in the creed or conduct of your opponents; but I rather think you will have to confess in the end, that it is a more difficult task than you imagined to make heretics of people who are not only no heretics, but who hate nothing in the world so much as heresy. In my last letter I succeeded in showing that you accuse them of one heresy after another, without being able to stand by one of the charges for any length of time; so that all that remained for you was to fix on their refusal to condemn "the sense of Jansenius," which you insist on their doing without explanation. You must have been sadly in want of heresies to brand them with, when you were reduced to this. For who ever heard of a heresy which nobody could explain? The answer was ready, therefore, that if Jansenius has no errors, it is wrong to condemn him; and if he has, you were bound to point them out, that we might know at least what we were condemning. This, however, you have never yet been pleased to do; but you have attempted to fortify your position by decrees, which made nothing in your favor, as they gave no sort of explanation of the sense of Jansenius, said to have been condemned in the five propositions. This was not the way to terminate the dispute. Had you mutually agreed as to the genuine sense of Jansenius, and had the only difference between you been as to whether that sense was heretical or not, in that case the decisions which might pronounce it to be heretical, would have touched the real question in dispute. But the great dispute being about the sense of Jansenius, the one party saying that they could see nothing in it inconsistent with the sense of St. Augustine and St. Thomas, and the other party asserting that they saw in it an heretical sense which they would not express. It is clear that a constitution which does not say a word about this difference of opinion, and which only condemns in general and without explanation the sense of Jansenius, leaves the point in dispute quite undecided.

You have accordingly been repeatedly told, that as your discussion turns on a matter of fact, you would never be able to bring it to a conclusion without declaring what you understand by the sense of Jansenius. But, as you continued obstinate in your refusal to make this explanation, I endeavored, as a last resource, to extort it from you, by hinting, in my last letter, that there was some mystery under the efforts you were making to procure the condemnation of this sense without explaining it, and that your design was to make this indefinite censure recoil some day or other, upon the doctrine of efficacious grace, by showing, as you could easily do, that this was exactly the doctrine of Jansenius. This has reduced you to the necessity of making a reply; for, had you pertinaciously refused, after such an insinuation, to explain your views of that sense, it would have been apparent, to persons of the smallest penetration, that you condemned it in the sense of efficacious grace — a conclusion which, considering the veneration in which the Church holds holy doctrine, would have overwhelmed you with disgrace.

You have, therefore, been forced to speak out your mind; and we find it expressed in your reply to that part of my letter in which I remarked, that "if Jansenius was capable of any other sense than that of efficacious grace, he had no defenders; but if his writings bore no other sense, he had no errors to defend." You found it impossible to deny this position, father; but you have attempted to parry it by the following distinction: "It is not sufficient," say you, "for the vindication of Jansenius, to allege that he merely holds the doctrine of efficacious grace, for that may be held in two ways — the one heretical, according to Calvin, which consists in maintaining that the will, when under the influence of grace, has not the power of resisting it; the other orthodox, according to the Thomists and the Sorbonists, which is founded on the principles established by the councils, and which is, that efficacious grace of itself governs the will in such a way that it still has the power of resisting it."

All this we grant, father; but you conclude by adding: "Jansenius would be orthodox, if he defended efficacious grace in the sense of the Thomists; but he is heretical, because he opposes the Thomists, and joins issue with Calvin, who denies the power of resisting grace." I do not here enter upon the question of fact, whether Jansenius really agrees with Calvin. It is enough for my purpose that you assert that he does, and that you now inform me that by the sense of Jansenius you have all along understood nothing more than the sense of Calvin. Was this all you meant, then, father? Was it only the error of Calvin that you were so anxious to get condemned, under the name of "the sense of Jansenius?" Why did you not tell us this sooner? You might have saved yourself a world of trouble; for we were all ready, without the aid of bulls or briefs, to join with you in condemning that error. What urgent necessity there was for such an explanation! What a host of difficulties has it removed! We were quite at a loss, my dear father, to know what error the popes and bishops meant to condemn, under the name of "the sense of Jansenius." The whole Church was in the utmost perplexity about it, and not a soul would relieve us by an explanation. This, however, has now been done by you, father—you, whom the whole of your party regard as the chief and prime mover of all their councils, and who are acquainted with the whole secret of this proceeding. You, then, have told us that the sense of Jansenius is neither more nor less than the sense of Calvin, which has been condemned by the council. Why, this explains everything. We know now that the error which they intended to condemn, under these terms—*the sense of Jansenius*—is neither more nor less than the sense of Calvin; and that, consequently, we, by joining with them in the condemnation of Calvin's doctrine, have yielded all due obedience to these decrees. We are no longer surprised at the zeal which the popes and some bishops manifested against "the sense of Jansenius." How, indeed, could they be otherwise than zealous against it, believing, as they did, the declarations of those who publicly affirmed that it was identically the same with that of Calvin?

I must maintain, then, father, that you have no further reason to quarrel with your adversaries; for they detest that doctrine as heartily as you do. I am only astonished to see that you are ignorant of this fact, and that you have such an imperfect acquaintance with their sentiments on this point, which they have so repeatedly expressed in their published works. I flatter myself that, were you more intimate with these writings, you would deeply regret your not having made yourself acquainted sooner, in the spirit of peace, with a doctrine which is in every respect so holy and so Christian, but which passion, in the absence of knowledge, now prompts you to oppose. You would find, father, that they not only hold that an effective resistance may be made to those feebler graces which go under the name of *exciting* or *inefficacious*, from their not terminating in the good with which they inspire us; but that they are, moreover, as firm in maintaining, in opposition to Calvin, the power which the will has to resist even efficacious and victorious grace, as they are in contending against Molina for the power of this grace over the will, and fully as jealous for the one of these truths as they are for the other. They know too well that man, of his own nature, has always the power of sinning and of resisting grace; and that, since he became corrupt, he unhappily carries in his breast a fount of concupiscence which infinitely augments that power; but that, notwithstanding this, when it pleases God to visit him with his mercy, he makes the soul do what he wills, and in the manner he wills it to be done, while, at the same time, the infallibility of the divine operation does not in any way destroy the natural liberty of man, in consequence of the secret and wonderful ways by which God operates this change. This has been most admirably explained by St. Augustine, in such a way as to dissipate all those imaginary inconsistencies which the opponents of efficacious grace suppose to exist between the sovereign power of grace over the free-will and the power which the free-will has to resist grace. For, according to this great saint, whom the popes and the Church have held to be a standard authority on this subject, God transforms the heart of man, by shedding abroad in it a heavenly sweetness, which surmounting the delights of the flesh, and inducing him to feel, on the one hand, his own mortality and nothingness, and to discover, on the other hand, the majesty and eternity of God, makes him conceive a distaste for the pleasures of sin, which interpose between him and incorruptible happiness. Finding his chiefest joy in the God who charms him, his soul is drawn towards him infallibly, but of its own accord, by a motion perfectly free, spontaneous, love-impelled; so that it would be its torment and punishment to be separated from him. Not but that the person has always the power of forsaking his God, and that he may not actually forsake him, provided he choose to do it. But how *could* he choose such a course, seeing that the will always inclines to that which is most agreeable to it, and that in the case we now suppose, nothing can be more agreeable than the possession of that *one good*, which comprises in itself all other good things? "Our actions are necessarily determined by that which affords us the greatest pleasure," St. Augustine says.

Such is the manner in which God regulates the free will of man without encroaching on its freedom, and in which the free will, which always may, but never will, resist his grace, turns to God with a movement as voluntary as it is irresistible, whensoever he is pleased to draw it to himself by the sweet constraint of his efficacious inspirations.

These, father, are the divine principles of St. Augustine and St. Thomas, according to which it is equally true that *we have the power of resisting grace*, contrary to Calvin's opinion, and that, nevertheless, to employ the language of Pope Clement VIII., in his paper addressed to the Congregation *de Auxiliis*, "God forms within us the motion of our will, and effectually disposes of our hearts, by virtue of that empire which his supreme majesty has over the volitions of men, as well as over the other creatures under heaven, according to St. Augustine."

On the same principle, it follows that we act of ourselves, and thus, in opposition to another error of Calvin, that we have merits which are truly and properly *ours*; and yet, as God is the first principle of our actions, and as, in the language of St. Paul, he "worketh in us that which is pleasing in his sight"; "our merits are the gifts of God," as the Council of Trent says.

By means of this distinction we demolish the profane sentiment of Luther, condemned by that Council, namely, that "we co-operate in no way whatever towards our salvation, any more than inanimate things"; and, by the same mode of reasoning, we overthrow the equally profane sentiment of the school of Molina, who will not allow that it is by the strength of divine grace that we are enabled to co-operate with it in the work of our salvation, and who thereby comes into hostile collision with that principle of faith established by St. Paul, "That it is God who worketh in us both to will and to do."

In fine, in this way we reconcile all those passages of Scripture which seem quite inconsistent with each other such as the following: "Turn ye unto God" — "Turn thou us, and we shall be turned" — "Cast away iniquity from you" — "It is God who taketh away iniquity from his people" — "Bring forth works meet for repentance" — "Lord, thou has wrought all our works in us" — "Make ye a new heart and a new spirit" — "A new spirit will I give you, and a new heart will I create within you," &c.

The only way of reconciling these apparent contrarieties, which ascribe our good actions at one time to God, and at another time to ourselves, is to keep in view the distinction, as stated by St. Augustine, that "our actions are ours in respect of the free will which produces them; but that they are also of God, in respect of his grace which enables our free will to produce them"; and that, as the same writer elsewhere remarks, "God enables us to do what is pleasing in his sight, by making us will to do even what we might have been unwilling to do."

It thus appears, father, that your opponents are perfectly at one with the modern Thomists, for the Thomists hold, with them, both the power of resisting grace, and the infallibility of the effect of grace; of which latter doctrine they profess themselves the most strenuous advocates, if we may judge from a common maxim of their theology, which Alvarez, one of the leading men among them, repeats so often in his book, and expresses in the following terms (disp. 72, n. 4): "When efficacious grace moves the free will, it infallibly consents; because the effect of grace is such, that, although the will has the power of withholding its consent, it nevertheless consents in effect." He corroborates this by a quotation from his master, St. Thomas: "The will of God cannot fail to be accomplished; and, accordingly, when it is his pleasure that a man should consent to the influence of grace, he consents infallibly, and even necessarily, not by an absolute necessity, but by a necessity of infallibility." In effecting this, divine grace does not trench upon "the power which man has to resist it, if he wishes to do so"; it merely prevents him from wishing to resist it. This has been acknowledged by your Father Petau, in the following passage (tom. i. p. 602): "The grace of Jesus Christ insures infallible perseverance in piety, though not by necessity; for a person may refuse to yield his consent to grace, if he be so inclined, as the council states; but that same grace provides that he shall never be so inclined."

This, father, is the uniform doctrine of St. Augustine, of St. Prosper, of the fathers who followed them, of the councils, of St. Thomas, and of all the Thomists in general. It is likewise, whatever you may think of it, the doctrine of your opponents. And let me add, it is the doctrine which you yourself have lately sealed with your approbation. I shall quote your own words: "The doctrine of efficacious grace, which admits that we have a power of resisting it, is orthodox, founded on the councils, and supported by the Thomists and Sorbonists." Now, tell us the plain truth, father; if you had known that your opponents really held this doctrine, the interests of your Society might perhaps have made you scruple before pronouncing this public approval of it; but, acting on the supposition that they were hostile to the doctrine, the same powerful motive has induced you to authorize sentiments which you know in your heart to be contrary to those of your Society; and by this blunder, in your anxiety to ruin their principles, you have yourself completely confirmed them. So that, by a kind of prodigy, we now behold the advocates of efficacious grace vindicated by the advocates of Molina — an admirable instance of the wisdom of God in making all things concur to advance the glory of the truth.

Let the whole world observe, then, that by your own admission, the truth of this efficacious grace, which is so essential to all the acts of piety, which is so dear to the Church, and which is the purchase of her Saviour's blood, is so indisputably Catholic, that there is not a single Catholic, not even among the Jesuits, who would not acknowledge its orthodoxy. And let it be noticed, at the same time, that, according to your own confession, not the slightest suspicion of error can fall on those whom you have so often stigmatized with it. For so long as you charged them with clandestine heresies, without choosing to specify them by name, it was as difficult for them to defend themselves, as it was easy for you to bring such accusations. But now, when you have come to declare that the error which constrains you to oppose them, is the heresy of Calvin which you supposed them to hold, it must be apparent to every one that they are innocent of all error; for so decidedly hostile are they to this, the only error you charge upon them, that they protest, by their discourses, by their books, by every mode, in short, in which they can testify their sentiments, that they condemn that heresy with their whole heart, and in the same manner as it has been condemned by the Thomists, whom you acknowledge, without scruple, to be Catholics, and who have never been suspected to be anything else.

What will you say against them now, father? Will you say that they are heretics still, because, although they do not adopt the sense of Calvin, they will not allow that the sense of Jansenius is the same with that of Calvin? Will you presume to say that this is matter of heresy? Is it not a pure question of fact, with which heresy has nothing to do? It would be heretical to say that we have not the power of resisting efficacious grace; but would it be so to doubt that Jansenius held that doctrine? Is this a revealed truth? Is it an article of faith which must be believed, on pain of damnation? Or is it not, in spite of you, a point of fact, on account of which it would be ridiculous to hold that there were heretics in the Church?

Drop this epithet, then, father, and give them some other name, more suited to the nature of your dispute. Tell them, they are ignorant and stupid — that they misunderstand Jansenius. These would be charges in keeping with your controversy; but it is quite irrelevant to call them heretics. As this, however, is the only charge from which I am anxious to defend them, I shall not give myself much trouble to show that they rightly understand Jansenius. All I shall say on the point, father, is, that it appears to me that were he to be judged according to your own rules, it would be difficult to prove him not to be a good Catholic. We shall try him by the test you have proposed. "To know," say you, "whether Jansenius is sound or not, we must inquire whether he defends efficacious grace in the manner of Calvin, who denies that man has the power of resisting it — in which case he would be heretical; or in the manner of the Thomists, who admit that it may be resisted — for then he would be Catholic." Judge, then, father, whether he holds that grace may be resisted, when he says, "That we have always a power to resist grace, according to the council; that free will may always act or not act, will or not will, consent or not consent, do good or do evil; and that man, in this life, has always these two liberties, which may be called by some contradictions." Judge, likewise, if he be not opposed to the error of Calvin, as you have described it, when he occupies a whole chapter (21st) in showing "that the Church has condemned that heretic who denies that efficacious grace acts on the free will in the manner which has been so long believed in the Church, so as to leave it in the power of free will to consent or not to consent; whereas, according to St. Augustine and the council, we have always the power of withholding our consent if we choose; and according to St. Prosper, God bestows even upon his elect the will to persevere, in such a way as not to deprive them of the power to will the contrary." And, in one word, judge if he does not agree with the Thomists, from the following declaration in chapter 4th: "That all that the Thomists have written with the view of reconciling the efficaciousness of grace with the power of resisting it, so entirely coincides with his judgment, that to ascertain his sentiments on this subject, we have only to consult their writings."

Such being the language he holds on these heads, my opinion is, that he believes in the power of resisting grace; that he differs from Calvin, and agrees with the Thomists, because he has said so; and that he is, therefore, according to your own showing, a Catholic. If you have any means of knowing the sense of an author otherwise than by his expressions; and if,

without quoting any of his passages, you are disposed to maintain, in direct
opposition to his own words, that he denies this power of resistance, and
that he is for Calvin and against the Thomists, do not be afraid, father, that
I will accuse you of heresy for that. I shall only say, that you do not seem
properly to understand Jansenius; but we shall not be the less on that
account children of the same Church.

How comes it, then, father, that you manage this dispute in such a
passionate spirit, and that you treat as your most cruel enemies, and as the
most pestilent of heretics, a class of persons whom you cannot accuse of any
error, nor of anything whatever, except that they do not understand Jansenius as you do? For what else in the world do you dispute about, except
the sense of that author? You would have them to condemn it. They ask
what you mean them to condemn. You reply, that you mean the error of
Calvin. They rejoin that they condemn that error; and with this acknowledgment (unless it is syllables you wish to condemn, and not the thing
which they signify), you ought to rest satisfied. If they refuse to say that
they condemn the sense of Jansenius, it is because they believe it to be that
of St. Thomas, and thus this unhappy phrase has a very equivocal meaning
betwixt you. In your mouth it signifies the sense of Calvin; in theirs the
sense of St. Thomas. Your dissensions arise entirely from the different
ideas which you attach to the same term. Were I made umpire in the
quarrel, I would interdict the use of the word Jansenius, on both sides; and
thus, by obliging you merely to express what you understand by it, it would
be seen that you ask nothing more than the condemnation of Calvin, to
which they willingly agree; and that they ask nothing more than the
vindication of the sense of St. Augustine and St. Thomas, in which you
again perfectly coincide.

I declare, then, father, that for my part I shall continue to regard them as
good Catholics, whether they condemn Jansenius, on finding him erro-
neous, or refuse to condemn him, from finding that he maintains nothing
more than what you yourself acknowledge to be orthodox; and that I shall
say to them what St. Jerome said to John, bishop of Jerusalem, who was
either accused of holding the eight propositions of Origen: "Either condemn Origen, if you acknowledge that he has maintained these errors, or
else deny that he has maintained them."

See, father, how these persons acted, whose sole concern was with
principles, and not with persons; whereas you who aim at persons more
than principles, consider it a matter of no consequence to condemn errors,
unless you procure the condemnation of the individuals to whom you
choose to impute them.

How ridiculously violent your conduct is, father! and how ill calculated to
insure success! I told you before, and I repeat it, violence and verity can
make no impression on each other. Never were your accusations more
outrageous, and never was the innocence of your opponents more discern-
ible: never has efficacious grace been attacked with greater subtility, and

never has it been more triumphantly established. You have made the most desperate efforts to convince people that your disputes involved points of faith; and never was it more apparent that the whole controversy turned upon a mere point of fact. In fine, you have moved heaven and earth to make it appear that this point of fact is founded on truth; and never were people more disposed to call it in question. And the obvious reason of this is, that you do not take the natural course to make them believe a point of fact, which is to convince their senses, and point out to them in a book the words which you allege are to be found in it. The means you have adopted are so far removed from this straightforward course, that the most obtuse minds are unavoidably struck by observing it. Why did you not take the plan which I followed in bringing to light the wicked maxims of your authors — which was to cite faithfully the passages of their writings from which they were extracted? This was the mode followed by the curés of Paris, and it never fails to produce conviction. But, when you were charged by them with holding, for example, the proposition of Father Lamy, that a "monk may kill a person who threatens to publish calumnies against himself or his order, when he cannot otherwise prevent the publication," — what would you have thought, and what would the public have said, if they had not quoted the place where that sentiment is literally to be found? or if, after having been repeatedly demanded to quote their authority, they still obstinately refused to do it? or if, instead of acceding to this, they had gone off to Rome, and procured a bull, ordaining men to acknowledge the truth of their statement? Would it not be undoubtedly concluded that they had surprised the pope, and that they would never have had recourse to this extraordinary method, but for want of the natural means of substantiating the truth, which matters of fact furnish to all who undertake to prove them? Accordingly, they had no more to do than to tell us that Father Lamy teaches this doctrine in *tome* 5, *disp.* 36, *n.* 118, *page* 544, *of the Douay edition*; and by this means everybody who wished to see it found it out, and nobody could doubt about it any longer. This appears to be a very easy and prompt way of putting an end to controversies of fact, when one has got the right side of the question.

How comes it, then, father, that you do not follow this plan? You said, in your book, that the five propositions are in Jansenius, word for word, in the identical terms — You were told they were not. What had you to do after this, but either to cite the page, if you had really found the words, or to acknowledge that you were mistaken. But you have done neither the one nor the other. In place of this, on finding that all the passages from Jansenius, which you sometimes adduce for the purpose of hoodwinking the people, are not "the condemned propositions in their individual identity," as you had engaged to show us, you present us with Constitutions from Rome, which, without specifying any particular place, declare that the propositions have been extracted from his book.

I am sensible, father, of the respect which Christians owe to the Holy

See, and your antagonists give sufficient evidence of their resolution ever to abide by its decisions. Do not imagine that it implied any deficiency in this due deference on their part, that they represented to the pope, with all the submission which children owe to their father, and members to their head, that it was possible he might be deceived on this point of fact — that he had not caused it to be investigated during his pontificate; and that his predecessor, Innocent X., had merely examined into the heretical character of the propositions, and not into the fact of their connection with Jansenius. This they stated to the commissary of the Holy Office, one of the principal examiners, stating, that they could not be censured, according to the sense of any author, because they had been presented for examination on their own merits; and without considering to what author they might belong: further, that upwards of sixty doctors, and a vast number of other persons of learning and piety, had read that book carefully over, without ever having encountered the proscribed propositions, and that they have found some of a quite opposite description: that those who had produced that impression on the mind of the pope, might be reasonably presumed to have abused the confidence he reposed in them, inasmuch as they had an interest in decrying that author, who has convicted Molina of upwards of fifty errors: that what renders this supposition still more probable is, that they have a certain maxim among them, one of the best authenticated in their whole system of theology, which is, "that they may, without criminality, calumniate those by whom they conceive themselves to be unjustly attacked;" and that, accordingly, their testimony being so suspicious, and the testimony of the other party so respectable, they had some ground for supplicating his holiness, with the most profound humility, that he would ordain an investigation to be made into this fact, in the presence of doctors belonging to both parties, in order that a solemn and regular decision might be formed on the point in dispute. "Let there be a convocation of able judges (says St. Basil on a similar occasion, Ep. 75); let each of them be left at perfect freedom; let them examine my writings; let them judge if they contain errors against the faith; let them read the objections and the replies; that so a judgment may be given in due form, and with proper knowledge of the case, and not a defamatory libel without examination."

It is quite vain for you, father, to represent those who would act in the manner I have now supposed as deficient in proper subjection to the Holy See. The popes are very far from being disposed to treat Christians with that imperiousness which some would fain exercise under their name. "The Church," says Pope St. Gregory, "which has been trained in the school of humility, does not command with authority, but persuades by reason, her children whom she believes to be in error, to obey what she has taught them." And so far from deeming it a disgrace to review a judgment into which they may have been surprised, we have the testimony of St. Bernard for saying that they glory in acknowledging the mistake. "The

Apostolic See (he says, Ep. 180) can boast of this recommendation, that it never stands on the point of honor, but willingly revokes a decision that has been gained from it by surprise; indeed, it is highly just to prevent any from profiting by an act of injustice, and more especially before the Holy See."

Such, father, are the proper sentiments with which the popes ought to be inspired; for all divines are agreed that they may be surprised, and that their supreme character, so far from warranting them against mistakes, exposes them the more readily to fall into them, on account of the vast number of cares which claim their attention. This is what the same St. Gregory says to some persons who were astonished at the circumstance of another pope having suffered himself to be deluded: "Why do you wonder," says he, "that we should be deceived, we who are but men? Have you not read that David, a king who had the spirit of prophecy, was induced, by giving credit to the falsehoods of Ziba, to pronounce an unjust judgment against the son of Jonathan? Who will think it strange, then, that we, who are not prophets, should sometimes be imposed upon by deceivers? A multiplicity of affairs presses on us, and our minds, which, by being obliged to attend to so many things at once, apply themselves less closely to each in particular, are the more easily liable to be imposed upon in individual cases." Truly, father, I should suppose that the popes know better than you whether they may be deceived or not. They themselves tell us that popes, as well as the greatest princes, are more exposed to deception than individuals who are less occupied with important avocations. This must be believed on their testimony. And it is easy to imagine by what means they come to be thus overreached. St. Bernard, in the letter which he wrote to Innocent II., gives us the following description of the process: "It is no wonder, and no novelty, that the human mind may be deceived, and is deceived. You are surrounded by monks who come to you in the spirit of lying and deceit. They have filled your ears with stories against a bishop, whose life has been most exemplary, but who is the object of their hatred. These persons bite like dogs, and strive to make good appear evil. Meanwhile, most holy father, you put yourself into a rage against your own son. Why have you afforded matter of joy to his enemies? Believe not every spirit, but try the spirits whether they be of God. I trust that, when you have ascertained the truth, all this delusion, which rests on a false report, will be dissipated. I pray the spirit of truth to grant you the grace to separate light from darkness, and to favor the good by rejecting the evil." You see, then, father, that the eminent rank of the popes does not exempt them from the influence of delusion; and I may now add, that it only serves to render their mistakes more dangerous and important than those of other men. This is the light in which St. Bernard represents them to Pope Eugenius: "There is another fault, so common among the great of this world, that I never met one of them who was free from it; and that is, holy father, an excessive credulity, the source of numerous disorders. From this proceed violent persecutions against the innocent, unfounded prejudices against the absent, and tremendous storms about nothing. This, holy father, is a universal evil, from the influence of which, if you are exempt, I shall only say, you are the only individual among all your compeers who can boast of that privilege."

I imagine, father, that the proofs I have brought are beginning to convince you that the popes are liable to be surprised. But, to complete your conversion, I shall merely remind you of some examples, which you yourself have quoted in your book, of popes and emperors whom heretics have actually deceived. You will remember, then, that you have told us that Apollinarius surprised Pope Damasius, in the same way that Celestius surprised Zozimus. You inform us, besides, that one called Athanasius deceived the Emperor Heraclius, and prevailed on him to persecute the Catholics. And lastly, that Sergius obtained from Honorius that infamous decretal which was burned at the sixth council, "by playing the busybody," as you say, "about the person of that pope."

It appears, then, father, by your own confession, that those who act this part about the persons of kings and popes, do sometimes artfully entice them to persecute the faithful defenders of the truth, under the persuasion that they are persecuting heretics. And hence the popes, who hold nothing in greater horror than these surprisals, have, by a letter of Alexander III., enacted an ecclesiastical statute, which is inserted in the canonical law, to permit the suspension of the execution of their bulls and decretals, when there is ground to suspect that they have been imposed upon. "If," says that pope to the Archbishop of Ravenna, "we sometimes send decretals to your fraternity which are opposed to your sentiments, give yourselves no distress on that account. We shall expect you either to carry them respectfully into execution, or to send us the reason why you conceive they ought not to be executed; for we deem it right that you should not execute a decree which may have been procured from us by artifice and surprise." Such has been the course pursued by the popes, whose sole object is to settle the disputes of Christians, and not to follow the passionate counsels of those who strive to involve them in trouble and perplexity. Following the advice of St. Peter and St. Paul, who in this followed the commandment of Jesus Christ, they avoid domination. The spirit which appears in their whole conduct is that of peace and truth. In this spirit they ordinarily insert in their letters this clause, which is tacitly understood in them all — "If it be so as we have heard it — if the facts be true." It is quite clear, if the popes themselves give no force to their bulls, except in so far as they are founded on genuine facts, that it is not the bulls alone that prove the truth of the facts, but that, on the contrary, even according to the canonists, it is the truth of the facts which renders the bulls lawfully admissible.

In what way, then, are we to learn the truth of facts? It must be by the eyes, father, which are the legitimate judges of such matters, as reason is the proper judge of things natural and intelligible, and faith of things supernatural and revealed. For, since you will force me into this discussion, you must allow me to tell you, that, according to the sentiments of the two greatest doctors of the Church, St. Augustine and St. Thomas, these three principles of our knowledge, the senses, reason, and faith, have each their separate objects, and their own degrees of certainty. And as God has been pleased to employ the intervention of the senses to give entrance to faith (for "faith cometh by hearing"), it follows, that so far from faith destroying the certainty of the senses, to call in question the faithful report of the senses would lead to the destruction of faith. It is on this principle that St. Thomas explicitly states that God has been pleased that the sensible accidents should subsist in the eucharist, in order that the senses, which judge only of these accidents, might not be deceived.

We conclude, therefore, from this, that whatever the proposition may be that is submitted to our examination, we must first determine its nature, to ascertain to which of those three principles it ought to be referred. If it relate to a supernatural truth, we must judge of it neither by the senses nor by reason, but by Scripture and the decisions of the Church. Should it concern an unrevealed truth, and something within the reach of natural reason, reason must be its proper judge. And if it embrace a point of fact, we must yield to the testimony of the senses, to which it naturally belongs to take cognizance of such matters.

So general is this rule, that, according to St. Augustine and St. Thomas, when we meet with a passage even in the Scripture, the literal meaning of which, at first sight, appears contrary to what the senses or reason are certainly persuaded of, we must not attempt to reject their testimony in this case, and yield them up to the authority of that apparent sense of the Scripture, but we must interpret the Scripture, and seek out therein another sense agreeable to that sensible truth; because, the Word of God being infallible in the facts which it records, and the information of the senses and of reason, acting in their sphere, being certain also, it follows that there must be an agreement between these two sources of knowledge. And as Scripture may be interpreted in different ways, whereas the testimony of the senses is uniform, we must in these matters adopt as the true interpretation of Scripture that view which corresponds with the faithful report of the senses. "Two things," says St. Thomas, "must be observed, according to the doctrine of St. Augustine: first, That Scripture has always one true sense; and secondly, That as it may receive various senses, when we have discovered one which reason plainly teaches to be false, we must not persist in maintaining that this is the natural sense, but search out another with which reason will agree."

St. Thomas explains his meaning by the example of a passage in Genesis, where it is written that "God created two great lights, the sun and the moon, and also the stars," in which the Scriptures appear to say that the moon is greater than all the stars; but as it is evident, from unquestionable demonstration, that this is false, it is not our duty, says that saint, obstinately to defend the literal sense of that passage; another meaning must be sought, consistent with the truth of the fact, such as the following, "That the phrase *great light*, as applied to the moon, denotes the greatness of that luminary merely as it appears in our eyes, and not the magnitude of its body considered in itself."

An opposite mode of treatment, so far from procuring respect to the Scripture, would only expose it to the contempt of infidels; because, as St. Augustine says, "when they found that we believed, on the authority of Scripture, in things which they assuredly knew to be false, they would laugh at our credulity with regard to its more recondite truths, such as the resurrection of the dead and eternal life." "And by this means," adds St. Thomas, "we should render our religion contemptible in their eyes, and shut up its entrance into their minds."

And let me add, father, that it would in the same manner be the likeliest means to shut up the entrance of Scripture into the minds of heretics, and to render the pope's authority contemptible in their eyes, to refuse all those the name of Catholics who would not believe that certain words were in a certain book, where they are not to be found, merely because a pope by mistake has declared that they are. It is only by examining a book that we can ascertain what words it contains. Matters of fact can only be proved by the senses. If the position which you maintain be true, show it, or else ask no man to believe it—that would be to no purpose. Not all the powers on earth can, by the force of authority, persuade us of a point of fact, any more than they can alter it; for nothing can make that to be not which really is.

It was to no purpose, for example, that the monks of Ratisbon procured from Pope St. Leo IX. a solemn decree, by which he declared that the body of St. Denis, the first bishop of Paris, who is generally held to have been the Areopagite, had been transported out of France, and conveyed into the chapel of their monastery. It is not the less true, for all this, that the body of that saint always lay, and lies to this hour, in the celebrated abbey which bears his name, and within the walls of which you would find it no easy matter to obtain a cordial reception to this bull, although the pope has therein assured us that he has examined the affair "with all possible diligence, and with the advice of many bishops and prelates; so that he strictly enjoins all the French to own and confess that these holy relics are no longer in their country." The French, however, who knew that fact to be untrue, by the evidence of their own eyes, and who, upon opening the shrine, found all those relics entire, as the historians of that period inform us, believed then, as they have always believed since, the reverse of what that holy pope had enjoined them to believe, well knowing that even saints and prophets are liable to be imposed upon.

It was to equally little purpose that you obtained against Galileo a decree from Rome, condemning his opinion respecting the motion of the earth. It will never be proved by such an argument as this that the earth remains stationary; and if it can be demonstrated by sure observation that it is the earth and not the sun that revolves, the efforts and arguments of all mankind put together will not hinder our planet from revolving, nor hinder themselves from revolving along with her.

Again, you must not imagine that the letters of Pope Zachary, excommunicating St. Virgilius for maintaining the existence of the antipodes, have annihilated the New World; nor must you suppose that, although he declared that opinion to be a most dangerous heresy, the king of Spain was wrong in giving more credence to Christopher Columbus, who came from the place, than to the judgment of the pope, who had never been there, or that the Church has not derived a vast benefit from the discovery, inasmuch as it has brought the knowledge of the Gospel to a great multitude of souls, who might otherwise have perished in their infidelity.

You see, then, father, what is the nature of matters of fact, and on what principles they are to be determined; from all which, to recur to our subject, it is easy to conclude, that if the five propositions are not in Jansenius, it is impossible that they can have been extracted from him; and that the only way to form a judgment on the matter, and to produce universal conviction, is to examine that book in a regular conference, as you have been desired to do long ago. Until that be done, you have no right to charge your opponents with contumacy; for they are as blameless in regard to the point of fact as they are of errors in point of faith — Catholics in doctrine, reasonable in fact, and innocent in both.

Who can help feeling astonishment, then, father, to see on the one side a vindication so complete and on the other accusations so outrageous! Who would suppose that the only question between you relates to a single fact of no importance, which the one party wishes the other to believe without showing it to them! And who would ever imagine that such a noise should have been made in the Church for nothing, as good St. Bernard says! But this is just one of the principal tricks of your policy, to make people believe that everything is at stake, when, in reality, there is nothing at stake; and to represent to those influential persons who listen to you, that the most pernicious errors of Calvin, and the most vital principles of the faith, are involved in your disputes, with the view of inducing them, under this conviction, to employ all their zeal and all their authority against your opponents, as if the safety of the Catholic religion depended upon it; whereas, if they came to know that the whole dispute was about this paltry point of fact, they would give themselves no concern about it, but would, on the contrary, regret extremely that, to gratify your private passions, they had made such exertions in an affair of no consequence to the Church. For, in fine, to take the worst view of the matter, even though it should be true that Jansenius maintained these propositions, what great misfortune would accrue from some persons doubting of the fact, provided they detested the propositions, as they have publicly declared that they do? Is it not enough that they are condemned by everybody, without exception, and that, too, in the sense in which you have explained that you wish them to be condemned? Would they be more severely censured by saying that Jansenius maintained them? What purpose, then, would be served by exacting this acknowledgment, except that of disgracing a doctor and bishop, who died in the communion of the Church? I cannot see how that should be accounted so great a blessing as to deserve to be purchased at the expense of so many disturbances. What interest has the state, or the pope, or bishops, or doctors, or the Church at large, in this conclusion? It does not affect them in any way whatever, father; it can affect none but your Society, which would certainly enjoy some pleasure from the defamation of an author who has done you some little injury. Meanwhile everything is in confusion, because you have made people believe that everything is in danger. This is the secret spring giving impulse to all those mighty commotions, which would cease immediately were the real state of the controversy once known. And therefore, as the peace of the Church depended on this explanation, it was, I conceive, of the utmost importance that it should be given, that, by exposing all your disguises, it might be manifest to the whole world that your accusations were without foundation, your opponents without error, and the Church without heresy.

Such, father, is the end which it has been my desire to accomplish; an end which appears to me, in every point of view, so deeply important to religion, that I am at a loss to conceive how those to whom you furnish so much occasion for speaking can contrive to remain in silence. Granting that they are not affected with the personal wrongs which you have committed against them, those which the Church suffers ought, in my opinion, to have forced them to complain. Besides, I am not altogether sure if ecclesiastics ought to make a sacrifice of their reputation to calumny, especially in the matter of religion. They allow you, nevertheless, to say whatever you please; so that, had it not been for the opportunity which, by mere accident, you afforded me of taking their part, the scandalous impressions which you are circulating against them in all quarters would, in all probability, have gone forth without contradiction. Their patience, I confess, astonishes me; and the more so, that I cannot suspect it of proceeding either from timidity or from incapacity, being well assured that they want neither arguments for their own vindication, nor zeal for the truth. And yet I see them religiously bent on silence, to a degree which appears to me altogether unjustifiable. For my part, father, I do not believe that I can possibly follow their example. Leave the Church in peace, and I shall leave you as you are, with all my heart; but so long as you make it your sole business to keep her in confusion, doubt not but that there shall always be found within her bosom children of peace, who will consider themselves bound to employ all their endeavors to preserve her tranquility.

Reflections on Geometry in General
On The Geometrical Mind and
The Art of Persuasion (1657–1658)

One can have three chief aims in the study of truth; the first, to discover it when one seeks for it; the second, to demonstrate it when one possesses it; the last, to distinguish it from falsehood when one examines it.

I am not speaking of the first. I am dealing particularly with the second, and it includes the third. For, if one knows the method for proving the truth, one will possess at the same time that of distinguishing it, since in examining if the proof that is given of it is in agreement with the rules that one knows, one will know whether it is demonstrated exactly.

Geometry, which excels in these three aims, has explained the art of discovering unknown truths; and this is what it calls analysis, concerning which it would be useless to discourse after so many excellent works which have been done.

That of demonstrating truths already discovered, and of clarifying them in such a way that the proof of them will be invincible is the only matter that I want to deal with; and for this I only have to explain the method that geometry employs; for it teaches it perfectly by its examples, although it produces no discourses about it. And because this art consists in two principal things, the one of proving each proposition individually, the other of arranging all the propositions in the best order, I shall make two sections about it, one of which will contain the rules for conducting geometrical demonstrations, that is to say, methodical and perfect ones, and the second will comprehend that of geometrical order, that is to say, methodical and faultless: so that the two together will include all that will be needed for

Translated by Richard H. Popkin.

conducting reasoning to prove and to distinguish truth, which I plan to present completely.

SECTION I: ON THE METHOD OF GEOMETRICAL DEMONSTRATIONS, THAT IS TO SAY METHODICAL AND PERFECT ONES

I cannot better explain the means that should be taken for making demonstrations convincing than by explaining those that geometry employs, and I cannot do this perfectly without first presenting the idea of a method still more eminent and faultless, but which men can never achieve: for what goes beyond geometry, transcends us; and nevertheless it is necessary to say something about it, even though it is impossible to make uses of it, and much more to succeed in the one than in the other.

And I have chosen this science only in order to attain it because it alone knows the true rules of reasoning, and, without limiting itself to the rules of the syllogism, which are so natural that one cannot be unaware of them, limits itself and bases itself on the true method of conducting reasonings in all things, which almost everyone is unaware of, and which is so advantageous to know that we find by experience that between minds of equal strength, when all things are equal, the one which possesses geometry surpasses the other, and acquires a completely new strength.

Therefore I wish to explain what a demonstration is by means of the examples of those of geometry, which is almost the sole human science which produces infallible ones, because it alone observes the true method, while all of the others are, by a natural necessity, in a kind of confusion which only the geometers know exceedingly well how to recognize.

This true method, which would lead to demonstrations of the highest excellence, if it were possible to attain it, would consist of two principle things: one, that of not employing any term whose meaning had not hitherto been clearly explained; the other, that of never setting forth any propositions except those that may be demonstrated from truths already known; that is to say, in a word, to define all terms and to prove all propositions. But to follow the same order that I am explaining, I have to state what I mean by "definition."

The only definitions that are recognized in geometry are those that logicians call "nominal definitions," that is to say, the arbitrary attribution of a name to things which have been clearly designated in perfectly known terms; and I am only speaking of these alone.

Their utility and use is that of clarifying and abridging discourse by expressing by the single name chosen what could otherwise only be stated by several terms; so that the chosen name however remains empty of all other meaning, if it has any, having no longer any other than that which one decides to give it. Here is an example. If it is necessary to distinguish amongst numbers those that are exactly divisible by two from those that are not so, in order to avoid repeating this condition, a name of this type is given: I call every number exactly divisible by two an "even number."

That is a geometrical definition, because after having clearly designated something, namely every number exactly divisible by two, a name is given that excludes all other meaning, if it has any, in order to give it that of the thing designated.

From this it appears that definitions are completely arbitrary, and that they are never subject to contradiction; for nothing is more permissible than to give a thing that one has clearly designated whatever name one wishes. One only has to be careful that one doesn't abuse the freedom one has of imposing names, by giving the same one to two different things. Not that this may not be permitted as long as we do not confuse the results, and do not move from one to the other.

But if one falls into this vice, one can oppose it by a most sure and infallible remedy, that of mentally substituting the definition for what is defined, and always having the definition so present that everytime one speaks, for example, of even number, one understands precisely that it is one that is divisible into two equal parts, and that these two things are so connected and inseparable in thought that as soon as one is conceived, the mind immediately joins the other to it.

For geometers and all those who act methodically only impose names to things in order to abridge reasoning, and not in order to diminish or to change the idea of the things that they reason about. For they claim that the mind being always supplied with the whole definition of the short terms, they only use them in order to avoid the confusion that the multitude of words bring.

Nothing more quickly and more completely dispels the captious surprises of the sophists than this method, which it is necessary always to have present, and which alone suffices for banishing all kinds of difficulties and equivocations.

This being well understood, I come back to explaining the true order, which consists, as I said, in defining everything and proving everything.

Certainly this method would be wonderful, but it is absolutely impossible. For it is evident that the first terms that one would like to define would presuppose others preceding them to serve as their explanation, and that even the first propositions one would like to prove presuppose others which precede them; and thus it is clear that one would never arrive at the first ones.

Also, by pushing matters further and further, one necessarily comes to primitive terms that can no longer be defined, and to principles that are so clear that no others can be found which would be helpful in proving them.

From which it appears that men are naturally and immutably impotent to deal with any science whatsoever in an absolutely complete order.

But it does not follow from this that every kind of order ought to be abandoned.

For there is one, and it is that of geometry, that is in truth inferior in that it is less convincing, but not in that it is less certain. It does not define everything and prove everything, and it is in this that it yields. But it only presupposes things that are clear and constant according to the natural light, and that is why it is perfectly true. Nature sustaining it for want of reasoning. This order, the most perfect among men, consists not in defining everything or demonstrating everything, nor as well in defining nothing or demonstrating nothing, but in maintaining itself in between by not defining things that are clear and understood by all men, and by defining all others; and by not proving all the things known by men, and by proving all the others. They equally sin against this order who undertake to define everything and to prove everything and who neglect to do it with regard to matters which are not evident in themselves.

This is what geometry teaches perfectly. It does not define any of these things—space, time, motion, number, equality—nor similar things of which there are many, because these terms so naturally designate the things that they signify, to those who understand the language, that the clarification of them that might be made would bring more obscurity than enlightenment.

For there is nothing feebler than the reasoning of those who want to define these primitive words. What need is there to explain what is understood by the word "man"? Isn't it sufficiently known what the thing is that one wants to designate by this term? And what aid did Plato think of bringing up, by saying that it is a two-legged animal without feathers? As if the idea that I naturally have of it, and that I cannot express, was not more distinct and certain than that that he gives me with his useless and even ridiculous explanation; since a man does not lose his humanity by losing his two legs, and a capon does not acquire it by losing its feathers.

There are some who go to the absurd length of explaining a word by the same word. I know of some who have defined light in this way: Light is a luminary motion of luminous bodies" [Compare what Pascal cited from Father Noel, in his reply to him, p. 55]; as if the words "luminary" and "luminous" could be understood without that of "light."

One cannot undertake to define "being" without falling into this absurdity: for one cannot define a word without beginning by saying "it is," whether it be expressed or understood. Therefore, in order to define "being," it would be necessary to say "it is," and thus to employ the word to be defined in the definition.

It thereby is clear enough that there are some words incapable of being defined; and if Nature had not made up for this defect by giving all men a similar idea, all our expressions would be confused. Instead we make use of them with the same assurance as if they had been explained in a manner completely free from ambiguity. For Nature herself has given us, without words, a clearer understanding of them than defining would give us through our explanations.

It is not because all men have the same idea of the essence of things that I say that it is impossible and useless to define.

For, as an example, time is of this type. Who can define it? And why try to, since all men comprehend what is meant in speaking of time, without it being further designated. However there are many different opinions concerning the essence of time. Some say that it is the motion of a created thing, others that it is the measure of the motion, etc. Also, it is not the nature of these things that I say is conceived by everyone. It is only simply the relation between the name and the thing; so that this expression, "time," carries everyone's thought towards the same object: which suffices to make it the case that this term has no need to be defined, although later on, in examining what time is, we come to differing views after having thought about it; for definitions are only made to designate the things that are named, and not to exhibit their natures.

It is not that it is not permissible to call the motion of a created thing by the name, "time"; for, as I earlier said, nothing is freer than definitions.

But, as a result of this definition, there will be two things that will be called by the name "time": one is that which everyone naturally understands by this word, and that all those who speak our language name by this term; the other will be the motion of a created thing, for it will also be called by this name according to this new definition.

It will then be necessary to avoid ambiguities, and not confuse conclusions. For it will not follow from this that the thing that is naturally understood by the word "time" would actually be the motion of a created thing. It was allowed to give the two things the same name. But it will not be permitted to make them agree in nature as well as in name.

Thus, if one sets forth this proposition, "Time is the motion of a created thing," it is necessary to inquire what is intended by this word, "time," that is to say, whether it is given its ordinary meaning that is accepted by all, or whether it is deprived of this in order to give it on this occasion that of the motion of a created thing. If it is stripped of all other meaning, there can be no contradiction, and this will be an arbitrary definition, as a result of which, as I have said, there will be two things that will have the same name. But if it is left with its ordinary meaning, and yet it is claimed that is meant by this word is the motion of a created thing, a contradiction can occur. This is no longer an arbitrary definition. It is a proposition that must be proved, unless it is self-evident; and then it will be a principle and an axiom, but never a definition, because in this enunciation it is not understood that the word "time" signifies the same thing as this: the motion of a created thing; but it is understood that what is conceived by the term "time" is this supposed motion.

If I were not aware of how necessary it is to understand this clearly, and how much it happens all the time both in ordinary discourse and in scientific reasoning, in similar circumstances to the one of which I have given an example, I would not have stopped at this. But it seems to me, from the experience that I have of confusion in disputes, that one cannot engage too much in this spirit of clarity, for the sake of which I am writing this entire treatise, more than for the subject which is treated in it.

For how many persons are there who think they have defined time when they have said that it is the measure of motion, while leaving it however its ordinary meaning! And nevertheless they have set forth a proposition, and not a definition. How many people are there likewise who think they have defined motion when they have said, "Motion is neither simply act nor mere potency, but the act of a being in potency"? And, moreover, if they leave the word "motion" its ordinary meaning, as they do, it is not a definition, but an assertion. And by this confusing definitions that are called "nominal" ones, which are true, arbitrary, lawful and geometrical definitions, with those that are called "real definitions," which are properly speaking not arbitrary, but subject to contradiction, they give themselves the freedom of forming one kind as well as the other. And as each person defines the same thing in his own way, with a freedom that is as forbidden in the latter kind of definitions as allowed in the former, they jumble up everything, and in abandoning all order and illumination, they become bewildered and go astray in inexplicable perplexities.

This will never happen by following the order of geometry. This judicious science carefully avoids defining its primitive terms, "space," "time," "motion," "equality," "greater than," "dimunition," "whole," and all the others that everyone understands by themselves. But, except for these, the rest of the terms that are employed are there so clarified and defined, that there is no need of a dictionary to understand any of them. So that, in a word, all these terms are perfectly intelligible, either by the natural light, or by the definitions that are given of them.

That is how it [geometry] avoids all the vices that be encountered on this first count, which consists in defining only those things which require definition. In the same way it deals with the other count, which consists in proving propositions that are not evident.

For when it has arrived at the basic known truths, it stops there and asks that they be accepted, there being nothing clearer by which to prove them. So that all that geometry proposes is perfectly demonstrated, either by the natural light, or by proofs.

Thus if this science does not define and demonstrate everything, it is solely because that is impossible for us. But as Nature furnishes all that this science does not, its order does not actually yield a perfection greater than a human one, but it possesses all that which men can achieve. It seemed to me proper to give from the beginning of this discourse this. . . .

It will perhaps be found strange that geometry is not able to define any of the things that are its principal objects. For it can define neither motion, nor numbers, nor space; and however these three things are those that it especially deals with, and on the basis of their study, it takes on these three different names of "mechanics," "arithmetic," "geometry," this last name applying to both the genus and the species.

But this should not be surprising, if it is observed that this admirable science, applying only to the simplest things, that same quality which makes them worthy of being its objects, makes them incapable of being defined. So that the lack of definition is more a perfection than a defect, because it comes not from their obscurity, but, on the contrary, from their extreme clarity, which is such that although it does not carry the conviction of demonstrations, it has all the certitude of them. It then supposes that it is known what is understood by these words: "motion," "number," "space"; and without stopping to uselessly define them, it penetrates into their natures, and reveals marvelous properties of them.

These three things, which make up the entire universe, according to these words, "God has made all things in weight, number and proportion" (Wisdom 11:21) have a reciprocal and necessary connection. For we cannot conceive of motion without something that moves; and this thing being one, this unity is the origin of all numbers; finally motion not being able to occur without space, we see these three things included in the first.

Time is even also comprehended in it: for motion and time are related to one another; swiftness and slowness, which are the differences of motions, having a necessary connection with time.

Thus there are properties common to all these things, the knowledge of which opens the mind to the greatest wonders of Nature.

The chief of these involves the two infinities that are encountered in all things: that one of greatness, the other of smallness.

For no matter how swift a motion may be, a one more swift can be conceived, and this one further increased, and so on to infinity, without ever reaching one which would be such that nothing more could be added to it. And, on the contrary, no matter how slow a motion may be, it can be slowed down even more, and more than that; and so to infinity, without ever reaching such a degree of slowness that we could not decrease further to an infinity of others without arriving at rest.

Likewise, no matter how large a number may be, a greater one can be conceived, and still one that surpasses that; and so on to infinity, without ever reaching one that can no longer be increased. And, so the contrary, no matter how small a number may be, as the hundredth or ten-thousandth part, a smaller one can be conceived, and always on to infinity, without ever reaching zero or nothing.

Likewise no matter how large a space may be, a larger one can be conceived, and one that will be more so; and so on to infinity, without ever reaching one that cannot be increased. And on the contrary, no matter how small a space may be, a lesser one can still be conceived, and continually to infinity, without ever reaching an indivisible one that no longer has any extension.

It is the same with time. A greater one can always be conceived, without a last one, and a lesser one without ever reaching an instant and a pure nothing of duration.

That is to say, in a word, that no matter what motion, what number, what space, what time there may be, there is always a greater one and a smaller one; so that they all maintain themselves between nothing and infinity, being always infinitely far from these extremes.

All these truths cannot be demonstrated, and yet they are the foundations and principles of geometry. But since the cause which makes them incapable of being demonstrated is not their obscurity, but on the contrary their extreme clarity, this lack of proof is not a defect, but rather a perfection.

From which it is seen that geometry cannot define its objects nor prove its principles; but for this sole and advantageous reason, that the ones and the others possess an extreme natural clarity, which convinces reason more forcefully than does argument.

For what is there more evident than this truth that a number, whatever it may be, can be increased? Can it not be doubled? That the swiftness of a motion can be doubled, and that a space can likewise be doubled?

And who can also doubt that a number, whatever it may be, may be divided in half, and also its half divided in half? For would this half be a nothing? and would two halves, which would be two zeros, make a number?

Likewise, cannot a motion, no matter how slow it may be, be decreased by half, so that it transverses the same space in double the time, and also with this latter motion? For would this be pure rest? And how would it be that these two halves of some speed, which would be two rests, could make up this first velocity?

Thus, cannot a space, no matter how small it may be, be divided in half, and these halves again? And how could it be made the case that these halves would be indivisible without extension, that who, when joined together, have made up the primary extension?

There is no natural knowledge in man that precedes these, and which surpasses them in clarity. Nevertheless, so that there may be examples of everything, we find minds, excellent in all other respects, who are shocked by these infinities, and who cannot in any way accept them.

I have never known anyone who thought that a space could not be increased. But I have seen some people, otherwise very capable, who have asserted that a space can be divided into two indivisible parts, however absurd this may be.

I have never tried to discover what it is in them that could be the cause of this obscurity, and I have found that there was only one chief one, which is that they could not conceive of a content divisible to infinity, from which they conclude that it is not so divisible.

It is a natural malady of man to believe that he possesses the truth directly. And, as a result of this, he is always disposed to deny everything that is incomprehensible to him. Instead he actually only knows falsehood, and he only ought to take as true those matters whose contrary appears false to him.

And that is why, every time that a proposition is inconceivable, one must suspend judgment about it, and not deny it because of this, but examine the contrary of it. And if it is found obviously false, one can boldly affirm the first, however incomprehensible it may be. Let us apply this rule to our subject.

There is no geometer who does not believe space is divisible to infinity. He can no more be one without this principle than be a man without a soul. And nevertheless, there are none of them who comprehend an infinite division. And we are only assured of this truth by this sole reason, which is certainly sufficient, that we understand perfectly that it is false that in dividing a space we can arrive at an indivisible part, that is to say, which would have no extension.

For what is there more absurd than to claim that by continually dividing a space, we finally reach a division such that in dividing it in two, each of the halves remains indivisible and without any extension, and that thus these two nothings of extension would together make an extension? For I would like to ask those who hold this idea, if they clearly conceive that these two indivisibles touch each other. If they do everywhere, they are only the same thing, and consequently the two together are indivisible; and if it is not everywhere, it is only then in a part. Therefore they have parts, thus they are not indivisible.

Let them admit, as they actually do state when they are pressed that their assertion is as inconceivable as the other. Then they acknowledge that it is not by our capacity of conceiving these matters that we ought to judge concerning their truth, since these two contraries, both being inconceivable, it is nonetheless necessarily the case that one of the two be true.

But with regard to these chimerical difficulties, which only have relation to our weakness, they oppose these natural lights and solid truths; if it was true that space was composed of a certain number of indivisibles, it would follow that two spaces, each of which was square, that is to say equal and the same on all sides, one being double the other, one would contain a number of these indivisibles double the number of indivisibles of the other. Let them carefully keep to this consequence, and let them use it next for arranging points in squares until they have encountered two cases in which one has double the points of the other, and then I will concede that they are superior to all the geometers in the world. But if it is naturally impossible, that is to say, if there is an invincible impossibility in arranging squares of points, of which one has double that of another, as I would even demonstrate here if the matter was worth stopping for, let them draw the conclusion from it.

And to ease the pains that they would have in certain matters, such as in conceiving that a space has an infinity of indivisibles, in view of the fact that we traverse them in so little time, during which we would have traversed this infinity of divisibles, it is necessary to warn them that they ought not to compare things as disproportionate as are the infinity of divisibles with the little time in which they are traversed: but that they compare the whole space with the whole time, and the infinite divisibles with the infinite instants of that time. And thus they will discover that we traverse an infinity of divisibles in an infinity of instants, and a little space in a little time; in which they will no longer find the disproportion that had astonished them.

And finally if they find it strange that a little space has as many parts as a large one, let them also understand that they are proportionally smaller, and let them look at the firmament through a small glass in order to familiarize themselves with this knowledge, by seeing every part of the sky in every part of the glass.

But if they cannot comprehend that parts so small, that they are imperceptible to us, can be divided as much as the firmament, there is no better remedy than to make them look with glasses which enlarge this delicate point into a prodigious mass; from which they will easily conceive that, with the help of another glass still more artfully contrived, they can be enlarged until they equal that firmament whose extent is admired. And since these objects now appear to them to be very easily divisible, let them remember that Nature can do infinitely more than art.

For finally who has assured them whether these glasses will have changed the natural size of these objects, or whether they will have, on the contrary, re-established the true one, that the shape of our eye had changed and abridged, as glasses do that diminish?

It is annoying to dwell on these trifles; but there are times for trifling.

It suffices to say to minds clear on this matter that two nothings of extension cannot make up an extension. But because there are some of them who claim to elude this light by this marvelous answer, that two nothings of extension can as well make up an extension as two unities neither of which is a number, make up a number by their combination; it is necessary in retort to them that they could oppose, in the same way, that twenty thousand men make up an army, although none of them is an army; that a thousand houses make up a city, although none of them is a city; or that the parts make up the whole, although none of them is the whole, or, to keep to the comparison of numbers, that two binaries make a quaternary, and ten tens a hundred, although none of them is it.

But it is not to have an exact mind to confuse by such unequal comparisons the immutable nature of things with their arbitrary and freely assigned
names, dependent on the caprices of the men who have made them up. For
it is clear that in order to facilitate, the name "army" has been given to
twenty thousand men, that of "city" to several houses, that of ten to ten
unities; and that from this liberty arises the names "unity," "binary,"
"quaternary," "ten," "a hundred," differing according to our fancies, although these things are actually of the same genus according to their
invariable nature, and although they are completely proportionate one to
another and differ only by greater or less, and although, as a result of these
names, the binary is not quaternary, nor a house a city, any more than the
city is a house. But still, although a house is not a city, it is nevertheless not
a nothing in a city. There is indeed some difference between not being a
thing and being a nothing.

For, in order that the matter be fundamentally understood, it is necessary to know that the only reason why unity is not ranked as a number is
that Euclid and the earliest writers who dealt with arithmetic, having
several properties in mind which applied to all numbers except unity, in
order to avoid often saying that for all numbers save unity, such and such a
condition is to be found, they have excluded unity from the signification of
the word "number," by the freedom that we have already said we have of
making definitions at our pleasure. Also, if they had so wished, in the same
way they might have excluded the binary and ternary from it, and all that
they pleased. For we are the master of it, provided that we give notice
about it; since, on the contrary, unity is placed, when we wish, in the ranks
of numbers, and likewise fractions. And, actually, we are obliged to do it in
general propositions to avoid saying each time, "for all numbers and unity
and fractions, such and such a property is found." And it is in this indefinite
sense that I have taken it in all that I have written about it.

But the same Euclid who removed unity from the name "number,"
which he was allowed to do, in order to explain however that it was not a
nothing, but was on the contrary of the same genus, defined homogeneous
magnitudes thusly. "Magnitudes," he says, "are said to be of the same
genus, when one being multiplied several times can exceed the other."
And consequently, since unity, being multiplied many times, can exceed
any number whatsoever, it is of the same genus as numbers precisely
according to its essence and its immutable nature, in the sense of the same
Euclid who desired that it not be called "number."

It is not likewise the case of an indivisible with regard to an extension.
For not only does it differ in name, which is arbitrary, but it differs in
genus, according to the same definition, since an indivisible, multiplied as
many times as one may wish, is so far from being able to exceed an
extension that it can never constitute anything but a single unique indivisible. This is natural and necessary as has already been shown. And since this

last proof is based on the definition of these two things, "indivisible" and "extension," we shall go on and complete the demonstration.

An indivisible is that which has no parts, and extension is that which has various separate parts.

On the basis of these definitions, I assert that two indivisibles being united do not constitute an extension.

For when they are united, they touch each other in a part; and thus the parts by which they touch each other are not separated, since otherwise they would not touch. Now, according to their definitions, they have no other parts at all. Therefore they have no separate parts. Therefore they are not an extension according to the definition of extension which involves the separation of parts.

The same thing will be shown about all other indivisibles that may be so joined, for the same reason. And consequently, an indivisible multiplied as many times as one likes, will never make up an extension. Therefore it is not of the same kind as extension, according to the definition of things of the same kind.

This is how it is demonstrated that indivisibles are not of the same genus as numbers. From this it follows that two unities can indeed make up a number, because they are of the same kind; and that two indivisibles do not make up an extension because they are not of the same kind.

From which one sees how little basis there is for comparing the relationship that exists between unity and numbers with that that exists between indivisibles and extension.

But if one wishes to find in numbers a comparison that justly represents what we consider in extension, it has to be the relation of zero to numbers. For zero is not of the same genus as numbers, because, when multiplied, it cannot surpass them: so that it is a genuine indivisible of number, as the indivisible is a genuine zero of extension. And a similar comparison will be found between rest and motion, and between an instant and time. For all these things are heterogeneous with regard to their magnitudes, because when multiplied infinitely, they can never make up anything but indivisibles, no more than can the indivisibles of extension, and for the same reason. And then a perfect correspondence between these things will be found: for all these magnitudes are infinitely divisible, without falling into their indivisibles, so that they all remain in the middle between infinity and nothing.

That is the wonderful relationship that nature has placed among these things, and the two marvelous infinities that she has set forth for men, not to conceive, but to admire. And to finish the consideration of this with a final observation, I will add that these two infinities, though infinitely different, are nevertheless related one to the other, in such a way that the knowledge of the one leads necessarily to the knowledge of the other.

For in numbers, from the fact that they can be continually increased, it follows absolutely that they can be continually decreased, and this is clear:

for if a number can be multiplied 100,000 times, for example, a one hundred thousandth part can also be taken of it by dividing it by the same number by which it is multiplied, and thus every factor of increase becomes a factor of division, by changing the whole thing into a fraction. So that infinite augmentation necessarily also includes infinite division.

And in space the same relationship is found between these two infinite contraries, that is to say that from the fact that a space can be infinitely extended, it follows that it can be infinitely diminished, as appears in this example. If we look through a glass at a vessel that is continuously moving away in a straight line, it is clear that the location of the transparent place where we see whatever point of the boat that we may wish always rises by a continual flux as the vessel moves away. Therefore, if the course of the vessel is continually extended on to infinity, this point will continually rise; and however it will never reach the point where the horizontal ray carried from the eye to the glass will fall, so that it will constantly approach it without ever getting there, endlessly dividing the space that remains under this horizontal point. From which we see the necessary consequence that results from the infinity of the extent of the vessel's course with regard to the infinite division and the infinite smallness of this small space remaining below this horizontal point.

Those who will not be satisfied by these reasons, and who will maintain the belief that space is not infinitely divisible, can in no way make a claim of geometrical demonstrations; and, although they may be capable of being clear about other matters, they will be very little clarified about these: for someone can easily be a most capable person and a bad geometer.

But those who do not clearly see these truths will be able to admire the greatness and power of Nature in this double infinity which surrounds us on all sides, and to learn by this marvelous consideration to know themselves, by seeing themselves located between an infinity and a numerical nothing, between an infinity and a nothing of motion, between an infinity and a temporal nothing. Concerning which one can learn to estimate one's own true worth, and to form reflections that are more valuable than all of the rest of geometry.

I felt obliged to make this reflection for those who, not understanding this double infinity at first, are capable of being convinced about it. And although there may be some who are sufficiently enlightened to do without this, it can nevertheless be the case that this discourse, which will be necessary for the ones, will not be completely useless for the others.

SECTION II: THE ART OF PERSUASION

The art of persuasion has a necessary relation to the way in which men consent to what is proposed to them, and to the conditions of the things which it is desired to make them believe.

No one is unaware that there are two avenues by which opinions are received in the soul, which are its two chief powers, the understanding and the will. The most natural is that of the understanding, for we should always consent only to demonstrated truths. But the more usual, although contrary to Nature, is that of the will; for all men are almost always led to believe not by proof, but by pleasures.

This way is base, unworthy and odd. Also everyone disavows it. Each claims to believe only and even to love only what he knows deserves it.

I am not speaking here of divine truths, which I should be far from letting fall under the art of persuasion, for they are infinitely above Nature. God alone can place them in the soul, and by whatever means He pleases.

I know that He has wished that they enter in the mind from the heart, and in the heart from the mind, in order to humiliate that superb power of reasoning that claims the right to be the judge of the things that the will chooses, and in order to cure that infirm will, which is entirely corrupted by its filthy attachments. And from thence it happens that instead when speaking of human affairs, we say that they must be known before being loved, which has become a proverb (*ignoti nulla cupido*; "We do not desire what we do not know"). The saints on the contrary say, when speaking of divine things, that they must be loved in order to be known, and that we only enter into truth by charity, from which they have made one of their most useful maxims.

From which it appears that God has established this supernatural order, completely contrary to the order which ought to be natural to men in natural matters. They have nevertheless corrupted this order by making of profane matters what they ought to make of holy matters, because actually we believe almost only what pleases us. And from this comes our remoteness from consenting to the truths of the Christian religion, all opposed to our pleasures. "Tell us agreeable things and we will listen to you," said the Jews to Moses, as if pleasure ought to regulate belief! And it is in order to punish this disorder by an order that conforms to Him, that God only sheds his light on minds after having subdued the rebellion of the will by an entirely celestial sweetness which charms it and transports it.

Therefore I am only talking about truths within our reach; and it is concerning these that I say that the mind and the heart are like gates through which they are received in the soul; but that very few enter through the mind, instead they are introduced in crowds by the rash caprices of the will, without the counselor of reason.

These powers or faculties each have their principles and prime movers of their actions.

Those of the mind are the truths that are natural and known to everybody, like the whole is greater than its part, besides several particular maxims that are accepted by some and not by others, but which, as soon as they are accepted, are powerful enough, even though false, to carry away belief, as the most true ones.

Those of the will concern certain desires that are natural and common to all men, such as the desire to be happy, that no one can avoid having, besides several particular objects that each pursues in order to reach it, and which, having the power to please us, are as strong, although actually pernicious, for making the will act, as if they constituted its genuine happiness.

That is what concerns the forces that lead us to consent.

But as to the qualities of things that ought to persuade us, they are very diverse.

Some are drawn, by a necessary consequence, from common principles and avowed truth. These can be infallibly persuasive. For, by showing the relationship they have to accepted principles, there is an inevitable necessity of conviction.

And it is impossible that they not be accepted in the soul as soon as we have linked them to those truths that it has already admitted.

There are some of them who have a close connection with the objects of our satisfaction; and these also are accepted with certainty, for as soon as the soul is shown that something can lead it to what it supremely loves, it is inevitable that she embraces it joyfully.

But those which have this connection completely both with admitted truth and the desires of the heart, are so sure of their effect that there is nothing which is more so in nature.

Just as, on the contrary, that which has relation neither to our beliefs nor our pleasures is troublesome, false, and completely alien to us.

In all these cases, there is no doubting at all. But there are some in which the things that it is desired that we believe are well established on the basis of known truths, but which are, at the same time, contrary to the pleasures which affect us the most. And these are in great danger of showing, by an expression that is only too common, what I was saying at the outset: that this imperious soul, which boasted of acting only by reason, follows a shameful and rash choice what a corrupted will desires, whatever resistance a too enlightened mind can oppose to this.

It is then that a dubious balance is made between truth and will, and that knowledge of one and feeling of the other create a struggle of which success is most uncertain, since it would be necessary, in order to judge it, to know all that goes on in the innermost part of man, that man himself almost never knows.

It seems from this that, whatever it may be that we want to convince some of, it is necessary to have regard to the person we want to persuade, concerning whom it is necessary to know his mind and his heart, what principles he accepts, what things he likes; and then to observe, concerning the matter in question, what connection it has with acknowledged principles, or with the objects of delight according to the charms attributed to the thing in question.

So that the art of persuasion consists as much in that of pleasing as in that of convincing, so much more are men governed by caprice than by reason!

Now concerning these two methods, one of convincing, the other of pleasing, I will only here give the rules of the former; assuming that we have accepted the principles, and remain steadfast in acknowledging them: otherwise I do not know if there would be a means for accommodating proofs to the inconstancy of our caprices.

But the way of pleasing is indeed incomparably more difficult, more subtle, more useful and more admirable. Also, if I do not deal with it, it is because I am not capable to do so, and I feel myself so unsuited to do so, that I believe the matter absolutely impossible.

It is not that I do not believe that there are rules as certain for pleasing as for demonstrating, not that he who knows them perfectly and employs them would not succeed in making kings and all sorts of persons love him as in demonstrating the elements of geometry to those who have sufficient imagination to understand the hypotheses involved.

But I consider, and perhaps it is my weakness that makes me do so, that it is impossible to achieve this. At least, I know that if anyone can do it it is someone I know, and that nobody else has clear and abundant understanding about it.

The reason for this extreme difficulty results from the fact that the principles of pleasure are not firm or stable. They differ in all men, and vary in each particular person with such diversity that there is no man who differs more from other men than from himself at different times. A man has different pleasures than a woman does. A rich man and a poor one have different ones. A prince, a warrior, a middle class person, a peasant, the old, the young, the healthy, the sick all vary. The slightest accidents affect them.

Now there is an art, and it is the one I set forth, for showing the connection of truths to their principles, whether of truth or of pleasure, provided that the principles that have once been accepted remain firm and are never denied.

But as there are few principles of this kind, and outside of geometry, which only deals with very simple lines, there are almost no truths concerning which we always remain in agreement, and still fewer objects of pleasure concerning which we do not change all the time, I do not know if there is a means of giving firm rules for harmonizing reasoning with the inconstancy of our caprices.

This art that I call the art of persuasion, and which is properly only the conduct of perfect methodical proofs, consists in three essential parts:

defining terms that are to be used by clear definitions; proposing principles or evident axioms for proving the thing in question; and always substituting mentally in the demonstration the definitions in place of what is defined.

And the basis of this method is evident, since it would be useless to prove and to undertake demonstrating it, if we had not previously clearly defined all the terms which are not intelligible. And likewise it must be the case that the demonstration is preceded by the demand for evident principles which are necessary for it, for if we are sure of the foundations, we cannot be sure of the building. And lastly it is necessary in demonstrating to substitute mentally the definitions for the thing defined, since otherwise we could be led astray by the various meanings that are encountered for the terms. And it is easy to see that by following this method we are sure of convincing, since the terms being completely understood and perfectly exempt from ambiguity according to their definitions, and the principles being accepted, if in the demonstrations we always substitute the definitions for the things defined, the invincible force of the conclusions can not fail to have its effect.

There can never be the slightest doubt about a demonstration in which these conditions are met; and where these are missing demonstrations can never have any strength.

Hence, it is of great importance to understand these conditions and to be in possession of them, and that is why, in order to make the matter easier and more immediate, I will set them all forth in these few rules which include all that is necessary for the perfection of definitions, axioms and demonstration, and consequently of the whole method of geometrical proofs of the art of persuasion.

Rules for definitions: (1) Not to undertake to define any of the things so known in themselves that we have no clearer terms for explaining them. (2) To admit no terms that are a little obscure or ambiguous, without definition. (3) To employ in the definition of terms only words perfectly known, or already explained.

Rules for axioms: (1) To admit no necessary principles without having asked if we accept them, no matter how clear and evident they may be. (2) Not to demand in axioms anything but matters perfectly evident in themselves.

Rules for demonstrations: (1) Not to undertake to demonstrate any things which are so evident in themselves that we have nothing clearer for proving them. (2) To prove all propositions that are slightly obscure, and to employ in their proof only most evident axioms, or propositions already accepted or demonstrated. (3) To always substitute mentally the definitions for the things defined, in order not to be deceived by the ambiguity of terms that the definitions have restricted.

There are the eight rules which contain all the precepts of solid and immutable proofs. Of which there are three of them which are not absolutely necessary, and that we can neglect without error; while it is even difficult and almost impossible to always observe exactly, although it is more perfect to do it as much as can be done. There are the first ones of each of three divisions.

For definitions: Not to define any terms that are perfectly known.

For axioms: Not to omit questioning any perfectly evident and simple axioms.

For demonstrations: Not to demonstrate any things very known in themselves.

For it is doubtless that it is not a great fault to define and explain things very clearly, although very clear in themselves, nor to omit to question in advance axioms which cannot be refused in the place where they are necessary, nor finally to prove the propositions that we accept without proof.

But the five other rules are absolutely necessary, and we cannot dispense with them without an essential defect and often without error. And that is why I am going to take them up again here in detail.

Rules necessary for definitions: To admit no terms that are a little obscure or ambiguous without definition. To employ in the definitions of terms only words perfectly known, or already explained.

Necessary rules for axioms: Not to demand in axioms anything but matters perfectly evident.

Necessary rules for demonstrations: To prove all propositions by only employing in their proof either axioms most evident in themselves or propositions already shown or accepted. Never to take advantage of the ambiguity of terms, by failing to substitute mentally the definitions which restrict or explain them.

There are the five rules which constitute all that is necessary for making proofs convincing, immutable, and, to say it all, geometrical; and the eight rules together make them still more perfect.

I pass now to that of the order in which we ought to arrange the propositions, in order to be in an excellent and geometrical series . . . After having established . . .

That is what the art of persuasion consists in, which is included in these two rules: to define all the names that are employed; to prove all, by mentally substituting the definitions for what is defined.

Concerning which it seems to me proper to anticipate these objections that could be raised. One, that this method offers nothing new.

The other, that it is very easy to learn, without it being necessary for that to study the elements of geometry, since it consists of these two words that are known at first reading.

And lastly that it is quite useless, since its use is restricted almost completely to strictly geometrical matters.

Concerning which it is then necessary to show that there is nothing so unknown, nothing more difficult to practice, and nothing more useful and more universal.

As to the first objection, which is that these rules are common in the world, that everything must be defined and everything must be proven, and that logicians themselves have placed them among the precepts of their art, I wish it were so, and that it were so well known that I should not have had the trouble of having to seek so carefully for the source of all the defects of reasoning that are really common. But this is so little the case that, if we leave out the geometers alone, who are of so small a number that they are unique in every nation and in long time spans, we see nobody else who knows this. It will be easy to make this understood by those who have completely comprehended the little that I have said about it; but if they have not perfectly understood it, I admit that they will learn nothing from it.

But if they have entered into the spirit of these rules, and if these have made enough of an impression to take root and become fixed, they will be aware of how much difference there is between what is said here, and what some logicians have perhaps described of it, approaching it by chance, in some portions of their work.

Those who have the spirit of discernment know how much difference there is between two similar words, according to the situation and circumstances that accompany them. Will we believe, actually, that two persons who had read and learned the same book by heart know it equally well when one understands it so that he knows all the principles, the strength of the conclusions, the answers to objections that can be made to it, and the whole plan of the work; while for the other it is dead words, and seeds, which though like those that have produced such fertile trees, have remained dry and unfruitful in the sterile mind which has received them in vain.

All those who say the same things do not possess them in the same way; and that is why the incomparable author of *The Art of Conferring* [Montaigne, see *Essais*, III, viii] devotes so much care to making clear that the capacity of a man should not be judged by the excellence of a *bon mot* that he has been heard to make. But instead of extending the admiration of a good discourse to the person making it, let us penetrate, says he, into the spirit from which it comes: let us try to discover if it is due to his memory or to a happy coincidence; let us receive it with coolness or contempt, in order to see if he will feel that we are not giving the esteem that is deserved to what he says. We will most often see that we will make him disavow it immediately, and that we will draw him very far from this better view that he does not believe and throw him into another completely base and ridiculous one. It is then necessary to examine in what way this view is attached to its author; how; whence, up to what point he possesses it: otherwise the hasty judgment will be a rash one.

I would like to ask reasonable persons if this principle, "Matter has a natural, invincible incapacity to think," and this one, "I think, therefore I am," are actually the same thing in the mind of Descartes and in the mind of St. Augustine, who said the same thing twelve hundred years earlier.

In actuality, I am very far from saying that Descartes is not the real author of these, even if he only learned them by reading that great saint; for I know how much of a difference there is between writing a word by chance without making a very long and extended reflection about it and perceiving in this word an admirable series of consequences that proves the distinction of material and spiritual natures, and making of it a firm and sustained principle of a whole system of physics, as Descartes claimed to do. For without examining if he succeeded effectively in his contention, I shall suppose that he has done so, and it is in terms of this supposition that I say that this word is as different in his writings from the same word in others who have stated it in passing, as a dead man from a man full of life and strength.

Someone will say something about himself without understanding the excellence of it, while another will understand a marvelous series of consequences which makes us say boldly that it is no longer the same word, and that he no more is indebted to the person from whom he learned it, than an admirable tree belongs to the person who threw out a seed, without thinking about or being aware of it, onto a fertile soil which profited it in terms of its own fertility.

The same ideas sometimes develop completely differently in someone other than their author: infertile in their natural soil, fruitful when transplanted.

But it most often happens that a good mind produces itself all the fruits of which its thoughts are capable, and that afterwards some others, having heard them admired, borrow them and adorn themselves with them, but without recognizing their excellence. And it is this then in which the difference of the same word in different mouths appears the most.

It is in this way that logic has perhaps borrowed the rules of geometry without understanding the force of them. And thus by placing them by chance among its own rules, it does not follow from this that they (the logicians) have entered into the spirit of geometry; and I shall be most adverse, if they show no other signs than mentioning it in passing, to placing them along side that science which teaches the true method for leading reason.

But, on the contrary, I shall be well disposed to exclude them from it, and almost irrevocably so. For to have said in passing, without having taken care that everything was included in it, and instead of following these lights, to go astray blindly into useless researches, to pursue what these offer but cannot give, is truly to show that one is scarcely far seeing, and much more so than if one had failed to follow these lights because one had not seen them.

The method for not erring is sought by everyone. The logicians claim to lead to it, the geometers alone to reach it, and except for their science, and those that imitate it, there are no genuine demonstrations. And the entire art is the precepts alone that we have stated: they alone suffice, they alone prove; all other rules are useless or harmful.

That is what I know from a long experience of all sorts of books and persons.

And on this point, I make the same judgment on those who say that the geometers give them nothing new by these rules, because they actually have them, but mixed up with a multitude of other useless or false ones, among which they cannot discern them, as concerning those who, seeking for a diamond of great value among a great number of false ones, but which they cannot distinguish, might boast, while holding that all together, of possessing the real one as much as he who, without stopping at this vile mass, places his hand on the chosen stone that is sought for, and for which all the rest are thrown away.

The defect of a false reasoning is a malady that is cured by these two remedies. There is another that has been made up of an infinity of useless herbs in which the good ones are wrapped up and in which they remain without effect due to the bad features of this mixture.

In order to discover all the sophisms and equivocations of captious reasonings, they have invented barbarous names which astonish those who hear them. And instead of being able to unravel all of the strands of this knot that is so entangled by pulling at the one of the ends assigned by the geometers, they have marked out a strange number of others in which those are contained, without their knowing which is the good one.

And thus by showing us a number of different roads that they say conduct us where we want to go, although there are only two of them that lead there, it is necessary to know how to mark them out specifically. It will be claimed that geometry, which assigns them exactly, only yields what one already had by the others, because they actually give the same thing and more, without heeding that this present lost its value by its abundance, and was diminished by adding to it.

Nothing is more common than good things. The only problem is to discern them. And it is certain that they are all natural and within our reach, and even known by everyone. But people do not know how to distinguish them. This is universal. It is not in extraordinary and bizarre things that the excellence of any genus whatsoever is found. People rise in order to attain it, and they are farther away from it. Most often it is necessary to lower oneself. The best books are the ones that those who read them believe they could have written. Nature, which alone is good, is entirely familiar and common.

I do not then doubt that these rules, being the true ones, ought to be simple, elementary, natural, as they are. It is not *Barbara* and *Baralipton* [two scholastic forms of syllogistic reasoning] which constitute reasoning.

It is not necessary to hoist up the mind. Strained and labored manners fill it with a foolish presumption by an unnatural elevation and a vain and ridiculous inflation, instead of with solid and vigorous nourishment.

And one of the chief reasons why those who enter into this knowledge of the right road that ought to be followed are diverted is the opinion that they set forth at the outset that the good things are inaccessible, by giving them names like "great," "lofty," "elevated," "sublime." Everything is lost this way. I would like to call them "low," "common," "familiar." These names apply better to them. I detest these inflated expressions . . .

Pensées (Thoughts)*

PART I. ORDER

1. The Psalms are chanted throughout the whole world.

Who renders testimony to Mohammed? Himself. Jesus desires His own testimony to be as nothing.

The quality of witness necessitates their existence always and everywhere, and he, miserable creature, is alone. (596)

2. *Order by dialogues.* What ought I to do? I see only darkness everywhere. Shall I believe I am nothing. Shall I believe I am God? (227)

3. "Why! Do you not say yourself that the heavens and the birds prove God?" No. "And does not your religion say so?" No. For although it is true in a sense for some souls to whom God gives this light, yet it is false with regard to the majority of men. (244)

4. A letter to incite to the search after God.

And then to make people seek Him among the philosophers, skeptics and dogmatists, who disquiet him who inquires of them. (184)

5. *Order.* A letter of exhortation to a friend to induce him to seek. And he will reply, "But what is the use of seeking? Nothing is seen." Then to reply to him, "Do not despair." And he will answer that he would be glad to find some light, but that, according to this very religion, if he believed in it, it will be of no use to him, and therefore he prefers not to seek. And to answer to that: The machine. (247)

6. *First part:* The misery of man without God.
    Second part: Happiness of man with God.

---

*Translated by W. F. Trotter, slightly revised by Richard H. Popkin.

(The order of the *pensées* and their classification follow the Lafuma edition. The corresponding numbers in the Brunschvicg edition appear at the end of each *pensée*.)

Or, *First part*: That nature is corrupt. Proved by nature itself.
    Second part: That there is a Redeemer. Proved by Scripture. (60)

7. *A letter which indicates the use of proofs by the machine.* Faith is different
from proof; the one is human, the other is a gift of God. *The just shall live by
faith* [Romans 1:17]. It is this faith that God Himself puts into the heart, of
which the proof is often the instrument, *faith comes by hearing*, but this faith
is in the heart, and makes us not say, *I know*, but *I believe*. (248)

8. *Order.* To see what is clear and indisputable in the whole state of the
Jews. (602)

9. In the letter *On Injustice* can come the ridiculousness of the law that the
eldest gets all. "My friend, you were born on this side of the mountain, it is
therefore just that your elder brother gets everything."
    "Why do you not kill me?" (291)

10. The miseries of human life have established all this: as men have seen
this, they have taken up diversion. (167)

11. *Order.* After the letter *That we ought to seek God* to write the letter *On
removing obstacles*; which is the discourse on "the machine," on preparing
the machine, on seeking by reason. (246)

12. *Order.* Men despise religion; they hate it, and fear it is true. To remedy
this, we must begin by showing that religion is not contrary to reason; that
it is venerable, to inspire respect for it; then we must make it lovable, to
make good men hope it is true; finally we must prove it is true.
    Venerable, because it has perfect knowledge of man, lovable because it
promises the true good. (187)

PART II. VANITY

16. *Vanity.* How wonderful it is that a thing so evident as the vanity of the
world is so little known, that it is a strange and surprising thing to say that it
is foolish to seek greatness? (161)

17. *Inconstancy and oddity.* To live only by work, and to rule over the most
powerful State in the world, are very opposite things. They are united in
the person of the great Sultan of the Turks. (113)

21. When we are too young, we do not judge well; so, also, when we are too
old. If we do not think enough, or if we think too much on any matter, we

get obstinate and infuriated with it. If one considers one's work immediately after having done it, one is entirely prepossessed in its favor; by delaying too long, one can no longer enter into the spirit of it. So with pictures seen from too far or too near; there is but one exact point which is the true place wherefrom to look at them: the rest are too near, too far, too high, or too low. Perspective determines that point in the art of painting. But who shall determine it in truth and morality? (381)

23. *The vanity of the sciences.* Physical science will not console me for the ignorance of morality in the time of affliction. But the science of ethics will always console me for the ignorance of the physical sciences. (67)

27. Man's nature is not always to advance; it has its advances and retreats.

Fever has its cold and hot fits; and the cold proves as well as the hot the greatness of the fire of fever.

The discoveries of men from age to age turn out the same. The kindness and the malice of the world in general are the same. *Change is usually pleasing to princes* [Horace, *Odes*, Book III, 29]. (354)

28. *Weakness.* Every pursuit of men is to get wealth; and they cannot have a title to show that they possess it justly, for they have only that of human caprice; nor have they strength to hold it securely. It is the same with knowledge, for disease takes it away. We are incapable both of truth and goodness. (436)

33. What astonishes me most is to see that all the world is not astonished at its own weakness. Men act seriously, and each follows his own mode of life, not because it is in fact good to follow since it is the custom, but as if each man knew certainly where reason and justice are. They find themselves continually deceived, and by a comical humility that it is their own fault, and not that of the art which they claim always to possess. But it is well there are so many such people in the world, who are not skeptics for the glory of skepticism, in order to show that man is quite capable of the most extravagant opinions, since he is capable of believing that he is not in a state of natural or inevitable weakness, but, on the contrary, of natural wisdom.

Nothing fortifies skepticism more than that there are some who are not skeptics; if all were so, they would be wrong. (374)

34. This sect derives more strength from its enemies than from its friends; for the weakness of man is far more evident in those who know it not than in those who know it. (376)

36. He who does not see the vanity of the world is himself vain. Indeed who do not see it but youths who are absorbed in fame, diversion, and the

thought of the future? But take away diversion, and you will see them dried up with weariness. They feel then their nothingness without knowing it; for it is indeed to be unhappy to be in insufferable sadness as soon as we are reduced to thinking of self, and have no diversion. (164)

38. Too much and too little wine. Give him none, he cannot find truth; give him too much, the same. (71)

43. A mere trifle consoles us, for a mere trifle distress us. (136)

44. *Imagination*. It is that deceitful part in man, that mistress of error and falsity, the more deceptive that she is not always so; for she would be an infallible rule of truth, if she were an infallible rule of falsehood. But being more generally false, she gives no sign of her nature, impressing the same character on the true and the false.

I do not speak of fools, I speak of the wisest men; and it is among them that the imagination has the great gift of persuasion. Reason protests in vain; it cannot set a true value on things.

This arrogant power, the enemy of reason, who likes to rule and dominate it, has established in man a second nature to show how all-powerful she is. She makes men happy and sad, healthy and sick, rich and poor; she compels reason to believe, doubt, and deny; she blunts the senses, or quickens them; she has her fools and sages; and nothing vexes us more than to see that she fills her devotees with a satisfaction far more full and entire than does reason. Those who have a lively imagination are a great deal more pleased with themselves than the wise can reasonably be. They look down upon men with haughtiness; they argue with boldness and confidence, others with fear and diffidence; and this gaiety of countenance often gives them the advantage in the opinion of the hearers, such favor have the imaginary wise in the eyes of judges of like nature. Imagination cannot make fools wise: but she can make them happy to the envy of reason which can only make its friends miserable: the one covers them with glory, the other with shame.

What but this faculty of imagination dispenses reputation, awards respect and veneration to persons, works, laws, and the great? How insufficient are all the riches of the earth without her consent!

Would you not say that his magistrate, whose venerable age commands the respect of a whole people, is governed by pure and lofty reason, and that he judges causes according to their true nature without considering those mere trifles which only affect the imagination of the weak? See him go to sermon, full of devout zeal, strengthening his reason with the ardor of his love. He is ready to listen with exemplary respect. Let the preacher appear, and let nature have given him a hoarse voice, or a comical cast of countenance, or let his barber have given him a bad shave, or let by chance his dress be more dirtied than usual, then however great the truths he announces, I wager our senator loses his gravity.

If the greatest philosopher in the world find himself upon a plank wider than actually necessary, but hanging over a precipice, his imagination will prevail, though his reason convince him of his safety. Many cannot bear the thought without a cold sweat. I will not state all its effects.

Every one knows that the sight of cats or rats, the crushing of a coal, etc. may unhinge the reason. The tone of voice affects the wisest, and changes the force of a discourse or a poem.

Love or hate alters the aspect of justice. How much greater confidence has a lawyer, retained with a large fee, in the justice of his cause! How much better does his bold manner make his case appear to the judges, deceived as they are by appearances! How ludicrous is reason, blown with a breath in every direction!

I should have to enumerate almost every action of men who scarce waver save under her assaults. For reason has been obliged to yield, and the wisest reason takes as her own principles those which the imagination of man has everywhere rashly introduced. He who would follow reason would only be called foolish by most people. We must judge by the opinion of the majority of mankind. Because it has pleased them, we must work all day for pleasures seen to be imaginary; and after sleep has refreshed our tired reason, we must then start up and rush after phantoms, and suffer the impressions of this mistress of the world. This is one of the sources of error, but it is not the only one.

Our judges have known well this mystery. Their red robes, the ermine in which they wrap themselves like furry cats, the courts in which they administer justice, the symbols, and all such august apparel were necessary; if the physicians had not their cassocks and their mules, if the doctors had not their square caps and their robes four times too wide, they would never have duped the world, which cannot resist so original an appearance. If judges had true justice, and physicians the art of healing, they would have no occasion for square caps; the majesty of these sciences would of itself be venerable enough. But having only imaginary knowledge, they must employ these silly tools that strike the imagination with which they have to deal; and thereby in fact they inspire respect. Soldiers alone are not disguised in this manner, because indeed their part is the most essential; they establish themselves by force, the others by show.

Therefore our kings seek out no disguises. They do not mask themselves in extraordinary costumes to appear such: but they are accompanied by guards and weapons carriers. Those armed and red-faced puppets who have hands and power for them alone, those trumpets and drums which go before them, and those legions round about them, make the stoutest tremble. They have not dress only. They have might. A refined reason is required to regard as an ordinary man the Grand Turk, in his superb seraglio, surrounded by forty thousand janissaries.

We cannot even see an advocate in his robe and with his cap on his head, without a favorable opinion of his ability. The imagination disposes of everything; it makes beauty, justice, and happiness, which is everything in the world. I should like very much to see an Italian work, of which I only know the title, which alone is worth many books, *Della opinione regina del mundo [Concerning opinion, the queen of the World]*. I approve of the book without knowing it, save the evil in it, if any. These are pretty much the effects of that deceptive faculty, which seems to have been expressly given us to lead us into necessary error. We have, however, many other sources of error.

Not only are old impressions capable of misleading us: the charms of novelty have the same power. Hence arise all the disputes of men, who taunt each other with following the false impressions of childhood or with running rashly after the new. Who keeps the proper mean? Let him appear and prove it. There is no principle, however natural to us from infancy, which may not be made to pass for a false impression either of education or of sense.

"Because," say some, "you have believed from childhood that a box was empty when you saw nothing in it, you have believed in the possibility of a vacuum. This is an illusion of your senses, strengthened by custom, which science must correct." "Because," say others, "you have been taught at school that there is no vacuum, you have perverted your common sense which clearly comprehended it, and must correct this by returning to your first state." Which has deceived you, your senses or your education?

We have another source of error in diseases. They spoil the judgment and the senses; and if the more serious produce a sensible change, I do not doubt that slighter ills produce a proportionate impression.

Our own interest is again a marvelous instrument for nicely putting out our eyes. The justest man in the world is not allowed to be a judge in his own cause; I know some who, in order not to fall into this self-love, have been perfectly unjust out of opposition. The sure way of losing a just cause has been to get it recommended to these men by their near relatives.

Justice and truth are two such subtle points, that our tools are too blunt to touch them accurately. If they reach the point, they either crush it, or lean all around, more on the false than on the true.

Man is so happily formed that he has no principle of the true, and several excellent ones of the false. Let us now see how many. But the most powerful cause of error is the war existing between the sense and reason. (82)

45. *We must thus begin the chapter on the deceptive powers.* Man is only a subject full of error, natural and ineffaceable, without grace. Nothing shows

him the truth. Everything deceives him. These two sources of truth, reason and the sense, besides both being wanting in sincerity, deceive each other in turn. The senses mislead the reason with false appearances, and receive from reason in their turn the same trickery which they apply to her; reason has her revenge. The passions of the soul trouble the senses, and make false impressions upon them. They rival each other in falsehood and deception. But besides those errors which arise accidentally and through lack of intelligence, with these heterogeneous faculties . . . (83)

47. We do not rest satisfied with the present! We anticipate the future as too slow in coming, as if in order to hasten its course; or we recall the past, to stop its too rapid flight. So imprudent are we that we wander in the times which are not ours, and do not think of the only one which belongs to us; and so idle are we that we dream of those times which are no more, and thoroughly overlook that which alone exists. For the present is generally painful to us. We conceal it from our sight, because it troubles us; and if it be delightful to us, we regret to see it pass away. We try to sustain it by the future, and think of arranging matters which are not in our power, for a time which we have no certainty of reaching.

Let each one examine his thoughts, and he will find them all occupied with the past and the future. We scarcely ever think of the present; and if we think of it, it is only to take light from it to arrange the future. The present is never our end. The past and the present are our means; the future alone is our end. So we never live, but we hope to live; and, as we are always preparing to be happy, it is inevitable that we should never be so. (172)

48. The mind of this sovereign judge of the world is not so independent that it is not liable to be disturbed by the first din about it. The noise of a cannon is not necessary to hinder its thoughts; it needs only the creaking of a weathercock or a pulley. Do not wonder if at present it does not reason well; a fly is buzzing in its ears; that is enough to render it incapable of good judgment. If you wish to be able to reach the truth, chase away that animal which holds its reason in check and disturbs that powerful intellect which rules towns and kingdoms. He is a comical god! A ridiculous hero! (366)

PART III. MISERY

53. The vileness of man in submitting himself to the brutes, and in even worshipping them. (429)

56. We are so unfortunate that we can only take pleasure in a thing on condition of being annoyed if it turn out ill, as a thousand things can do,

and do every hour. He who should find the secret of rejoicing in the good, without troubling himself with its contrary evil, would have hit the mark. It is perpetual motion. (181)

58. Tyranny consists in the desire of universal power beyond its scope.

There are different assemblies of the strong, the fair, the sensible, the pious, in which each man rules at home, not elsewhere. And sometimes they meet, and the strong and the fair foolishly fight as to who shall be master, for their mastery is of different kinds. They do not understand one another, and their fault is the desire to rule everywhere. Nothing can effect this, not even might, which is of no use in the kingdom of the wise, and is only mistress of external actions.

Tyranny. So these expressions are false and tyrannical: "I am fair, therefore I must be feared. I am strong, therefore I must be loved. I am . . ."

Tyranny is the wish to have in one way what can only be had in another. We render different duties to different merits; and the duty of love to the pleasant; the duty of fear to the strong; duty of belief to the learned.

We must render these duties; it is unjust to refuse them, and unjust to ask others. And so it is false and tyrannical to say, "He is not strong, therefore I will not esteem him; he is not able, therefore I will not fear him." (332)

60. On what shall man found the order of the world which he would govern? Shall it be on the caprice of each individual? What confusion! Shall it be on justice? Man is ignorant of it.

Certainly had he known it, he would not have established this maxim, the most general of all that obtain among men, that each should follow the custom of his own country. The glory of true equity would have brought all nations under subjection, and legislators would not have taken as their model the fancies and caprice of Persians and Germans instead of this unchanging justice. We would have seen it set up in all the States on earth and in all times; whereas we see neither justice nor injustice which does not change its nature with change in climate. Three degrees of latitude reverse all jurisprudence; a meridian decides the truth. Fundamental laws change after a few years of possession; right has its epochs; the entry of Saturn into the Lion marks to us the origin of such and such a crime. A strange justice that is bounded by a river! Truth on this side of the Pyrenees, error on the other side.

Men admit that justice does not consist in these customs but that it resides in natural laws, common to every country. They would certainly maintain it obstinately, if reckless chance which has distributed human laws had encountered even one which was universal; but the farce is that the caprice of men has so many vagaries that there is no such law.

Theft, incest, infanticide, parricide, have all had a place among virtuous actions. Can anything be more ridiculous than that a man should have the right to kill me because he lives on the other side of the water, and because his ruler has a quarrel with mine, though I have none with him?

Doubtless there are natural laws; but good reason once corrupted has corrupted all. *Nothing more is ours (what we call ours is by convention)* [Cicero, *De Finibus*, Lib. V, 21]. *It is by virtue of senatorial decrees and votes of the people that crimes are committed* [Seneca, Epistles, XCV]. *Just as we once used to suffer for our vices, we now suffer for our laws* [Tacitus, *Annals* [Lib. III, 25].

The result of this confusion is that one affirms the essence of justice to be the authority of the legislator; another, the interest of the sovereign; another, present custom, and this is the most sure. Nothing, according to reason alone, is just in itself; all changes with time. Custom creates the whole of equity, for the simple reason that it is accepted. It is the mystical foundation of its authority; whoever carries it back to its first principles destroys it. Nothing is so faulty as those laws which correct faults. He who obeys them because they are just, obeys a justice which is imaginary, and not the essence of law; it is quite self-contained, it is law and nothing more. He who will examine its motive will find it so feeble and so trifling that if he be not accustomed to contemplate the wonders of human imagination, he will marvel that one century has gained for it so much pomp and reverence. The art of opposition and of revolution is to unsettle established customs, sounding them even to their source, to point out their want of authority and justice. We must, it is said, get back to the natural and fundamental laws of the State, which an unjust custom has abolished. It is a game certain to result in the loss of all; nothing will be just on the balance. Yet people readily lend their ear to such arguments. They shake off the yoke as soon as they recognize it; and the great profit by their ruin, and by that of these curious investigators of accepted customs. But for a contrary mistake men sometimes think they can justly do everything which is not without an example. That is why the wisest of legislators said that it was necessary to deceive men for their own good; and another, a politician *When he asks about the truth that is to bring him freedom, it is a good thing that he should be deceived* [St. Augustine, *City of God*, Book IV, 27]. We must not see the fact of usurpation; law was once introduced without reason, and has become reasonable. We must make it regarded as authoritative, eternal, and conceal its origin, if we do not wish that it should soon come to an end. (294)

61. *Justice.* As custom determines what is agreeable, so also does it determine justice. (309)

65. *Variety.* Theology is a science, but at the same time how many sciences? A man is a whole; but if we dissect him, will he be the head, the heart, the

stomach, the veins, each vein, each portion of a vein, the blood, each humor in the blood.

A town, a country-place, is from afar a town and a country-place. But, as we draw near, there are houses, trees, tiles, leaves, grass, ants, limbs of ants, in infinity. All this is contained under the name of country-place. (115)

66. *Injustice.* It is dangerous to tell the people that the laws are unjust, for they obey them only because they think them just. Therefore it is necessary to tell them at the same time that they must obey them because they are laws, just as they must obey superiors, not because they are just, but because they are superiors. In this way all sedition is prevented, if this can be made intelligible, and it be understood what is the proper definition of justice. (326)

68. When I consider the short duration of my life, swallowed up in the eternity before and after, the little space which I fill, and even can see, engulfed in the infinite immensity of spaces of which I am ignorant, and which know me not, I am frightened, and am astonished at being here rather than there; for there is no reason why here rather than there, why now rather than then. Who has put me here? By whose order and direction, have this place and time been allotted to me, *as the remembrance of a guest that tarrieth but a day* [John:21:16]. (205)

69. *Misery.* Solomon and Job have been known and best spoken of the misery of man; the former the most fortunate, and the latter the most unfortunate of men; the former knowing the vanity of pleasures from experience, the latter the reality of evils. (174)

70. If our condition were truly happy, we would not need diversion from thinking of it in order to make ourselves happy. (165)

72. One must know oneself. If this does not serve to discover truth, it at least serves as a rule of life, and there is nothing better. (66)

75. Ecclesiastes shows that man without God is in total ignorance and inevitable misery. For it is wretched to have the wish, and not the power. Now he would be happy and assured of some truth, and yet he can neither know, nor desire not to know. He cannot even doubt. (389)

76. But perhaps this subject goes beyond the capacity of reason. Let us therefore examine her solutions to problems within her powers. If there be anything to which her own interest must have made her apply herself most

seriously, it is the inquiry into her own sovereign good. Let us see, then, wherein these strong and clear-sighted souls have placed it, and whether they agree.

One says that the sovereign good consists in virtue, another in pleasure, another in the knowledge of nature, another in truth, *Happy the man who could know the reasons for things,* [Virgil, *Georgics,* Book II, 490], another in total ignorance, another in indolence, others in disregarding appearances, another in wondering at nothing—*To be surprised at nothing is almost the only way to find happiness and to keep it* [Horace, *Epistles,* Lib. I, vi, I.], and the true skeptics in their indifference, doubt, and perpetual suspense, and others, wiser, think to find a better definition. We are well satisfied.

To transpose after the laws to the following title.

We must see if this fine philosophy has gained nothing certain from so long and so intent study; perhaps at least the soul will know itself. Let us hear the ruler of the world on this subject. What have they thought of her substance. Have they been more fortunate in locating her? What have they found out about her origin, duration, and departure?

Is then the soul too noble a subject for their feeble lights? Let us then abase her to matter and see if she knows whereof is made the very body which she animates, and those others which she contemplates and moves at her will. What have those great dogmatists, who are ignorant of nothing, known of this matter? [Page references are given to the edition of Montaigne's *Essays* that Pascal had at hand.]

This would doubtless suffice, if reason were reasonable. She is reasonable enough to admit that she had been unable to find anything durable, but she does not despair of reaching it; she is as ardent as ever in this search, and is confident she has within her the necessary power for this conquest. We must therefore conclude, and, after having examined her powers in their effects, observe them in themselves, and see if she had a nature and a grasp capable of laying hold of the truth. (73)

PART IV. BOREDOM

77. *Pride.* Curiosity is only vanity. Most frequently we wish to know only to talk. Otherwise we would not take a sea voyage in order never to talk of it, and for the sole pleasure of seeing without hope of ever communicating it. (152)

79. The weariness which is felt by us in leaving pursuits to which we are attached. A man dwells at home with pleasure; but if he sees a woman who charms him, or if he enjoys himself in play for five or six days, he is miserable if he returns to his former way of life. Nothing is more common than that. (128)

PART V. CAUSES OF EFFECTS

83. The world is a good judge of things, for it is in natural ignorance, which is man's true state. The sciences have two extremes which meet. The first is pure natural ignorance in which all men find themselves at birth. The other extreme is that reached by great intellects, who, having run through all that men can know, find they know nothing, and come back again to that same ignorance from which they set out; but this is a learned ignorance which is conscious of itself. Those between the two, who have departed from natural ignorance and have not been able to reach the other, have some smattering of this vain knowledge, and pretend to be wise. These trouble the world, and are bad judges of everything. The people and the wise constitute the world; these despise it, and are despised. They judge badly of everything, and the world judges rightly of them. (327)

84. *Descartes.* We must say summarily: This is made by figure and motion, for it is true. But to say what these are, and to compose the machine is ridiculous. For it is useless, uncertain, and painful. And were it true, we do not think all philosophy is worth one hour of pain. (79)

87. *True Justice.* We have it no more; if we had it, we should take conformity to the customs of a country as the rule of justice. It is here that, not finding justice, we have found force, etc. (297)

89. *The reason of effects.* It is wonderful that men would not have me honor a man clothed in brocade, and followed by seven or eight lackeys! Why! He will have me thrashed, if I do not salute him. This custom is a farce. It is the same with a horse in fine trappings in comparison with another! Montaigne is a fool not to see what difference there is, to wonder at our finding any, and to ask the reason. "Indeed," says he, "how comes it," etc. (315)

90. *The reason of effects.* Degrees. The people honor persons of high birth. The semi-learned despise them, saying that birth is not a personal, but a chance superiority. The learned honor them, not for popular reasons, but for secret reasons. Devout persons, who have more zeal than knowledge, despise them, in spite of that consideration which makes them honored by the learned, because they judge them by a new light which piety gives them. But perfect Christians honor them by another and higher light. So arise a succession of opinions for and against, according to the light one has. (337)

92. *The reason of effects.* It is then true to say that all the world is under a delusion; for although the opinions of the people are sound, they are so as conceived by them, since they think the truth to be where it is not. Truth is

indeed in their opinions, but not at the point where they imagine it. Thus it is true that we must honor noblemen, but not because noble birth is real superiority, etc. (335)

93. *The reason of effects.* Continual alternation of pro and con.

We have then shown that man is foolish, by the estimation he makes of things which are not essential; and all these opinions are destroyed. We have next shown that all these opinions are very sound, and that thus, since all these vanities are well founded, the people are so foolish as is said. And so we have destroyed the opinion which destroyed that of the people.

But we must now destroy this last proposition, and show that it remains always true that the people are foolish, though their opinions are sound, because they do not perceive the truth where it is, and, as they place it where it is not, their opinions are always very false and very unsound. (328)

95. *Sound opinions of the people.* To be elegant is not altogether foolish, for it proves that a great number of people work for one. It shows by one's hair, that one has a valet, a perfumer, etc., by one's hand, thread, lace . . . etc. Now it is not merely superficial nor merely outward show to have many arms to command. The more arms one has, the more powerful one is. To be spruce is to show one's power. (316)

98. How is it that a cripple does not offend us, but that a fool does? Because a cripple recognizes that we walk straight, whereas a fool declares that it is we who are silly; if it were not so, we should feel pity and not anger.

Epictetus asks still more strongly: "Why are we not angry if we are told that we have a headache, and why are we angry if we are told that we reason badly, or choose wrongly?" (80)

99. The reason is that we are quite certain that we have not a headache, or are not lame, but we are not so sure that we make a true choice. So having assurance only because we see with our whole sight, it puts us into suspense and surprise when another with his whole sight sees the opposite, and still more so when a thousand others deride our choice. For we must prefer our own lights to those of so many others, and that is bold and difficult. There is never this contradiction in the feelings towards a cripple.

Man is so made by continually telling him he is a fool he believes it, and by continually telling it to himself he makes himself believe it. For man holds an inward talk with his self alone, which it behooves him to regulate well. *Evil communications corrupt good manners* [I Corinthians 15:33]. We must keep silent as much as possible and talk with ourselves only of God, whom we know to be true; and thus we convince ourselves of the truth. (535)

103. *Justice, might.* It is right that what is just should be obeyed; it is necessary that what is strongest should be obeyed. Justice without might is helpless; might without justice is tyrranical. Justice without might is gainsaid, because there are always offenders; might without justice is condemned. We must then combine justice and might, and for this end make what is just strong, and what is strong just.

Justice is subject to dispute; might is easily recognized and is not disputed. So we cannot give might to justice, because might has gainsaid justice, and has declared that it is she herself who is just. And thus being unable to make what is just strong, we have made what is strong just. (298)

PART VI. GREATNESS

109. *Against skepticism.* It is, then, a strange fact that we cannot define these things without obscuring them, while we speak of them with all assurance. We assume that all conceive of them in the same way; but we assume it quite gratuitously, for we have no proof of it. I see, in truth, that the same words are applied on the same occasions, and that every time two men see a body change its place, they both express their view of this same fact by the same word, both saying that it is moved; and from this conformity of application we derive a strong conformity of ideas. But this is not absolutely or finally convincing, though there is enough to support a bet on the affirmative, since we know that we often draw the same conclusions from different premises.

This is enough, at least, to obscure the matter; not that it completely extinguishes the natural light which assures us of these things. The Academic skeptics [the skeptics in Plato's Academy like Arcesilaus and Carneades] would have won. But this dulls it, and troubles the dogmatists to the glory of the skeptical crowd, which consists in this doubtful ambiguity, and in a certain doubtful dimness from which our doubts cannot take away all the clearness, nor our own natural lights chase away all the darkness. (392)

110. We know the truth, not only by the reason, but also by the heart, and it is in this last way that we know first principles; and reason, which has no part in it, tries in vain to impugn them. The skeptics, who have only this for their object, labor to no purpose. We know that we do not dream, and however impossible it is for us to prove it by reason, this inability demonstrates only the weakness of our reason, but not, as they affirm, the uncertainty of all our knowledge. For the knowledge of first principles, as space, time, motion, number, is as sure as any of those which we get from reasoning. And reason must trust these intuitions of the heart, and must base them on every argument. (We have intuitive knowledge of the tri-di-

mensional nature of space, and of the infinity of number, and reason then shows that there are no two square numbers one of which is double to the other. Principles are intuited, propositions are inferred, all with certainty, though in different ways.) And it is as useless and is absurd for reason to demand from the heart proofs of her first principles, before admitting them, as it would be for the heart to demand from reason an intuition of all demonstrated propositions before accepting them.

This inability ought, then, to serve only to humble reason, which would judge all, but not to impugn our certainty, as if only reason were capable of instructing us. Would to God, on the contrary, that we had never need of it, and that we knew everything by instinct and intuition! But nature has refused us this boon. On the contrary she has given us but very little knowledge of this kind, and all the rest can be acquired only by reasoning.

There, those to whom God has imparted religion by intuition are very fortunate and justly convinced. But to those who do not have it, we can give it only by reasoning, waiting for God to give them spiritual insight, without which faith is only human, and useless for salvation. (282)

111. I can well conceive a man without hands, feet, head (for it is only experience which teaches us that the head is more necessary than feet). But I cannot conceive man without thought; he would be a stone or a brute. (339)

112. Instinct and reason, marks of two natures. (344)

113. *A thinking reed.* It is not from space that I must seek my dignity, but from the government of my thought. I shall have no more if I possess worlds. By space the universe encompasses and swallows me up like an atom; by thought I comprehend the world. (348)

PART VII. CONTRADICTIONS

119. *Contraries. After having shown the vileness and the greatness of man.* Let man now know his value. Let him love himself, for there is in him a nature capable of good; but let him not for this reason love the vileness which is in him. Let him despise himself, for this capacity is barren; but let him not therefore despise this natural capacity. Let him hate himself, let him love himself; he has within him the capacity of knowing the truth and of being happy, but he possesses no truth either constant or satisfactory.

I would then lead man to the desire of finding truth; to be free from passions, and ready to follow it where he may find it, knowing how much his knowledge is obscured by the passions. I would indeed that he should hate in himself the lust which determined his will by itself, so that it may not blind him in making his choice, and may not hinder him when he has chosen. (423)

121. It is a danger to make man see too clearly his equality with the brutes without showing him his greatness. It is also dangerous to make him see his greatness too clearly, apart from his vileness. It is still more dangerous to leave him in ignorance of both. But it is very advantageous to show him both. Man must not think that he is on a level either with the brutes or with the angels, nor must he be ignorant of both sides of his nature; but he must know both. (418)

122. *At Port-Royal. Greatness and Wretchedness.* Wretchedness being deduced from greatness, and greatness from wretchedness, some have inferred man's wretchedness all the more because they have taken his greatness as a proof of it, and others have inferred his greatness with all the more force, because they have inferred it from his very wretchedness. All that the one party has been able to say in proof of his greatness has only served as an argument of his wretchedness to the others, because the greater our fall, the more wretched we are, and *vice versa.* The one party is brought back to the other in an endless circle, it being certain that in proportion as men possess light they discover both the greatness and the wretchedness of man. In a word man knows that he is wretched. He is therefore wretched because he is so; but he is really great because he knows it. (416)

125. What are our natural principles but principles of custom? In children they are those that they have received from the habits of their fathers, as hunting in animals. A different custom will cause different natural principles. This is seen in experience; and if there are some natural principles ineradicable by custom, there are also some customs opposed to nature, ineradicable by nature, or by a second custom. This depends on disposition. (92)

127. The nature of man may be viewed in two ways: the one according to its end, and then he is great and incomparable; the other according to the multitude, just as we judge of the nature of the horse and the dog, popularly, by seeing its fleetness; and then man is abject and vile. These are two ways which make us judge of him differently, and which occasion such disputes among philosophers. The one denies the assumption of the other. One says, "He is not born for this end, for all of his actions are repugnant to it." The other says, "He foresakes his end, when he does these base actions." (415)

128. Two things instruct man about his whole nature; instinct and experience. (396)

130. If he exalt him, I humble him; if he humbles himself, I exalt him, and I always contradict him, till he understands that he is an incomprehensible monster. (420)

131. The chief argument of the skeptics — I pass over the lesser ones — are that we have no certainty of the truth of these principles apart from faith and revelation, except in so far as we naturally perceive them in ourselves. Now this natural intuition is not a convincing proof of their truth; since, having no certainty, apart from faith, whether man was created by a good God, or by a wicked demon, or by chance, it is doubtful whether these principles given to us are true, or false or uncertain, according to our origin. Again no person is certain, apart from faith, whether he is awake or sleeps, seeing that during sleep we believe that we are awake as firmly as we do when we are awake; we believe that we see space, figure and motion; we are aware of the passage of time, we measure it; and in fact we act as if we were awake. So that half of our life being passed in sleep, we have on our own admission no idea of truth, whatever we may imagine. As all our intuitions are then illusions, who knows whether the other half of our life, in which we think we are awake, is not another sleep a little different from the former, from which we awake when we suppose ourselves asleep?

And who doubts that, if we dreamt in company, and the dreams chanced to agree, which is common enough, and if we were always alone when awake, we should believe that matters were reversed? In short, as we often dream that we dream, heaping dream upon dream, may it not be that this half of our life, wherein we think ourselves awake, is itself only a dream on which the others are grafted, from which we wake at death, during which we have as few principles of truth and good as during natural sleep, these different thoughts which disturb us being perhaps only illusions like the flight of time and the vain fancies of our dreams?

These are the chief arguments on one side and the other.

I omit minor ones, such as the skeptical talk against the impressions of custom, education, manners, country, and the like. Though these influence the majority of common folk, who dogmatize only on shallow foundations, they are upset by the least breath of the skeptics. We have only to see their books if we are not sufficiently convinced of this, and we shall very quickly become so, perhaps too much.

I notice the only strong point of the dogmatists, namely that, speaking in good faith and sincerely, we cannot doubt natural principles. Against this the skeptics set up in one word the uncertainty of our origin, which includes that of our nature. The dogmatists have been trying to answer this objection ever since the world began.

So there is an open war among men, in which each must take a part, and side either with dogmatism or skepticism. For he who thinks to remain neutral is above all a skeptic. This neutrality is the essence of the sect; he who is against them is essentially for them. In this appear their advantage. They are not for themselves; they are neutral, indifferent, in suspense as to all things, even themselves being no exception.

What then shall man do in this state? Shall he doubt everything? Shall he doubt whether he is awake, whether he is being pinched, or whether he is being burned? Shall he doubt whether he doubts? Shall he doubt whether he exists? We cannot go as far as that; and I lay it down as a fact that there never has been a real complete skeptic. Nature sustains our feeble reason, and prevents it raving to that extent.

Shall he then say, on the contrary, that he certainly possesses truth — he who when pressed ever so little, can show no title to it, and is forced to let go his hold?

What a chimera then is man! What a novelty! What a monster, what a chaos, what a contradiction, what a prodigy! Judge of all things, imbecile worm of the earth; depositary of truth, a sink of uncertainty and error; the pride and refuse of the universe!

Who will unravel this tangle? Nature confutes the skeptics, and reason confutes the dogmatists. What then will you become, O men! who try to find out by your natural reason what is your true condition? You cannot avoid one of these sects, nor adhere to one of them.

Know then, proud man, what a paradox you are to yourself. Humble yourself, weak reason; be silent foolish nature; learn that man infinitely transcends man, and learn from your Master your true condition, of which you are ignorant. Hear God.

For in fact, if man had never been corrupt, he would enjoy in his innocence both truth and happiness with assurance; and if man had always been corrupt, he would have no idea of truth or bliss. But, wretched as we are, and more so than if there were no greatness in our condition, we have an idea of happiness, and cannot reach it. We perceive an image of truth, and possess only a lie. Incapable of absolute ignorance and of certain knowledge, we have been manifestly in a degree of perfection from which we have unhappily fallen.

It is, however, an astonishing thing that the mystery furthest removed from our knowledge, namely that of the transmission of sin, should be a fact without which we can have no knowledge of ourselves. For it is beyond doubt that there is nothing which more shocks our reason than to say that the sin of the first man has rendered guilty those, who, being so removed from this source, seem incapable of participation in it. This transmission does not only seem to us impossible, it seems also very unjust. For what is more contrary to the rules of our miserable justice than to damn eternally an infant incapable of will, for a sin wherein he seems to have so little a share, that it was committed six thousand years before he was in existence? Certainly nothing offends us more rudely than this doctrine, and yet, without this mystery, the most incomprehensible of all, we are incomprehensible to ourselves. The knot of our condition takes its twists and turns in this abyss, so that man is more inconceivable without this mystery than this mystery is inconceivable to man.

Whence it seems that God, willing to render the difficulty of our existence unintelligible to ourselves, has concealed the knot so high, or, better speaking, so low, that we are quite incapable of reaching it; so that it is not by the proud exertions of our reason, but by the simple submissions of reason, that we can truly know ourselves.

These foundations, solidly established on the inviolable authority of religion, makes us know that there are two truths of faith equally certain; the one, that man, in the state of creation, or in that of grace, is raised above all nature, made like unto God and sharing in His divinity; the other, that, in the state of corruption and sin, he is fallen from this state and made like unto the beasts.

These two propositions are equally sound and certain. Scripture manifestly declares this to us, when it says in some places: *My delights were with the sons of men*, Proverbs 8:31; and in other places, *I will pour out my spirit upon all flesh*, Joel 2:28. *Ye are gods*, Psalms 82:6; and in other places, *All flesh is grass*, Isaiah 11:6. *Man is like the beasts that perish*, Psalms 49:12. *I said in my heart concerning the state of the sons of men*, Ecclesiastes 3:18.

Whence it clearly seems that man by grace is made like unto God, and a partaker in His divinity, and that without grace he is like unto the brute beasts. (434)

PART VIII. DIVERSION

132. *Diversion.* If man were happy, he would be the more so, the less he was diverted, like the Saints and God — Yes; but is it not to be happy to have a faculty of being amused by diversion? — No, for that comes from elsewhere and from without, and thus is dependent, and therefore subject to be disturbed by a thousand accidents, which brings inevitable griefs. (170)

133. *Diversion.* As men are not able to fight against death, misery, ignorance, they have taken it into their heads, in order to be happy, not to think of them at all. (168)

134. Despite these miseries, man wishes to be happy, and only wishes to be happy, and cannot wish not to be so. But how will he set about it? To be happy he would have to make himself immortal; but, not being able to do so, it has occurred to him to prevent himself from thinking of death. (169)

135. I feel that I might not have been; for the Ego consists in my thoughts. Therefore I, who think, would not have been, if my mother had been killed before I had life. I am not then a necessary being. In the same way I am not eternal or infinite; but I see plainly that there exists in nature a necessary Being, eternal and infinite. (469)

136. *Diversion.* When I have occasionally set myself to consider the different distractions of men, the pains and perils to which they expose themselves at court or in war, whence arise so many quarrels, passions, bold and often bad ventures, etc., I have discovered that all the unhappiness of men arises from one single fact that they cannot stay quietly in their own chamber. A man who has enough to live on, if he knew how to stay with pleasure at home would not leave it to go to sea or to beseige a town. A commission in the army would not be bought so dearly, but that it is found insufferable not to budge from the town; and men only seek conversation and entertaining games, because they cannot remain with pleasure at home.

But on further consideration, when, after finding the cause of all our ills, I have sought to discover the reason of it, I have found that there is one very real reason, namely, the natural poverty of our feeble and mortal condition, so miserable that nothing can comfort us when we think of it closely.

Whatever condition we picture to ourselves, if we muster all the good things which it is possible to possess, royalty is the finest position in the world. Yet, when we imagine a king attended with every pleasure he can feel, if he be without diversion, and be left to consider and reflect on what he is, this feeble happiness will not sustain him; he will necessarily fall into forebodings of danger, of revolutions which may happen, and finally, of death and inevitable disease; so that if he be without what is called diversion, he is unhappy, and more unhappy that the least of his subjects who plays and diverts himself.

Hence it comes that play and the society of women, war and high posts, are sought after. Not that there is in fact any happiness in them, or that men imagine true bliss to consist in money won at play, or in the hare which they hunt; we would not take these as a gift. We do not seek that easy and peaceful lot which permits us to think of our unhappy condition, nor the dangers of war, nor the labors of office, but the bustle which averts these thoughts of ours, and amuses us.

Reasons why we like the chase better than the quarry.

Hence it comes people so much love noise and stir; hence it comes that the prison is so horrible a punishment; hence it comes that the pleasure of solitude is a thing incomprehensible. And it is in fact the greatest source of happiness in the condition of kings, that people try incessantly to divert them, and to procure for them all kinds of pleasures.

The king is surrounded by persons whose only thought is to divert the king, and to prevent his thinking of self. For he is unhappy, king though he be, if he think of himself.

This is all that men have been able to discover to make themselves happy. And those who philosophize on the matter, and who think men unreasonable for spending a whole day chasing a hare that they would not have bought, hardly know our nature. The hare in itself would not screen us from the sight of death and calamities; but the chase which turns away our attention from these, does screen us.

The advice given to Pyrrhus to take the rest which he was about to seek with so much labor, was full of difficulties.

To bid a man live quietly is to bid him to live happily. It is to advise him to be in a perfectly happy state, in which he thinks at leisure without therein a cause of distress. This is to misunderstand nature.

As people who naturally understand their own condition avoid nothing so much as rest, so there is nothing they leave undone in seeking turmoil. Now that they have an instinctive knowledge of true happiness. . . .

So we are wrong in blaming them. Their error does not lie in seeking excitement, if they seek it only as a diversion; the evil is that they seek it as if the possession of the objects of their quest would make them really happy. In this respect it is right to call their quest a vain one. Hence in all this both the censurers and censured do not understand man's true nature.

And thus, when we take exception against them, that what they seek with such fervor cannot satisfy them, if they replied — as they should do if they considered the matter thoroughly — that they sought in it only a violent and impetuous occupation which turned their thoughts from themselves, and that they therefore chose an attractive object to charm and ardently attract them, they would leave their opponents without replying. But they do not make this answer, because they do not know themselves. They do not know that it is the chase, and not the quarry, which they seek.

Dancing. We must consider rightly where to place our feet — A gentleman sincerely believes that hunting is great and royal sport; but a beater is not of this opinion.

They imagine that if they obtained such a post, they would then rest with pleasure, and are insensible of the insatiable nature of their desire. They think they are truly seeking quiet, and they are only seeking excitement.

They have a secret instinct which impels them to seek amusement and occupation abroad, and which arises from the sense of their constant unhappiness. They have another secret instinct, a remnant of the greatness of our original nature, which teaches them that happiness in reality consists only in rest, and not in being stirred up. And of these two contrary instincts they form with themselves a confused idea, which hides itself from their view in the depths of their soul, inciting them to aim at rest through excitement, and always to fancy that the satisfaction which they do not have will come to them, if, by surmounting whatever difficulties confront them, they can thereby open the door to rest.

Thus passes away all man's life. People seek rest in a struggle against difficulties; and when they have conquered these, rest becomes insufferable. For we think either of the misfortunes we have or of those which threaten us. And even if we should see ourselves sufficiently sheltered on all sides, weariness of its own accord would not fail to arise from the depths of the heart wherein it has its natural roots, and to fill the mind with its poison.

Thus so wretched is man that he would weary even without any cause for weariness from the peculiar state of his disposition; and so frivolous is he, that though full of a thousand reasons for weariness, the least thing, such as playing billiards or hitting a ball, is sufficient to amuse him.

But will you say what object has he in all this? The pleasure of bragging tomorrow among his friends that he has played better than some one else. So others wait in their own rooms to show to the learned that they have solved a problem in algebra, which no one had hitherto been able to solve. Many more expose themselves to extreme perils, in my opinion as foolishly, in order to boast afterwards that they have captured a town. Lastly, others wear themselves out in studying all these things, not in order to become wiser, but only in order to prove that they know them; and these are the most senseless of the band, since they are so knowingly, whereas one may suppose of the others, that if they knew it, they would no longer be foolish.

This man spends his life without weariness in playing every day for a small stake. Give him each morning the money he can win each day, on condition that he does not play; you make him miserable. It will perhaps be said that he seeks the amusement of play and not the winnings. Make him then play for nothing; he will not become excited over it, and will feel bored. It is then not the amusement alone that he seeks; a languid and passionless amusement will weary him. He must get excited over it, and deceive himself by the fancy that he will be happy to win what he would not have as a gift on condition of not playing; and he must make for himself an object of passion, and excite over it his desire, his anger, his fear, to obtain his imagined end, as children are frightened at the face they have blackened.

Whence comes it that this man, who lost his only son a few months ago, or who this morning was in such trouble through being distressed by lawsuits and quarrels, now no longer thinks of them? Do not wonder; he is quite taken up in looking out for the boar which his dogs have been hunting so hotly for the last six hours. He requires nothing more. However full of sadness a man may be, he is happy for the time, if you can prevail upon him to enter into some amusement; and however happy a man may be, he will soon be discontented and wretched if he be not diverted and occupied by some passion or pursuit which prevents weariness from overcoming him. Without amusement there is no sadness. And this also constitutes the happiness of persons in high position, that they have a number of people to amuse them, and have the power to keep themselves in this state.

Consider this. What is it to be superintendent, chancellor, first president, but to be in a condition wherein from early morning a large number of people come from all quarters to see them, so as not to leave them an hour in the day in which they can think of themselves? And when they are in disgrace and sent back to their country houses, where they lack neither wealth nor servants to help them on occasion, they do not fail to be wretched and desolate, because no one prevents them from thinking of themselves. (139)

137. *Diversion.* Is not the royal dignity sufficiently great in itself to make its possessor happy by the mere contemplation of what he is? Must he be diverted from this thought like ordinary folk? I see that a person is made happy by diverting him from the view of his domestic sorrows so as to occupy all his thoughts with the care of dancing well. But will it be the same with a king and will he be happier in the pursuit of these idle amusements than in the contemplation of his greatness? And what more satisfactory object could be presented to his mind? Would it not be a deprivation of his delight for him to occupy his soul with the thought of how to adjust his steps to the cadence of an air, or how to throw a ball skillfully, instead of leaving it to enjoy quietly the contemplation of the majestic glory which encompassess him? Let us make trial; let us leave a king all alone to reflect on himself quite at leisure, without any gratification of the senses, without any care in his mind, without society; and we will see that a king without diversion is a man full of wretchedness. So this is carefully avoided, and near the persons of kings there never fail to be a great number of people who see to it that amusement follows business, and who watch all the time of their leisure to supply them with delights and games, so that there is no blank in it. In fact, kings are surrounded with persons who are wonderfully attentive in taking care that the king be not alone, and in a state to think of himself, knowing well that he will be miserable, king though he be, if he meditate on himself.

In all this I am not talking of Christian kings as Christians, but only as kings. (142)

138. *Diversion.* Death is easier to bear without thinking of it, than is the thought of death without peril. (166)

PART IX. PHILOSOPHERS

140. Had Epictetus seen the way perfectly, he would have said to men, "You follow a wrong road"; he shows that there is another, but he does not lead to it. It is the way of willing what God wills. Jesus Christ alone leads to it. *I am the way, the truth, the life,* [John 14:6].

The vices of Zeno himself.

142. *Against the philosophers who believe in God without Jesus Christ.*

Philosophers. They believe that God alone is worthy to be loved and admired; and that they have desired to be loved and admired of men, and do not know their own corruption. If they feel full of feelings, of love, and admiration, and find therein their chief delight, very well, let them think themselves good. But if they find themselves averse to Him, if they have no inclination but the desire to establish themselves in the esteem of men, and if their whole perfection consists only in making men — but without constraint — find their happiness in loving them, I declare that this perfection is horrible. What! they have known God, and have not desired solely that men should love Him, but that men should stop short at them! They have wanted to be the object of the voluntary delight of men. (463).

143. *Philosophers.* We are full of things which take us out of ourselves.

Our instinct makes us feel that we must seek our happiness outside ourselves. Our passions impel us outside, even when no objects present themselves to excite them. External objects tempt us of themselves, and call to us, even when we are not thinking of them. And thus philosophers have said in vain, "Retire within yourselves, you will find your good there." We do not believe them, and those who believe them are the most empty and the most foolish. (464)

146. *The Stoics.* They conclude that what has been done once can always be done, and since the desire of glory imparts some power to those whom it possesses, others can do likewise. There are feverish movements which health cannot imitate.

Epictetus concludes that since there are consistent Christians, every man can easily be so. (350)

PART X. THE SOVEREIGN GOOD.

147. *The sovereign good. Dispute about the sovereign good — That you may be content with yourself and the good things innate in you* [Seneca, Epistles, XX, 8]. There is a contradiction, for in the end they advise suicide. Oh! What a happy life, from which we are to free ourselves as from the plague! (361)

148. *Second part—That man without faith cannot know the true good, nor justice.*

All men seek happiness. This is without exception. Whatever different means they employ, they all tend to this end. The cause of some going to war, and of others avoiding it, is the same desire in both, attended with different views. They will never take the least step but to this object. This is the motive of every action, of every man, even of those who hang themselves.

And yet after such a great number of years, no one without faith has reached the point to which all continually look. All complain, princes and subjects, noblemen and commoners, old and young, strong and weak, learned and ignorant, healthy and sick, of all countries, all times, all ages, and all conditions.

A trial so long, so continuous, and so uniform, should certainly convince us of our inability to reach the good by our own efforts. But the example teaches us little. No resemblance is ever so perfect that there is not some slight difference; and hence we expect that our hope will not be deceived on this occasion as before. And thus, while the present never satisfies us, experience dupes us, and from misfortune to misfortune leads us to death, their eternal crown.

What is then that this desire and this inability proclaim to us, but that there was once in man a true happiness of which there now remain to him only the mark and empty trace, which he in vain tries to fill from all his surrounding, seeking them from things absent the help he does not obtain from things present? But these are all inadequate, because the infinite abyss can only be filled by an infinite and immutable object, that is to say, only by God Himself.

He only is our true good, and since we have foresaken Him, it is a strange thing that there is nothing in nature which has not been serviceable in taking His place; the stars, the heavens, earth, the elements, plants, cabbages, leeks, animals, insects, calves, serpents, fever, pestilence, war, famine, vices, adultery, incest. And since man has lost the true good, everything can appear equally good to him, even his own destruction, though so opposed to God, to reason, and to the whole course of nature.

Some seek good in authority, others in scientific research, others in pleasure. Others, who are in fact nearer the truth, have considered it necessary that the universal good, which all men desire, should not consist in any of the particular things which can only be possessed by one man, and which, when shared, afflict their possessors more by the want of the part he has not, than they please him by the possession of what he has. They have learned that the true good should be such as all can possess at once, without diminution, and without envy, and which no one can lose against his will. And their reason is that this desire being natural to man, since it is necessarily in all, and that it is impossible not to have it, they infer from it . . . (428)

PART XI. AT PORT-ROYAL

149. *At Port-Royal. The beginning, after having explained the incomprehensibility.* The greatness and the wretchedness of man are so evident that the true religion must necessarily teach us both that there is in man some great source of greatness, and a great source of wretchedness. It must then give us a reason for these astonishing contradictions.

In order to make man happy, it must prove to him that there is a God; that we ought to love Him, that our true happiness is to be in Him, and our sole evil is to be separated from Him; it must recognize that we are full of darkness which prevents us from knowing and loving Him; and that thus, as our duties compel us to love God, and our lusts turn us away from Him, we are full of unrighteousness. It must give us an explanation of our opposition to God and to our own good. It must teach us the remedies for these infirmities, and the means of obtaining these remedies. Let us therefore examine all the religions of the world, and see if there be any other than the Christian which is sufficient for this purpose.

Shall it be that of the philosophers, who put forward as the chief good, the good which is in ourselves? Is this the true good? Have they found the remedy for our ills? Is man's pride cured by placing him on an equality with God? Have those who have made us equal to the brutes, or the Mohammedans who have offered us earthly pleasures as the chief good even in eternity, produced the remedy for our lusts? What religion, then will teach us to cure pride and lust? What religion will in fact teach us our good, our duties, the weakness which turns us from them, the cause of this weakness, the remedies which can cure it, and the means of obtaining these remedies?

All other religions have not been able to do so. Let us see what the wisdom of God will do.

"Expect neither truth," she says, "nor consolation from men. I am she who formed you, and who alone can teach you what you are. But you are now no longer in the state in which I formed you. I created man holy, innocent, perfect. I filled him with light and intelligence. I communicated to him my glory and my wonders. The eye of man saw then the majesty of God. He was not then in the darkness which blinds him, nor subject to mortality and woes which afflict him. But he has not been able to sustain so great glory without falling into pride. He wanted to make himself his own center, and independent of my help. He withdrew himself from my rule; and on making himself equal to me by the desire of finding his happiness in himself, I abandoned him to himself. And setting in revolt the creatures that were subject to him, I made them his enemies; so that man is now become like the brutes, and so estranged from me that there scarce remains to him a dim vision of his Author. So far has all his knowledge been extinguished or disturbed! The senses, independent of reason, and often the masters of reason, have led him into pursuit of pleasure. All creatures either torment or tempt him, and domineer over him, either subduing him by their strength, or fascinating him by their charms, a tyranny more awful and more imperious.

"Such is the state in which men now are. There remains to them some feeble instinct of the happiness of their former state; and they are plunged in the evils of their blindness and their lust, which have become their second nature.

"From this principle which I disclose to you, you can recognize the cause of those contradictions which have astonished all men, and have divided them into parties holding so different views. Observe, now, all the feelings of greatness and glory which the experience of so many woes cannot stifle, and see if the cause of them must not be in another nature."

At Port-Royal tomorrow (Prosopopoea). "It is in vain, O men, that you seek within yourselves the remedy for your ills. All your light can only reach the knowledge that not in yourselves will you find truth or good. The philosophers have promised you that, and you have been unable to do it. They neither know what is your true good, nor what is your true state. How could they have given remedies for your ills, when they did not even know them? Your chief maladies are pride, which takes you away from God, and lust, which binds you to earth; and they have done nothing else but cherish one or the other of these diseases. If they gave you God as an end, it was only to administer to your pride; they made you think that you are by nature like Him, and conformed to Him. And those who saw the absurdity of this claim put you on another precipice, by making you understand that your nature was like that of the brutes, and led you to seek your good in the lusts which are shared by the animals. This is not the way to cure you of your unrighteousness, which these wise men never knew. I alone can make you understand who you are. . . ."

Adam, Jesus Christ.

If you are united to God, it is by grace, and not by nature. If you are humbled, it is by penitence, not by nature.

Thus this double capacity . . .

You are not in the state of your creation.

As these two states are open, it is impossible for you not to recognize them. Follow your own feelings, observe yourselves, and see if you do not find the lively characteristics of these two natures. Could so many contradictions be found in a simple subject?

Incomprehensible — Not all that is incomprehensible ceases to exist. Infinite number, An infinite space equal to a finite.

Incredible that God should unite Himself to us — This consideration is drawn only from the sight of our vileness. But if you are quite sincere over it, follow it as far as I have done, and recognize that we are indeed so vile that we are incapable in ourselves of knowing if His mercy cannot make us capable of Him. For I would know how this animal, who knows himself to be so weak, has the right to measure the mercy of God, and set limits to it, suggested by his own fancy. He has so little knowledge of what God is, that he does not know what he himself is, and, completely disturbed at the sight of his own state, dares to say that God cannot make him capable of communion with Him.

But I would ask him if God demands anything else from him than the knowledge and love of Him, and why, since his nature is capable of love and knowledge, he believes that God cannot make Himself be loved by him. Doubtless he knows at least that he exists, and that he loves something. Therefore, if he sees anything in the darkness wherein he is, and if he finds some object of his love among the things on earth, why, if God impart to him some ray of His essence, will he not be capable of knowing and loving Him in the manner on which it shall please Him to communicate Himself to us? There must then be certainly an intolerable presumption in arguments of this sort, although they seem founded on an apparent humility, which is neither sincere nor unreasonable, if it does not make us admit that, not knowing of ourselves what we are, we can only learn it from God.

"I do not mean that you should submit your belief to me without reason, and I do not aspire to overcome by tyranny. In fact, I do not claim to give you a reason for everything. And to reconcile these contradictions, I intend for you to see clearly, by convincing proofs, those divine signs in me, which may convince you of what I am, and may gain authority for me by wonders and proofs, those divine signs which you cannot reject; so that you may then believe without. . . . the things which I teach you, since you will find no other ground for rejecting them, except that you cannot know of yourselves if they are true or not.

"God has willed to redeem men, and to open salvation to those who seek it. But men render themselves so unworthy of it, that it is right that God should refuse to some, because of their obduracy, what He grants to others from a compassion which is not due to them. If He had willed to overcome the obstinacy of the most hardened, He could have done so by revealing Himself so manifestly to them that they could not have doubted the truth of His essence; as it will appear at the last day, with such thunders and such a convulsion of nature, that the dead will rise again, and the blindest will see Him.

"It is not in this manner that He has willed to appear in His advent of mercy, because, as so many make themselves unworthy of His mercy, He has willed to leave them in the loss of the good which they do not want. It was not then right that He should appear in a manner manifestly divine, and completely capable of convincing all men; but it was also not right that He should come in so hidden a manner that He could not be known by those who sincerely seek Him with all their heart, and to be so hidden from those who flee from Him with all their heart. He so regulates the knowledge of Himself that he has given signs of Himself, visible to those who seek Him, and not to those who seek Him not. There is enough light for those who desire to see, and enough obscurity for those who have a contrary disposition." (430)

PART XII. BEGINNING

150. Infidels, who profess to follow reason, ought to be exceedingly strong in reason. What say they then? "Do we not see," say they, "that the brutes live and die like men, and Turks like Christians? They have their ceremonies, their prophets, their learned men, their saints, their monks, like us," etc. (Is this contrary to Scripture? Does it not say all this?)

If you care but little to know the truth, here is enough of it to leave you in repose. But if you desire with all your heart to know it, it is not enough; look at it in detail. This would be sufficient for a question in philosophy; but not here, where it concerns your all. And yet, after a trifling reflection of this kind, we go to amuse ourselves, etc. Let us inquire of this same religion whether it does not give a reason for this obscurity; perhaps it will teach it to us. (226)

151. We are fools to depend upon the society of our fellow-men. Wretched as we are, powerless as we are, they will not aid us; we shall die alone. We should therefore act as if we were alone, and in that case should we build fine houses, etc. We should seek the truth without hesitation; and, if we refuse it, we show that we value the esteem of men more than the search for truth. (211)

152. Between us and heaven or hell there is only life, which is the frailest thing in the world. (213)

153. What then do you promise me, in addition to certain troubles, but ten years of self-love (for ten years is the chance), to try hard to please without success? (238)

154. *Chances.* We must live differently in the world, according to these different assumptions: (1) that we could always remain in it; (2) that it is

certain that we shall not remain here long, and uncertain if we shall remain here one hour. This last assumption is our condition. (237)

155. Heart, instinct, principles. (281)

156. To pity the atheists who seek, for are they not unhappy enough? To inveigh against those who make a boast of it. (190)

157. Atheism shows strength of mind, but only to a certain degree. (225)

158. According to the doctrine of chance, you ought to put yourself to the trouble of searching for the truth; for if you die without worshipping the True Cause, you are lost. — "But," say you, "if He had wished me to worship Him, He would have left me signs of His will." — He has done so, but you neglect them. Seek them, therefore; it is well worth it. (236)

159. If we ought to devote eight hours of life, we ought to devote a hundred years. (204)

160. There are only three kinds of persons; those who serve God, having found Him, others who are occupied in seeking Him, not having found Him; while the remainder live without seeking Him, and without having found Him. The first are reasonable and happy, the last are foolish and unhappy; those between are unhappy and reasonable. (157)

161. Atheists ought to say what is perfectly evident; now it is not perfectly evident that the soul is material. (221)

162. To begin by pitying unbelievers; they are wretched enough by their condition. We ought only to revile them where it is beneficial; but this does them harm.

163. A man in a dungeon, ignorant whether his sentence be pronounced, and having only one hour to learn it, but this hour enough, if he knew that it is pronounced, to obtain its repeal, would act unnaturally in spending that hour, not in ascertaining his sentence, but in playing cards. So it is against nature that man, etc. It is making heavy the hand of God.

Thus not only the zeal of those who seek Him proves God, but also the blindness of those who seek Him not. (200)

164. *Dungeon.* I approve of not examining the opinion of Copernicus, but this . . . ! It concerns all our life to know whether the soul be mortal or immortal. (218)

165. The last act is tragic, however happy all the rest of the play is; at the

last a little earth is thrown upon our head, and that is the end for ever. (210)

166. We run carelessly to the precipice, after we have put some thing before us to prevent us from seeing it. (183)

PART XIII. SUBMISSION AND USE OF REASON

167. Submission is the use of reason in which consists true Christianity. (269)

168. How I hate these follies of not believing in the Eucharist, etc.! If the Gospels be true, if Jesus Christ be God, what difference is there? (224)

169. I should not be a Christian, but for the miracles, said St. Augustine. (812)

170. *Submission.* We must know where to doubt, where to feel certain, where to submit. He who does not do so, understands not the force of reason. There are some who offend against these rules, either by affirming everything as demonstrative, from want of knowing what demonstration is; or by doubting everything, from want of knowing where to submit; or by submitting in everything, from want of knowing where they must judge. (268)

171. *They received the word with all readiness of mind, and searched the Scriptures daily, whether those things were so* [Acts 17:2]. (695)

172. The conduct of God, who disposes all things kindly, is to put religion into the mind by reason, and into the heart by grace, But to will to put it into the mind and heart by force and threats is not to put religion there, but terror. (185)

173. If we submit everything to reason, our religion will have no mysterious or supernatural element. If we offend the principles of reason, our religion will be absurd and ridiculous. (273)

174. *Saint Augustine.* Reason would never submit, if did not judge that there are some occasions on which it ought to submit. It is then right for it to submit, when it judges that it ought to submit. (270)

175. It will be one of the confusions of the damned to see that they are condemned by their own reason, by which they claimed to condemn the Christian religion. (563)

176. Those who do not love the truth take as a pretext that it is disputed, and that a multitude deny it. And so their error arises only from this, that they do not love either truth or charity. Thus they are without excuse. (261)

177. Contradiction is a bad sign of truth; several things which are certain are contradicted; several things which are false pass without contradiction. Contradiction is not a sign of falsity, nor the want of contradiction a sign of truth. (384)

179. I say there are few true Christians, even as regards faith. There are many who believe but from superstition. There many who do not believe solely from wickedness. Few are between the two. In this I do not include those who are of truly pious character, nor all those who believe from a feeling in their heart. (256)

180. Jesus performed miracles, then the apostles, and the first saints in great number; because the prophecies not being yet accomplished, but in the process of being accomplished by them, the miracles alone bore witness to them. It was foretold that the Messiah should convert the nations. How could this prophecy be fulfilled without the conversion of the nations? And how could the nations be converted to the Messiah, if they did not see this final effect of the prophecies which prove Him? Therefore, till He had died, risen again, and converted the nations, all was not accomplished, and so miracles were needed during all this time. Now they are no longer needed against the Jews; for the accomplished prophecies constitute a lasting miracle. (838)

181. Piety is different from superstition.
   To carry piety as far as superstition is to destroy it.
   The heretics reproach us for this superstitious submission. This is to do what they reproach us for. . . .
   Infidelity, not to believe in the Eucharist, because it is not seen.
   Superstition to believe propositions. Faith, etc. (255)

182. There is nothing so comfortable to reason as this disavowal of reason. (272)

183. Two extremes: to exclude reason, to admit reason only. (253)

184. Had it not been for the miracles, there would have been no sin in not believing in Jesus Christ. (811)

185. Faith indeed tells what the senses do not tell, but not the contrary of what they see. It is above them and not contrary to them. (265)

187. It is not a rare thing to have to reprove the world for too much docility. It is a natural vice like credulity, and as pernicious. Superstition. (254)

188. The last proceeding of reason is to recognize that there is an infinity of things which are beyond it. It is but feeble if it does not see so far as to know this. But if natural things are beyond it, what will be said of superstition? (267)

PART XIV. EXCELLENCE

189. We know God only by Jesus Christ. Without this mediator all communion with God is taken away; through Jesus Christ we know God. All those who have claimed to know God, and to prove Him without Jesus Christ, have had only weak proofs. But in proof of Jesus Christ we have the prophecies which are solid and palpable proofs. And these prophecies, being accomplished and proved true by the event, mark the certainty of these truths, and therefore the divinity of Christ. In Him then, and through Him, we know God. Apart from Him, and without the Scripture, without original sin, without a necessary mediator promised and come, we cannot absolutely prove God, nor teach right doctrine and right morality. But through Jesus Christ, and in Jesus Christ, we prove God, and teach morality and doctrine. Jesus Christ is then the true God of men.

But we know at the same time our wretchedness; for this God is none other than the Savior of our wretchedness. So we can only know God well by knowing our iniquities. Therefore those who have known God, without knowing their wretchedness, have not glorified Him, but have glorified themselves. *For after that . . . the world by wisdom knew not God, it pleased God by the foolishness of preaching to save them that believe* [I Corinthians 1:21]. (547)

190. *Preface.* The metaphysical proofs of God are so remote from the reasoning of men, and so complicated, that they make little impression; and if they should be of service to some, it would be only during the moment that they see such demonstration; but an hour afterwards they fear they have been mistaken.

What they gained by curiosity they lost through pride [St. Augustine, *Sermons*, no. 141].

This is the result of the knowledge of God obtained without Jesus Christ; it is communion without a mediator with the God whom they have known without a mediator. Whereas those who have known God by a mediator know their own wretchedness. (543)

191. It is not only impossible but useless to know God without Jesus

Christ. They have not departed from Him, but approached; they have not humbled themselves, but . . .

The better one is the worse one becomes if one ascribes this excellence to oneself [St. Bernard, *Sermons on the Canticles,* no. 84]. (549)

192. The knowledge of God without that of man's misery causes pride. The knowledge of man's misery without that of God causes despair. The knowledge of Jesus Christ constitutes the middle course, because in Him we find both God and our misery. (527)

PART XV. TRANSITION

193. *Prejudice leading to error.* It is a deplorable thing to see all men deliberating on means alone, and not on the end. Each thinks how he will acquit himself in his condition; but as for the choice of condition, or of country, chance gives them to us.

It is a pitiable thing to see many Turks, heretics, and infidels follow the way of their fathers for the sole reason that each has been imbued with the prejudice that it is the best. And that fixes for each man his condition of locksmith, soldier, etc.

Hence savages care nothing for Providence. (98)

194. Why is my knowledge limited? Why my stature? Why my life to one hundred years rather than a thousand? What reason has nature had for giving me such, and for choosing this number rather than another in the infinity of those from which there is no more reason to choose one than another, trying nothing else? (208)

195. Since we cannot be universal and know all that is to be known of everything, we ought to know a little about everything. For it is far better to know something about everything than to know all about one thing. This universality is the best. If we can have both, still better; but if we must choose, we ought to choose the former. And the world feels this and does so; for the world is often a good judge. (37)

198. When I see the blindness and the wretchedness of man, when I regard the whole silent universe, and man without light, left to himself, and, as it were, lost in this corner of the universe, without knowing who has put him there, what he has come to do, what will become of him at death, and incapable of all knowledge, I became terrified, like a man who should be carried in his sleep to a dreadful desert island, and should awake without knowing where he is, and without means of escape. And thereupon I wonder how people in a condition so wretched do not fall into despair. I see

other persons around me of a like nature. I ask them if they are better informed than I am. They tell me that they are not. And, thereupon these wretched and lost beings, having looked around them, and seen some pleasing objects, have given and attached themselves to them. For my own part, I have not been able to attach myself to them, and considering how strongly it appears that there is something else than what I see, I have examined whether this God has not left some sign of Himself.

I see many contradictory religions, and consequently all false save one. Each wants to be believed on its own authority, and threatens unbelievers. I do not therefore believe them. Every one can say this; every one can call himself a prophet. But I see that Christian religion wherein prophecies are fulfilled; and that is what every one cannot do. (693)

199. *Man's disproportion.* This is where our innate knowledge leads us. If this be not true, there is no truth in man; and if it be true, he finds therein great cause for humiliation, being compelled to abase himself in one way or another. And since he cannot exist without this knowledge, I wish that, before entering on deeper researches into nature, he would consider her both seriously and at leisure, that he would reflect upon himself also, and knowing what proportion there is. . . . Let man then contemplate the whole of nature in her full and grand majesty, and turn his vision from the low objects which surround him. Let him gaze on that brilliant light, set like an eternal lamp to illuminate the universe; let the earth appear to him a point in comparison with the vast circle described by the sun; and let him wonder at the fact that this vast circle is itself but a fine point in comparison with that described by the stars in their revolution around the firmament. But if our view be arrested there, let our imagination pass beyond; it will sooner exhaust the power of conception than nature that of supplying material for conception. The whole visible world is only an imperceptible atom in the ample bosom of nature. No idea approaches it. We may enlarge our conceptions beyond all imaginable space; we only produce atoms in comparison with the reality of things. It is an infinite sphere, the center of which is everywhere, the circumference nowhere. In short it is the greatest sensible mark of the almighty power of God, that imagination loses itself in that thought.

Returning to himself, let man consider what he is in comparison with all existence; let him regard himself as lost in this remote corner of nature; and from the little cell in which he finds himself lodged, I mean the universe, let him estimate at their true value the earth, kingdoms, cities, and himself. What is a man in the Infinite?

But to show him another prodigy equally astonishing, let him examine the most delicate things he knows. Let a mite be given him, with its minute body and parts incomparably more minute, limbs with their joints, veins in the limbs, blood in the veins, humors in the blood, drops in the humors, vapors in the drops. Dividing these last things again, let him exhaust his powers of conception, and let the last object at which he can arrive be now that of discourse. Perhaps he will think that here is the smallest point in nature. I will let him see therein a new abyss. I will paint for him not only the visible universe, but all that he can conceive of nature's immensity in the womb of this abridged atom. Let him see therein an infinity of universes, each of which has its firmament, the planets, its earth, in the same proportion as in the visible world; in each earth animals, and in the last mites, in which he find again all that the first had, finding still in these others the same thing without end and without cessation. Let him lose himself in wonders as amazing in their littleness as the others in their vastness. For who will not be astounded at the fact that our body, which a little while ago was imperceptible in the universe, itself imperceptible in the bosom of the whole, is now a colossus, a world, or rather a whole, in respect of the nothingness which we cannot reach? He who regards himself in this light will be afraid of himself, and observing himself sustained in the body given him by nature between those two abysses of the Infinite and Nothing, will tremble at the sight of these marvels; and I think that, as his curiosity changes into admiration, he will be more disposed to contemplate them in silence than to examine them with presumption.

For in fact what is man in nature? A Nothing in comparison with the Infinite, an All in comparison with the Nothing, a mean between nothing and everything. Since he is infinitely removed from comprehending the extremes, the end of things and their beginning are hopelessly hidden from him in an impenetrable secret; he is equally incapable of seeing the Nothing from which he was made, and the Infinite in which he is swallowed up.

What will he do then, but perceive the appearance of the middle of things, in an eternal despair of knowing either their beginning or their end. All things proceed from the Nothing, and borne towards the Infinite. Who will follow these marvellous processes? The Author of these wonders understands them. None other can do so.

Through failure to contemplate these Infinites, men have rashly rushed into the examination of nature, as though they bore some proportion to her. It is strange that they have wished to understand the beginnings of things, and thence to arrive at the knowledge of the whole, with a presumption as infinite as their object. For surely this design cannot be formed without presumption or without a capacity infinite like nature.

If we are well informed, we understand that, as nature has graven her image and that of her Author on all things, they almost all partake of her double infinity. Thus we see that all the sciences are infinite in the extent of their researches. For who doubts that geometry, for instance, has an infinite infinity of problems to solve? They are also infinite in the multitude and fineness of their premises; for it is clear that those which are put forward as ultimate are not self-supporting, but are based on others which again having others for their support, do not permit of finality. But we represent some as ultimate for reason, in the same way as in regard to material objects we call that an indivisible point beyond which our senses can no longer perceive anything, although by its nature it is infinitely divisible.

Of these Infinites of science, that of greatness is the most palpable, and hence a few persons have pretended to know all things. "I will speak of the whole," said Democritus.

But the infinitely little is the least obvious. Philosophers have much oftener claimed to have reached it, and it is here they have all stumbled. This has given rise to such common titles as *First Principles, Principles of Philosophy,* and the like, as ostentatious in fact, though not in appearance, as that one which blinds us, *Of All that Can be Known* [by Pico della Mirandola].

We naturally believe ourselves far more capable of reaching the center of things than of embracing their circumference. The visible extent of the world visibly exceeds us; but as we exceed little things, we think ourselves more capable of knowing them. And yet we need no less capacity for attaining the Nothing than the All. Infinite capacity is required for both, and it seems to me that whoever shall have understood the ultimate principles of being might also attain to the knowledge of the Infinite. The one depends on the other, and one leads to the other. These extremes meet and reunite by force of distance, and find each other in God, and in God alone.

Let us then take our compass; we are something, and we are not everything. The nature of our existence hides from us knowledge of first beginnings which are born of the Nothing, and the littleness of our being conceals from us the sight of the Infinite.

Our intellect holds the same position in the world of thought as our body occupies in the expanse of nature.

Limited as we are in every way, this state which holds the mean between the extremes is present in all our impotence. Our senses perceive no extreme. Too much sound deafens us; too much light dazzles us; too great distance or proximity hinders our view. Too great length and too great brevity of discourse tend to obscurity; too much truth is paralyzing. (I know some who cannot understand that to take four from nothing leaves nothing.) First principles are too self-evident for us; too much pleasure disagrees with us. Too many consonances are annoying in music; too many benefits irritate us; we wish to have the wherewithal to over-pay our debts. *Kindness is welcome to the extent that it seems the debt can be paid back. When it goes too far gratitude turns into hatred* [Tacitus, *Annals*, Lib. IV, 18]. We feel neither extreme heat nor extreme cold. Excessive qualities are prejudicial to us and not perceptible by the senses; we do not feel but suffer them.

Extreme youth and extreme age hinder the mind, as also too much and too little education. In short, extremes are for us as though they were not, and we are not within their notice. They escape us or we them.

This is our true state, that is what makes us incapable of certain knowledge and absolute ignorance. We sail within a vast sphere, ever drifting in uncertainty, driven from end to end. When we think to attach ourselves to any point and to fasten to it, it wavers and leaves us; and if we follow it, it eludes our grasp, slips past us, and vanishes for ever. Nothing stays for us. This is our natural condition, and yet most contrary to our inclination; we burn with desire to find solid ground and an ultimate sure foundation whereon to build a tower reaching to the Infinite. But our whole groundwork cracks, and the earth opens to abysses.

Let us therefore not look for certainty and stability. Our reason is always deceived by fickle shadows; nothing can fix the finite between the two Infinites, which both enclose and fly from it.

If this be well understood, I think that we shall remain at rest, each in the state wherein nature has placed him. As this sphere which has fallen to us as our lot is always distant from either extreme, what matter it that man should have a little more knowledge of the universe? If he has it, he but gets a little higher. Is he not always infinitely removed from the end, and is not the duration of our life equally removed from eternity, even if it lasts ten years longer?

In comparison with these Infinites all finites are equal, and I see no reason for fixing our imagination on one more than on another. The only comparison which we make of ourselves to the finite is painful to us.

If man made himself the first object of study, he would see how incapable he is of going further. How can a part know the whole? But he may perhaps aspire to know at least the parts to which he bears some proportion. But the parts of the world are all so related and linked to one another, that I believe it impossible to know one without the other and without the whole.

Man, for instance, is related to all he knows. He needs a place wherein to abide, time through which to live, motion in order to live, elements to compose him, warmth and food to nourish him, air to breathe. He sees light; he feels bodies; in short, he is in a dependent alliance with everything. To know man, then, it is necessary to know how it happens that he needs air to live, and, to know the air, we must first know how it is thus related to the life of man, etc. Flame cannot exist without air; therefore to understand the one, we must understand the other.

Since everything then is cause and effect, dependent and supporting, mediate and immediate, and all is held together by a natural though imperceptible chain, which binds together things most distant and most different, I hold it equally impossible to know the parts without knowing the whole, and to know the whole without knowing the parts in detail.

The eternity of things in itself or in God must all astonish our brief duration. The fixed and constant immobility of nature, in comparison with the continual change which goes on within us, must have the same effect.

And what completes our incapability of knowing things, is the fact that we are simple, and that we are composed of two opposite natures, different in kind, soul and body. For it is impossible that our rational part should be other than spiritual, and if any one maintain that we are simply corporeal, this would far more exclude us from the knowledge of things, there being nothing so inconceivable as to say that matter knows itself. It is impossible to imagine how it should know itself.

So if we are simply material, we can know nothing at all; and if we are composed of mind and matter, we cannot know perfectly things which are simple, whether spiritual or corporeal. Hence it comes that almost all philosophers have confused ideas of things, and speak of material things in spiritual terms, and of spiritual things in material terms. For they say boldly that bodies have a tendency to fall, that they seek after their center, that they fly from destruction, that they fear the void, that have inclinations, sympathies, antipathies, all of which attributes pertain only to mind. And in speaking of minds, they consider them as in a place, and attribute to them movement from one place to another; and these are qualities which belong only to bodies.

Instead of receiving the ideas of these things in their purity, we color them with our own qualities, and stamp with our composite being all the simple things which we contemplate.

Who would not think, seeing us compose all things of mind and body, but that this mixture would be quite intelligible to us? Yet it is the very thing we least understand. Man is to himself the most wonderful object in nature, for he cannot conceive what the body is, still less what the mind is, and least of all how a body should be united to a mind. This is the consummation of his difficulties, and yet it is his very being. *The way in which minds are attached to bodies is beyond man's understanding, and yet this is what man is* [Saint Augustine, *City of God*, Book 21, 10]. Finally, to complete the proof of our weakness, I shall conclude with these two considerations. . . . (72)

200. Man is but a reed, the most feeble thing in nature; but he is a thinking reed. The entire universe need not arm itself to crush him. A vapor, a drop of water suffices to kill him. But, if the universe were to crush him, man would still be more noble than that which killed him, because he knows that he dies and the advantage which the universe has over him, the universe knows nothing of this.

All our dignity consists, then, in thought. By it we must elevate ourselves, and not by space and time which we cannot fill. Let us endeavor, then, to think well; this is the principle of morality. (347)

201. The eternal silence of these infinite spaces frightens me. (206)

202. Comfort yourselves. It is not from yourselves that you should expect grace; but, on the contrary, it is in expecting nothing from yourselves, that you must hope for it. (517)

PART XVI. THE FALSITY OF OTHER RELIGIONS

203. Mohammed was without authority. His reasons then should have been very strong, having only their own force. What does he say then, that we must believe him? (595)

204. *The falseness of other religions.* They have no witnesses. Jews have. God defies other religions to produce such signs [Isaiah 43:9, 44:8]. (592)

205. If there is one sole source of everything, there is one sole end of everything; everything through Him, everything for Him. The true religion, then, must teach us to worship Him only, and to love Him only. But as we find ourselves unable to worship what we know not, and to love any other object but ourselves, the religion which instructs us in these duties must instruct us also of this inability, and teach us also the remedies for it. It teaches us that by one man all was lost, and the bond broken between God and us, and that by one man the bond is renewed.

We are born so averse to this love of God, and it is so necessary that we must be born guilty, or God would be unjust. (489)

208. Without this divine knowledge what could men do but either become elated by the inner feeling of their past greatness which still remains to them, or become despondent at the sight of their present weakness? For, not seeing the whole truth, they could not attain to perfect virtue. Some considering nature as corrupt, others as incurable, they could not escape either pride or sloth, the two sources of all vice; since they cannot but either abandon themselves to it through cowardice, or escape it by pride. For if they knew the excellence of men, they were ignorant of his corruption; so they easily avoided sloth, but fell into pride. And if they recognized the infirmity of nature, they were ignorant of its dignity; so that they could easily avoid vanity, but it was to fall into despair. Thence arise the different schools of the Stoics and Epicureans, the Dogmatists, Academic Skeptics, etc.

The Christian religion alone has been able to cure these two vices, not by expelling the one through means of the other according to the wisdom of the world, but by expelling both according to the simplicity of the Gospel. For it teaches the righteous that it raises them even to a participation in divinity itself; that in this lofty state they still carry the source of all corruption, which renders them during all their life subject to error, misery, death and sin; and it proclaims to the most ungodly that they are capable of the grace of their Redeemer. So making those tremble whom it justifies, and consoling those whom it condemns, religion so justly tempers fear with hope through that double capacity of grace and of sin, common to all, that it humbles infinitely more than reason alone can do, but without despair; and it exalts infinitely more than natural pride, but without inflating; thus making it evident that alone being exempt from error and vice, it alone fulfills the duty of instructing and correcting human beings.

Who then can refuse to believe and adore this heavenly light? For is it not clearer than day that we perceive within ourselves ineffaceable marks of excellence? And is it not equally true that we experience every hour the results of our deplorable condition? What does this chaos and monstrous confusion proclaim to us but the truth of these two states, with a voice so powerful that it is impossible to resist it? (435)

209. *The difference between Jesus and Mahomet.* Mahomet was not foretold; Jesus Christ was foretold.

Mahomet slew; Jesus Christ caused His own to be slain.

Mahomet forebade reading; the Apostles ordered reading.

In fact the two are so opposed, that if Mahomet took the way to succeed from a worldly point of view, Jesus Christ, from the same point of view, took the way to perish. And instead of concluding that, since Mahomet succeeded, Jesus Christ might well have succeeded, we ought to say that since Mahomet succeeded, Jesus Christ should have failed. (599)

210. All men naturally hate one another. They employ lust as far as possible in the service of the public weal. But this is only a pretence and a false image of love; for at bottom it is only hate. (451)

211. From lust men have found and extracted excellent rules of policy, morality, and justice; but in reality this vile root of man, is only covered, it is not taken away. (453)

212. Jesus Christ is a God whom we approach without pride, and before whom we humble ourselves without despair. (528)

214. The true religion must have as a characteristic the obligation to love God. This is very just, and yet no other religion has commanded this; ours has done so. It must also be aware of human lust and weakness; ours is so. It must have adduced remedies for this; one is prayer. No other religion has asked of God to love and follow Him. (491)

215. *After having understood the whole nature of man.* That a religion may be true, it must have knowledge of our nature. It ought to know its greatness and littleness, and the reason of both. What religion but the Christian has known this? (433)

216. The true religion teaches our duties; our weaknesses, pride, and lust; and the remedies, humility and mortification. (493)

218. It is not by what is obscure in Mahomet, and which may be interpreted in a mysterious sense, that I would have him judged, but by what is clear, as his paradise and the rest. In that he is ridiculous. And since what is clear is ridiculous, it is not right to take his obscurities for mysteries.

It is not the same with the Scripture. I agree that there are in it obscurities as strange as those of Mahomet; but there are admirably clear passages, and the prophecies are manifestly fulfilled. The cases are therefore not on a par. We must not confound, and put on one level things which only resemble each other in their obscurity, and not in the clearness, which requires us to reverence the obscurities. (598)

219. Other religions, as the pagan, are more popular, for they consist in externals. But they are not for educated people. A purely intellectual religion would be more suited to the learned, but it would be of no use to the common people. The Christian religion is alone adapted to all, being composed of externals and internals. It raises the common people to the internals, and humbles the proud to the external; it is not perfect without the two, for the people must understand the spirit of the letter, and the learned must submit their spirit to the letter. (251)

220. No other religion has proposed to human beings to hate themselves. No other religion then can please those who hate themselves and who seek a Being truly lovable. And these, if they had never heard of the religion of a God humiliated, would embrace it at once. (468)

PART XVII. TO MAKE RELIGION LOVABLE

221. Jesus Christ for all. Moses for a nation.

The Jews blessed in Abraham: "I will bless those that bless thee." But: "All nations blessed in his seed." *It is a light thing that thou shouldst be my servant* [Isaiah 49:6]. *A light to lighten the Gentiles* [Luke 2:32].

He hath not dealt so with any nation, said David [Psalms 147:20], speaking of the Law. But, in speaking of Jesus Christ, we must say: *He hath dealt so with every nation. It is a light thing,* etc. [Isaiah]. So it belongs to Jesus Christ to be universal. Even the Church offers sacrifices only for the faithful. Jesus Christ offered that of the cross for all. (774)

222. The carnal Jews and the heathen have their calamities, and Christians also. There is no Redeemer for the heathen, for they do not so much as hope for one. There is no Redeemer for the Jews; they hope for Him in vain. There is a Redeemer only for Christians (see *Perpetuity*). (747)

PART XVIII. FUNDAMENTALS

223. To the chapter on *Fundamentals* must be added that on *Typology* touching the reason for types: why Jesus Christ was prophesied as to His first coming; why prophesied obscurely as to the manner. (570)

224. Unbelievers are the most credulous. They believe the miracles of Vespasian, in order not to believe those of Moses. (816)

225. As Jesus Christ remained unknown among men, so His truth remains among common opinions without external difference. Thus the Eucharist among ordinary bread. (789)

226. All faith consists in Jesus Christ and in Adam, and all morality in lust and in grace. (523)

227. What have they to say against the resurrection, and against the child-bearing of the Virgin? Which is the more difficult, to produce a man or an animal, or to reproduce it? And if they had never seen any species of animals, could they have conjectured whether they were produced without connection with each other? (223)

228. What do the prophets say of Jesus Christ? That he will be clearly God? No; but that He is a God truly hidden; that He will be slighted; that none will think that it is He; that He will be a stone of stumbling, upon which many will stumble, etc. Let people then reproach us no longer for want of clarity, since we make a profession of it.
    But, it is said, there are obscurities. And without that, no one would have stumbled over Jesus Christ, and this is one of the formal pronouncements of the prophets. *Shut their eyes* [Isaiah: 6:10]. (751)

229. This religion taught to her children what men have only been able to discover by their greatest knowledge. (444)

231. If we would say that people are too insignificant to deserve communion with God, we must indeed be very great to judge of it. (511).

232. We understand nothing of the works of God, if we do not take as a principle that He has willed to blind some, and enlighten others. (566)

233. Jesus Christ does not say that He is not of Nazareth, in order to leave the wicked in their blindness; nor that He is not Joseph's son. (796)

234. God prefers rather to incline the will than the intellect. Perfect clarity would be of use to the intellect, and would harm the will. To humble pride. (581)

235. Jesus Christ came to blind those who saw clearly, and to give sight to the blind; to heal the sick, and leave the healthy to die; to call to repentance, and to justify sinners, and to leave the righteous in their sins; to fill the needy, and leave the rich empty. (771)

236. There is sufficient clearness to enlighten the elect, and sufficient obscurity to humble them. There is sufficient obscurity to blind the reprobate, and sufficient clearness to condemn them, and make them inexcusable [Saint Augustine, Montaigne, *Apology for Raimond Sebond*].

The geneology of Jesus Christ is the Old testament is intermingled with so many others that are useless, that it cannot be distinguished. If Moses had kept only the record of the ancestors of Christ, that might have been too plain. If he had not noted that of Jesus Christ, it might not have been sufficiently plain. But, after all, whoever looks closely sees that of Jesus Christ expressly traced through Tamar, Ruth, etc.

Those who ordained these sacrifices, knew their uselessness; those who have declared their uselessness, have not ceased to praise them.

If God had permitted only one religion, it has been too easily known; but when we look at it closely, we clearly discern the truth amidst their confusion.

The premiss. Moses was a clever man. If, then, he ruled himself by his reason, he would say nothing clearly which was directly against reason.

Thus all the very apparent weaknesses are strength. Example; the two genealogies in Saint Matthew and Saint Luke. What can be clearer than that this was not concerted? (578)

237. If Jesus Christ had only come to sanctify, all Scripture and all things would tend to that end; and it would be quite easy to convince unbelievers. If Jesus Christ had only come to blind, all His conduct would be confused; and we would have no means of convincing unbelievers. But as He came *for a sanctuary and a stone of stumbling*, as Isaiah says [Isaiah 8:14], we cannot convince unbelievers, and they cannot convince us. But by this very fact we convince them; since we say that in His whole conduct there is no convincing proof on one side or the other. (795)

239. Man is not worthy of God, but he is not incapable of being made worthy.

It is unworthy of God to unite Himself in wretched man; but it is not unworthy of God to pull him out of his misery. (510)

240. *Proof.* Prophecies with their fulfillment; what has preceded and what has followed Jesus Christ. (705)

241. *Source of contradictions.* A God humiliated, even to the death on the cross; a Messiah triumphing over death by his own death. Two natures in Jesus Christ, two advents, two states of man's nature. (765)

242. *That God has willed to hide himself.* If there were only one religion, God would indeed be manifest. The same would be the case, if there were no martyrs but in our religion.

God being thus hidden, every religion which does not affirm that God is hidden, is not true; and every religion which does not give the reason of it, is not instructive. Our religion does all this: *Verily thou art a God that hidest thyself* [Isaiah 45:15]. (585)

243. The heathen religion has no foundation at the present day. It is said once to have had a foundation by oracles which spoke. But what are the books which assure us of this? Are they so worthy of belief on account of the virtue of their authors? Have they been preserved with such care that we can be sure that they have not been meddled with?

The Mahometan religion has for a foundation the Koran and Mahomet. But has the prophet, who was to be the last hope of the world, been foretold? What sign has he that every other man has not, who chooses to call himself a prophet? What miracles does he himself say that he has done? What mysteries has he taught, even according to his own tradition? What was the morality, what the happiness held out by him?

The Jewish religion must be differently regarded in the tradition of the Holy Bible, and in the tradition of the people. Its morality and happiness are absurd in the tradition of the people, but are admirable in that of the Holy Bible. (And all religion is the same; for the Christian religion is very different in the Holy Bible and in the causists.) The foundation is admirable; it is the ancient book in the world, and the most authentic; and whereas Mahomet, in order to make his own book continue in existence, forbade men to read it, Moses, for the same reason, ordered every one to read his.

Our religion is so divine that another divine religion has only been the foundation of it. (601)

244. Objection of atheists: "But we have no light." (228)

PART XIX. TYPOLOGY

248. *Types.* The prophets prophesied by symbols of a girdle, a beard and burnt hair, etc. (653)

251. He who will give the meaning of Scripture, and does not take it from Scripture, is an enemy of Scripture [St. Augustine, *De Doctrina Christina*].

252. Two errors: 1. To take everything literally. 2. To take everything spiritually. (648)

255. God, in order to cause the Messiah to be known by the good and not to be known by the wicked, made Him to be foretold in this manner. If the manner of the Messiah had been clearly foretold, there would have been no obscurity, even for the wicked. If the time had been obscurely foretold, there would have been obscurity, even for the good. For their goodness of heart would not have made them understand, for instance, that the closed *mem* [the Hebrew letter] signifies six hundred years. But that time has been clearly foretold, and the manner in types.

By this means, the wicked, taking the promised blessings for material blessings, have fallen into error, in spite of the clear prediction of the time; and the good have not fallen in error. For the understanding of the promised blessings depends on the heart, which calls "good" that which it loves; but the understanding of the promised time does not depend on the heart. And thus the clear prediction of the blessings, deceive the wicked alone.

Either the Jews or the Christians must be wicked. (758)

256. The carnal Jews understood neither the greatness nor the humiliation of the Messiah foretold in their prophecies. They misunderstood Him in His foretold greatness, as when He said that the Messiah should be lord of David, through his son, and that He was before Abraham, who had seen Him. They did not believe Him so great as to be eternal, and they likewise misunderstood Him in His humiliation and in His death. "The Messiah," said they, "abideth for ever, and this man says that he shall die." Therefore they believed Him neither mortal nor eternal; they sought in Him for a carnal greatness. (662)

257. *Contradiction.* We can only describe a good character by reconciling all contrary qualities, and it is not enough to keep up a series of harmonious qualities, without reconciling contradictory ones. To understand the meaning of an author, we must make all the contrary passages agree.

Thus, to understand Scripture, we must have a meaning in which all the contrary passages are reconciled. It is not enough to have one which suits many concurring passages; but it is necessary to have one which reconciles even contradictory passages.

Every author has a meaning in which all the contradictory passages agree, or he has no meaning at all. We cannot affirm the latter of Scripture and the prophets; they undoubtedly are full of good sense. We must then seek for a meaning which reconciles all discrepancies.

The true meaning is not that of the Jews; but in Jesus Christ all the contradictions are reconciled.

The Jews could not reconcile the cessation of the royalty and principality, foretold by Hosea, with the prophecy of Jacob.

If we take the law, and the kingdom as realities, we cannot reconcile all the passages. They must then necessarily be only types. We cannot even reconcile the passages of the same author, nor of the same book, nor sometimes of the same chapter, which indicates copiously what was the meaning of the author. As when Ezekiel 20 says that man will live by the commandments of God and will not live by them. (684)

259. *Types.* If the law and the sacrifices are the truth, it must please God, and must not displease Him. If they are types, they must be both pleasing and displeasing.

Now in all Scripture they are both pleasing and displeasing. It is said that the law shall be changed; and the sacrifice shall be changed; that they shall be without law, without a prince, and without a sacrifice; that a new covenant shall be made; that the law shall be renewed; that the precepts which they have received are not good; that their sacrifices are abominable; that God has demanded none of them.

It is said, on the contrary, that the law shall abide for ever; that this covenant shall be for ever; that sacrifice shall be eternal; that the scepter shall never depart from among them, because it shall not depart from them till the eternal King comes.

Do all these passages indicate what is real? No. Do they then indicate what is typical? No, but what is either real or typical. But the first passages, excluding as they do reality, indicate that all this is only typical [i.e., figurative].

All these passages together cannot be applied to reality; all can be said to be typical; therefore they are not spoken of reality, but of the type.

The Lamb slain from the foundation of the world, perpetual sacrifice [Ezekiel 46:14]. (685)

260. *Types.* A portrait conveys absence and presence, pleasure and pain. The reality excludes absence and pain.

To know if the law and the sacrifices are a reality or a type, we must see if the prophets, in speaking of these things, confined their view and their thought to them, so that they saw only the old covenant; or if they saw therein something else of which they were the representation, for in a portrait we see the thing figured. For this we need only examine what they say of them.

When they say that it will be eternal, do they mean to speak of that covenant which they say will be changed; and so of the sacrifices, etc?

A cipher has two meanings. When we find out an important letter in which we discover a clear meaning, and in which it is nevertheless said that the meaning is veiled and obscure, that it is hidden, so that we might read the letter without seeing it, and interpret it without understanding it, what must we think but that here is a cipher with a double meaning, and the more so if we find obvious contradictions in the literal meaning? The prophets have clearly said that Israel would be always loved by God, and that the law would be eternal; and they have said that their meaning would not be understood, and that it was veiled.

How greatly then ought we to value those who interpret the cipher, and teach us to understand the hidden meaning, especially if the principles which they educe are perfectly clear and natural! That is what Jesus Christ did, and the Apostles. They broke the seal; He rent the veil, and revealed the spirit. They have taught us through this that the enemies of man are his passions; that the Redeemer would be spiritual, and His reign spiritual; that there would be two advents, one in lowliness to humble the proud, the other in glory to exalt the humble; that Jesus Christ would be both God and man. (678)

261. The time of the first advent was foretold; the time of the second is not so; because the first was to be obscure, and the second is to be brilliant, and so manifest that even His enemies will recognize it. But, as He was first to come only in obscurity, and to be known only of those who searched the Scriptures . . . (757)

262. What could the Jews, His enemies, do. If they receive Him, they give proof of Him by their reception; for then the guardians of the expectation of the Messiah receive Him. If they reject Him, they give proof of Him by their rejection. (762)

263. *Contradictions.* The scepter till the Messiah — without king or prince.
The eternal law — changed.
The eternal covenant — a new covenant.
Good laws — bad precepts [Ezekiel]. (686)

264. The Jews were accustomed to great and striking miracles, and so, having had the great miracles of the Red Sea, and of the land of Canaan as an epitome of the great deeds of their Messiah, they therefore looked for more striking miracles, of which those of Moses were only the patterns. (746)

266. We might perhaps think that, when the prophets foretold that the scepter should not depart from Judah until the eternal King came, they

spoke to flatter the people, and that their prophecy was proved false by Herod. But to show that this was not their meaning, and that, on the contrary, they knew well that this temporal kingdom should cease, they said that they would be without a king and without a prince, and for a long time [Hosea 3:4]. (719)

267. *Types.* When once this secret is disclosed, it is impossible not to see it. Let us read the Old Testament in this light, and let us see if the sacrifices were real; if the fatherhood of Abraham was the true cause of the friendship of God; and if the promised land was the true place of rest. No. They are therefore types. Let us in the same way examine all those ordained ceremonies, all those commandments which are not of charity, and we shall see that they are types.

All these sacrifices and ceremonies were then either types or nonsense. Now these are things too clear, and too lofty, to be thought nonsense.

To know if the prophets confined their view in the Old Testament, or saw therein other things. (680)

269. There are some that see clearly that man has no other enemy than lust, which turns him from God, and not some enemies; and that he has no other good than God, and not a rich land. Let those who believe that the good of man is in the flesh, and evil in what turns him away from sensual pleasures, satiate themselves with them, and die in them. But let those who seek God with all their heart, who are only troubled at not seeing Him, who desire only to possess Him, and have as enemies only those who turn them away from Him, who are grieved at seeing themselves surrounded and overwhelmed with such enemies, take comfort. I proclaim to them happy news. There exists a Redeemer for them. I shall show Him to them. I shall show that there is a God for them. I shall show Him to others. I shall make them see that a Messiah has been promised, who should deliver them from their enemies, and that One has come to free them from their iniquities, but not from their enemies.

When David foretold that the Messiah would deliver His people from their enemies, one can believe that in the flesh these would be Egyptians; and then I cannot show that the prophecy was fulfilled. But one can well believe also that the enemies would be their sins; for indeed the Egyptians were not their enemies, but their sins were so. This word, enemies, is therefore ambiguous. But if he says elsewhere, as he does, that He will deliver His people from their sins, as indeed do Isaiah and others, the ambiguity is removed, and the double meaning of enemies is reduced to the simple meaning of iniquities. For if he had sins in his mind, he could well denote them as enemies; but if he thought of enemies he could not designate them as iniquities.

Now Moses, David, and Isaiah used the same terms. Who will say then that they have not the same meaning, and that David's meaning, which is plainly iniquities when he spoke of enemies, was not the same as that of Moses when speaking of enemies.

Daniel 9 prays for the deliverance of the people from the captivity of their enemies. But he was thinking of sins, and, to show this, he says that Gabriel came to tell him that his prayer was heard, and there were only seventy weeks to wait, after which the people would be freed from iniquity, sin would have an end, and the Redeemer, the Holy of Holies, would bring *eternal* justice, not legal, but eternal. (692)

270. *Types.* The Jews have grown old in these earthly thoughts, that God loved their father Abraham, his flesh and what sprung from it; that on account of this He had multiplied them, and distinguished them from all other nations, without allowing them to intermingle; that when they were languishing in Egypt, He brought them out with all these great signs in their favor; that He fed them with manna in the desert, and led them into a very rich land; that He gave them kings and a well-built temple, in order to offer up beasts before Him, by the shedding of whose blood they should be purified; and that at last He was to send them the Messiah to make them masters of all the world, and foretold of the time of His coming.

The world having grown old in these carnal errors, Jesus Christ came at the time foretold, but not with the expected glory; and thus men did not think it was He. After His death, Saint Paul came to teach men that all these things had happened in allegory; that the kingdom of God did not consist in the flesh, but in the spirit; that the enemies of men were not the Babylonians, but the passions; that God delighted not in the temples made with hands, but in a pure and contrite heart; that the circumcision of the body was unprofitable, but that of the heart was needed; that Moses had not given them the bread from heaven, etc.

But God, not having desired to reveal these things to this people who were unworthy of them, and having nevertheless desired to foretell them, in order that they might be believed, foretold the time clearly, and expressed the things sometimes clearly, but very often in figures, in order that those who loved symbols might consider them, and those who loved what was symbolized might see it therein.

All that tends not to charity is figurative.

The sole aim of the Scripture is charity.

All which tends not to the sole end is the type of it. For since there is only one end, all which does not lead to it in express terms is figurative.

God thus varies the sole precept of charity to satisfy our curiosity, which seeks for variety, by that variety which still leads us to the one thing needful. For one thing alone is needful, and we love variety; and God satisfies both by these varieties, which lead to the one thing needful.

The Jews have so much loved the shadows, and have so strictly expected them, that they have misunderstood the reality, when it came in the time and the manner foretold.

The Rabbis take the breasts of the Spouse for types, and all that does not express the only end they have, namely temporal good.

And Christians take even the Eucharist as a type of the glory at which they aim. (670)

271. Jesus Christ did nothing but teach men that they loved themselves, that they were slaves, blind, sick, wretched, and sinners; that He must deliver them, enlighten, bless, and heal them; that this would be effected by hating self, and by following Him through suffering and the death on the cross. (545)

272. *Types.* When the word of God, which is really true, is false literally, it is true spiritually. *Sit thou at my right hand* [Psalms 110:1]; this is false literally, therefore it is true spiritually.

In these expressions, God is spoken of after the manner of men; and this means nothing else but that the intention which men have in giving a seat at their right hand, God will have also. It is then an indication of the intention of God, not of His manner of carrying it out.

Thus, when it is said, "God has received the odor of your incense, and will in recompense give you a rich land [Genesis 8:21], that is equivalent to saying that the same intention which man would have, who, pleased with your perfumes, should in recompense give you a rich land, God will have towards you, because you have had the same intention as a man has towards him to whom he presents perfumes. So *the anger of the Lord is kindled* [Isaiah 5:25], a "jealous God," etc. For, the things of God being inexpressible, they cannot be spoken of otherwise, and the Church makes us of them even today: *for he hath strengthened the bars* [Psalms 147:13], etc.

It is not allowable to attribute to Scripture the meaning which is not revealed to us that it has. Thus, to say that the closed *mem* of Isaiah signifies six hundred, has not been revealed. It might be said that the *tsade* [another Hebrew letter] and the defective *he* [another Hebrew letter] may signify mysteries. But it is not allowable to say so, and still less to say this is the way of the philosopher's stone. But we say that the literal meaning is not the true meaning, because the prophets have themselves said so. (687)

273. Those who have a difficulty in believing seek a reason in the fact that the Jews do not believe. "Were this so clear," say they, "why did the Jews not believe? And they almost wish that they had believed, so as not to be kept back by the example of their refusal. But it is their very refusal that is the foundation of our faith. We should be much less disposed to faith, if they were on our side. We should then have a more ample pretext. The wonderful thing is to have made the Jews great lovers of the things foretold, and great enemies of their fulfillment. (745)

274. *Proof of the two Testaments at once.* To prove the two at one stroke, we

need only see if the prophets in one are fulfilled in the other. To examine the prophecies, we must understand them. For if we believe they have only one meaning, it is certain that the Messiah has not come; but if they have two meanings, it is certain that He has come in Jesus Christ.

The whole problem then is to know if they have two meanings.

That the Scripture has two meanings, which Jesus Christ and the Apostles have given, is shown by the following proofs:

1. Proof by Scripture itself.

2. Proof by the Rabbis. Moses Maimonides says that it has two aspects, and that the prophets have prophesied Jesus Christ only.

3. Proof by the Kabbala.

4. Proof by the mystical interpretation which the Rabbis themselves give to Scripture.

5. Proof by the principles of the Rabbis, that there are two meanings; that there are two advents of the Messiah, a glorious and a humiliating one, according to their desert; that the prophets have prophesied of the Messiah only—Law is not eternal, but must change at the coming of the Messiah —that then they shall no more remember the Red Sea; that the Jews and the Gentiles shall be mingled.

6. Proof by the key which Jesus Christ and the Apostles give us. (642)

276. If one of two persons, who are telling silly stories, uses language with a double meaning, understood in his own circle, while the other uses it with only one meaning, any one not in the secret, who hears them both talk in this manner, will pass upon them the same judgment. But if afterwards, in the rest of their conversation one says angelic things, and the other always dull commonplaces, he will judge that the one spoke in mysteries, and not the other; the one having sufficiently shown that he is incapable of such foolishness, and capable of being mysterious; and the other that he is incapable of mystery, and capable of foolishness.

The Old Testament is a cipher. (691)

PART XX. RABBINISM

278. [last line] Principles of Rabbinism: two Messiahs. (446)

PART XXI. PERPETUITY

279. One saying of David, or of Moses, as for instance that "God will circumcize the heart," enables us to judge of their spirit. If all their other expressions were ambiguous, and left us in doubt whether they were philosophers or Christians, one saying of this kind would in fact determine all the rest, as one sentence of Epictetus decides the meaning of all the rest to be the opposite. So far ambiguity exists, but not afterwards. (690)

280. State would perish if they did not often make their laws give way to necessity. But religion has never suffered this, or practiced it. Indeed, there must be these compromises, or miracles. It is not strange to be saved by yieldings, and this is not strictly self-preservation; besides, in the end they perish entirely. None has endured a thousand years. But the fact that this religion has always maintained itself, inflexible as it is, proves its divinity. (614)

281. *Perpetuity.* That religion has always existed on earth, which consists in believing that man has fallen from a state of glory and communion with God into a state of sorrow, penitence, and estrangement from God, but that after this life we shall be restored by a Messiah who should have come. All things have passed away, and this has endured, for which all things are.

Men have in the first age of the world been carried away into every kind of debauchery, and yet there were saints, as Enoch, Lamech, and others, who waited patiently for the Christ promised from the beginning of the world. Noah saw the wickedness of men at its height; and he was held worthy to save the world in his person, by the hope of the Messiah of whom he was a type. Abraham was surrounded by idolatry, when God made known to him the mystery of the Messiah, whom he welcomed from afar. In the time of Isaac and Jacob abomination was spread all over the earth; but these saints lived in faith; and Jacob, dying and blessing his children, cried in a rapture which made him break off his discourse, "I await, O my God, the Savior whom Thou hast promised" [Genesis 49:18]. The Egyptians were infected both with idolatry and magic; the very people of God were led astray by their example. Yet Moses and others believed Him who they saw not, and worshipped Him, looking to the eternal gifts which He was preparing for them.

The Greeks and Latins then set up false deities; the poets made a hundred different theologies, while the philosophers separated into a thousand different sects; and yet in the heart of Judea there were always chosen men who foretold the coming of the Messiah, which was known to them alone.

He came at length in the fullness of time, and time has since witnessed the birth of so many schisms and heresies, so many political revolutions, so many changes in all things; yet this Church, which worships Him who has always been worshipped, has endured uninterruptedly. It is a wonderful, incomparable, and altogether divine fact that this religion, which has always endured, has always been attacked. It has been a thousand times on the eve of universal destruction, and every time it has been in that state, God has restored it by extraordinary acts of His power. This is astonishing, also that it has preserved itself without yielding to the will of tyrants. For it is not strange that a State endures, when its laws are sometimes made to give way to necessity, but. . . . (see the passage indicated in Montaigne). (613)

282. *Perpetuity*. The Messiah has always been believed in. The tradition from Adam was fresh in Noah and in Moses. Since then the prophets have foretold him, while at the same time foretelling other things, which, being from time to time fulfilled in the sight of men, showed the truth of their mission, and consequently that of their promises touching the Messiah. Jesus Christ performed miracles, and the Apostles also, who converted all the heathen; and for all the prophecies being thereby fulfilled, the Messiah is for ever proved. (616)

284. The only religion contrary to nature, to common sense, and to our pleasure, is that alone which has always existed.

No religion but our own has taught that man is born in sin. No sect of philosophers has said this. Therefore none have declared the truth.

No sect or religion has always existed on earth, but the Christian religion. (606)

285. If the ancient Church was in error, the Church is fallen. If she should be in error today, it is not the same thing; for she has always the superior maxim of tradition from the hand of the ancient Church; and so this submission and this conformity to the ancient Church prevail and correct all. But the ancient Church did not assume the future Church, and did not consider her, as we assume and consider the ancient. (867)

286. There are two kinds of men in each religion: among the heathen, worshippers of beasts, and the worshippers of the one only God of natural religion; among the Jews, the carnal and the spiritual, who were the Christians of the old law; among Christians, the coarser-minded, who are the Jews of the new law. The carnal Jews looked for a carnal Messiah; the coarser Christians believe that the Messiah has dispensed them from the love of God; true Jews and true Christians worship a Messiah who makes them love God. (609)

287. Whoever judges the Jewish religion by its coarser forms will understand it. It is to be seen in the Holy Bible, and in the tradition of the prophets, who have made it plain enough that they did not interpret the law according to the letter. So our religion is divine in the Gospel, in the Apostles, and in tradition; but it is absurd in those who tamper with it.

The Messiah, according to the carnal Jews, was to be a great temporal prince. Jesus Christ, according to carnal Christians, has come to dispense us from the love of God, and to give us sacraments which shall do everything without our help. Such is not the Christian religion, nor the Jewish. True Jews and true Christians have always expected a Messiah who should make them love God, and by that love triumph over their enemies. (607)

289. The carnal Jews hold a midway place between Christians and heathens. The heathens knew not God, and love the world only. The Jews know the true God, and love the world only. The Christians know the true God, and love not the world. Jews and heathens love the same good. Jews and Christians know the same God.

The Jews were of two kinds; the first had only heathen affections, the other had Christian affections. (608)

PART XXII. PROOFS OF MOSES

290. The longevity of the patriarchs, instead of causing the loss of past history, conduced, on the contrary, to its preservation. For the reason why we are sometimes insufficiently instructed in the history of our ancestors, is that we have never lived long with them, and that they are often dead before we have attained the age of reason. Now, when men lived so long, children lived long with their parents. They conversed long with them. But what else could be the subject of their talk save the history of their ancestors, since to that all history was reduced, and men did not study science or art, which now form a large part of daily conversation? We see also that in these days tribes took particular care to preserve their genealogies. (626)

291. This religion, so great in miracles, saints, blameless Fathers, learned and great witnesses, martyrs, established kings as David, and Isaiah, a prince of the blood, and so great in science, after having displayed all her miracles and all her wisdom, rejects all this, and declares that she has neither wisdom nor signs, but only the cross and foolishness.

For those, who, by these signs and that wisdom, have deserved your belief, and who have proved to you their character, declare to you that nothing of all this can change you, and render you capable of knowing and loving God, but the power of the foolishness of the cross without wisdom and signs, and not the signs without this power. Thus our religion is foolish in respect to the effective cause, and wise in respect to the wisdom which prepares it. (587)

PART XXIII. PROOFS OF JESUS CHRIST

298. *Order. Against the objection that Scripture has no order.*
The heart has its own order; the intellect has its own, which is by principle and demonstration. The heart has another. We do not prove that we ought to be loved by enumerating in order the causes of love; that would be ridiculous.

Jesus Christ and Saint Paul employ the rule of love, not of intellect; for they would warm, not instruct. It is the same with Saint Augustine. The order consists chiefly in digressions on each point to indicate the end, and keep it always in sight. (283)

300. Jesus Christ is an obscurity (according to what the world calls obscurity), such that historians, writing only of important matters of states, have hardly noticed Him. (786)

305. *Proofs of Jesus Christ.* Captivity, with the assurance of deliverance within seventy years, was not real captivity. But now they are captives without any hope.

God has promised them that even though He should scatter them to the ends of the earth, nevertheless if they were faithful to His law, He would assemble them together again. They are very faithful to it, and remain oppressed. (638)

306. The Jews, in testing if He were God, have shown that He was man. (763)

307. The Church has had as much difficulty in showing that Jesus Christ was man, against those who denied it, as in showing that He was God; and the probabilities were equally great. (764)

308. The infinite distance between mind and body as a symbol of the infinitely more infinite distance between mind and charity; for charity is supernatural.

All the glory of greatness has no luster for people in search of understanding.

The greatness of clever men is invisible to kings, to the rich, to chiefs, and to all the worldly great.

The greatness of wisdom, which is nothing if not of God, is invisible to the carnal-minded and to the clever. These are three orders differing in kind.

Great geniuses have their power, their glory, their greatness, their victory, their luster, and have no need of worldly greatness, with which they are not in keeping. They are seen, not by the eye, but by the mind; this is sufficient.

The saints have their power, their glory, their victory, their luster, and need no worldly or intellectual greatness, with which they have no affinity; for these neither add anything to them, nor take away anything from them. They are seen of God, and the angels, and not of the body, nor of the curious mind. God is enough for them.

Archimedes, apart from his rank, would have the same veneration. He fought no battles for the eyes to feast upon; but he has given his discoveries to all men. Oh! how brilliant he was to the mind!

Jesus Christ, without riches, and without any external exhibition of his knowledge, is in His own order of holiness. He did not invent; He did not reign. But He was humble, patient, holy, holy to God, terrible to devils, without any sin. Oh! in what great pomp and in what wonderful splendor, He is come to the eyes of the heart, which perceive wisdom!

It would have been useless for Archimedes to have acted the prince in his books on geometry, although he was a prince.

It would have been useless for our Lord Jesus Christ to come like a king, in order to shine forth in His kingdom of holiness. But He came there appropriately in the glory of His own order.

It is most absurd to take offense at the lowliness of Jesus Christ, as if His lowliness were in the same order as the greatness which He came to manifest. If we consider this greatness in His life, in His passion, in His obscurity, in His death, in the choice of His disciples, in their desertion, in His secret resurrection, and the rest, we shall see it to be so immense, that we shall have no reason for being offended at a lowliness which is not of that order.

But there are some who can only admire worldly greatness, as though there were no intellectual greatness; for mind knows all these and itself; and these bodies nothing.

All bodies, the firmament, the stars, the earth and its kingdoms, are not equal to the lowest mind; for mind knows all these and itself; and these bodies nothing.

All bodies together, and all minds together, and all their products, are not equal to the least feeling of charity. This is of an order infinitely more exalted.

From all bodies together, we cannot obtain one little thought; this is impossible, and of another order. From all bodies and minds, we cannot produce a feeling of true charity; this is impossible, and of another and supernatural order. (793)

310. *Proof of Jesus Christ.* The supposition that the apostles were impostors is very absurd. Let us think it out. Let us imagine those twelve men, assembled after the death of Jesus Christ, plotting to say that He was risen. By this they attack all powers. The heart of man is strangely inclined to fickleness, to change, to promises, to gain. However little any of them might have been led astray by all these attractions, nay more, by the fear of prisons, tortures, and death, they were lost. Let us follow up this thought. (801)

311. It is a wonderful thing, and worthy of particular attention, to see this Jewish people existing so many years in perpetual misery, it being neces-

sary as a proof of Jesus Christ, both that they should exist to prove Him, and that they should be miserable, because they crucified Him; and though to be miserable, and to exist are contradictory, they nevertheless still exist in spite of their misery. (640)

321. Any man can do what Mahomet has done; for he performed no miracles. He was not foretold. No man can do what Christ has done. (600)

322. The apostles were either deceived or deceivers. Either supposition has difficulties; for it is not possible to mistake a man raised from the dead . . .
   While Jesus Christ was with them, He could sustain them. But, after that, if He did not appear to them, who inspired them to act? (802)

325. That He would teach men the perfect way.
   And there has never come, before Him or after Him, any man who has taught anything divine approaching to this. (733)

326. And what crowns all this is prediction, so that it should not be said that it is chance which has done it.
   Whosoever, having only a week to live, will not find out that it is expedient to believe that all this is not a stroke of chance. . . .
   Now, if the passions had no hold on us, a week and a hundred years would amount to the same thing. (694)

329. That Jesus Christ would be small in his beginning, and would then increase. The little stone of Daniel.
   If I had no wise heard of the Messiah, nevertheless, after such wonderful predictions of the course of the world which I see fulfilled, I see that He is divine. And I know that these same books foretold a Messiah, I should be sure that He would come; and seeing that they place His time before the destruction of the second temple, I should say that He had come. (734)

332. *Prophecies.* If one man alone had made a book of predictions about Jesus Christ, as to the time and the manner, and Jesus Christ had come in comformity to these prophecies, this would have infinite weight.
   But there is much more here. Here is a succession of men during four thousand years, who consequently and without variation, come, one after another, to foretell this same event. Here is a whole people who announce it, and who have existed for four thousand years, in order to give corporate testimony of the assurances which they have, and from which they cannot be diverted by whatever threats and persecutions people may make against them. This is far more important. (710)

335. The prophecies are the strongest proof of Jesus Christ. It is for them also that God has made most provision; for the event which has fulfilled them is a miracle existing since the birth of the Church to the end. So God has raised up prophets during sixteen hundred years, and, during four hundred years afterwards. He has scattered all these prophecies among all the Jews, who carried them into all parts of the world. Such was the preparation for the birth of Jesus Christ, and, as His Gospel was to be believed by all the world, it was not only necessary that there should be prophecies to make it believed, but that these prophecies should exist throughout the whole world, in order to make it embraced by the whole world. (706)

336. One must be bold to predict the same thing in so many ways. It was necessary that the four idolatrous or pagan monarchies, the end of the kingdom of Judah, and the seventy weeks, should happen at the same time, and all this before the second temple was destroyed. (709)

339. The prophecies having given different signs which should all happen at the advent of the Messiah, it was necessary that all these signs should occur at the same time. So it was necessary that the fourth monarchy should have come, when the seventy weeks of Daniel were ended; and that the scepter should have then departed from Judah. And all this happened without any difficulty. Then it was necessary that the Messiah should come; and Jesus Christ then came, who was called the Messiah. And all this again was without difficulty. This indeed shows the truth of the prophecies. (738)

PART XXVI. CHRISTIAN MORALITY

351. Christianity is strange. It bids man recognize that he is vile, even abominable, and bids him desire to be like God. Without such a counterpoise, this dignity would make him horribly vain, or this humiliation would make him terribly abject. (537)

352. Misery induces despair, pride induces presumption. The Incarnation shows man the greatness of his misery by the greatness of the remedy which he required. (526)

354. There is no doctrine more appropriate to man than this, which teaches him his double capacity of receiving, and of losing grace, because of the double peril to which he is exposed, of despair and of pride. (524)

357. None is so happy as a true Christian, nor so reasonable, virtuous or aimiable. (541)

360. *Morality.* God having made the heavens and the earth, which do not feel the happiness of their being, He has willed to make beings who should know it, and who should compose a body of thinking members. For our members do not feel the happiness of their union, of their wonderful intelligence, of the care which has been taken to infuse into their minds, and to make them grow and endure. How happy they would be if they saw and felt it! But for this they would need to have intelligence to know it, and good-will to consent to that of the universal soul. But if, having received intelligence, they employed it to retain nourishment for themselves without allowing it to pass to the other members, they would be not only unjust, but also miserable, and would hate rather than love themselves; their blessedness, as well as their duty, consisting in their consent to the guidance of the whole soul to which they belong, which loves them better than they love themselves. (482)

372. To be a member is to have neither life, being, nor movement, except through the spirit of the body, and for the body.

The separate member, seeing no longer the body to which it belongs, has only a perishing and dying existence. Yet it believes it is a whole, and seeing not the body on which it depends, it believes it depends only on self, and desires to make itself both center and body. But not having in itself a principle of life, it only goes astray, and is astonished in the uncertainty of its being; perceiving in fact that it is not a body, and still not seeing that it is a member of a body. In short, when it comes to know itself, it has returned as it were to its own home, and loves itself only for the body. It deplores its past wanderings.

It cannot by its nature love any other thing, except for itself and to subject it to self, because each thing loves itself more than all. But in loving the body, it loves itself, because it only exists in it, by it, and for it. *But he that is joined unto the Lord is one spirit* [I Corinthians 6:17].

The body loves the hand; and the hand, if it had a will, should love itself in the same way as it is loved by the soul. All love which goes beyond this is unfair.

He that is joined unto the Lord is one spirit. We love ourselves, because we are members of Jesus Christ. We love Jesus Christ, because He is the body of which we are members. All is one, one is in the other, like the Three Persons. (483)

373. We must love only God and hate self only.

If the foot had always been ignorant that it belonged to the body, and that there was a body on which it depended, if it had only had the knowledge and the love of self, and if it came to know that it belonged to a body on which it depended, what regret, what shame for its past life, for having been useless to the body which inspired its life, which would have annihilated it if it had rejected it and separated it from itself, as it kept itself apart from the body! What prayers for its preservation in it! And with what submission would it allow itself to be governed by the will which rules the body, even to consenting if necessary, to be cut off, or it would lose its character as member! For every member must be quite willing to perish for the body, for which alone the whole is. (477)

374. If the feet and the hands had a will of their own, they could only be in their order in submitting this particular will to the primary will which governs the whole body. Apart from that, they are in disorder and mischief; but in willing only the good of the body, they accomplish their own good. (475)

375. Philosophers have consecrated the vices by placing them in God Himself. Christians have consecrated the virtues. (503)

PART XXVII. CONCLUSION

377. The knowledge of God is very far from the love of Him. (280)

378. "Had I seen a miracle," say men, "I should become converted." How can they be sure they would do a thing of the nature of which they are ignorant? They imagine that this conversion consists in a worship of God which is like commerce, and in a communion such as they picture to themselves. True religion consists in annihilating self before that Universal Being, whom we have so often provoked, and who can justly destroy us at any time; in recognizing that we can do nothing without Him, and have deserved nothing from Him but His displeasure. It consists in knowing that there is an unconquerable opposition between us and God, and that without a mediator there can be no communion with Him. (470)

380. Do not wonder to see simple people believe without reasoning. God imparts to them love of Him and hatred of self. He inclines their heart to believe. Men will never believe with a saving and real faith, unless God inclines their heart; and they will believe as soon as He inclines it. And this is what David knew well, when he said: *Incline my heart unto thy testimonies* [Psalms 119:36]. (284)

381. Those who believe without having read the Testaments, do so because they have an inward disposition entirely holy, and all that they hear

of our religion conforms to it. They feel that a God has made them; they desire only to love God; they desire to hate themselves only. They feel that they have no strength in themselves; that they are incapable of coming to God; and that if God does not come to them, they can have no communion with Him. And they hear our religion say that men must love God only, and hate self only; but that all being corrupt and unworthy of God, God made Himself man to unite Himself to us. No more is required to persuade men who have this disposition in their heart, and who have this knowledge of their duty and of their inefficiency. (286)

382. Those whom we see to be Christians without the knowledge of the prophets and evidences, nevertheless judge of their religion as well as those who have that knowledge. They judge of it by the heart, as others judge of it by the intellect. God Himself inclines them to believe, and thus they are most effectively convinced.

I confess indeed that one of those Christians who believe without proofs will not perhaps be capable of convincing an infidel who will say the same of himself. But those who know the proofs of religion will prove without difficulty that such a believer is truly inspired by God, though he cannot prove it himself.

For God having said in His prophecies (which are undoubtedly prophecies), that in the reign of Jesus Christ He would spread His spirit abroad among nations, and that the youths and maidens and children of the Church would prophesy; it is certain that the Spirit of God is in these, and not in the others. (287)

PAPERS UNCLASSIFIED BY PASCAL

418. [The Wager] *Infinite — nothing.* Our soul is cast into a body, where it finds number, time, dimension. Thereupon it reasons, and calls this nature necessity, and can believe nothing else.

Unity joined to infinity adds nothing to it, no more than one foot to an infinite measure. The finite is annihilated in the presence of the infinite, and becomes a pure nothing. So our spirit before God, so our justice before divine justice. There is not so great a disproportion between our justice and that of God, as between unity and infinity.

The justice of God must be vast like His compassion. Now justice to the outcast is less vast, and ought less to offend our feelings than mercy towards the elect.

We know that there is an infinite, and are ignorant of its nature. As we know it to be false that numbers are finite, it is therefore true that there is an infinity in number. But we do not know what it is. It is false that it is even, it is false that it is odd; for the addition of a unit can make no change in its nature. Yet it is a number, and every number is odd or even (this is certainly true of every finite number). So we may well know that there is a God without knowing what He is. Is there not one substantial truth, seeing that there are so many things which are not the truth itself?

We know that the existence and nature of the finite, because we also are finite and have extension. We know the existence of the infinite, and are ignorant of its nature, because it has extension like us, but not limits like us. But we know neither the existence nor the nature of God, because He has neither extension nor limits.

But by faith we know His existence; in glory we shall know His nature. Now, I have already shown that we may well know the existence of a thing, without knowing its nature.

Let us now speak according to natural lights.

If there is a God, He is infinitely incomprehensible, since, having neither parts nor limits. He has no affinity to us. We are then incapable of knowing either what He is or if He is. This being so, who will dare to undertake the decision of the question? Not we, who have no affinity to Him.

Who then will blame Christians for not being able to give a reason for their belief, since they profess a religion for which they cannot give a reason? They declare, in expounding it to the world, that it is a foolishness; and then you complain that they do not prove it! If they proved it, they would not keep their word; it is in lacking proofs, that they are not lacking in sense. "Yes, but although this excuses those who offer it as such, and takes away from them the blame of putting it forward without reason, it does not excuse those who receive." Let us then examine this point, and say, "God is, or He is not." But to which side shall we incline? Reason can decide nothing here. There is an infinite chaos which separated us. A game is being played at the extremity of this infinite distance where heads or tails will turn up. What will you wager? According to reason, you can do neither the one thing nor the other; according to reason, you can defend neither of the propositions.

Do not then reprove for error those who have made a choice; for you know nothing about it. "No, but I blame them for having made, not this choice, but a choice; for again both he who chooses heads and he who chooses tails are equally at fault, they are both in the wrong. The true course is not to wager at all."

Yes; but you must wager. It is not optional. You are embarked. Which will you choose then? Let us see. Since you must choose, let us see which interests you least. You have two things to lose, the true and the good; and two things to stake, your reason and your will, your knowledge and your happiness; and your nature has two things to shun, error and misery. Your reason is no more shocked in choosing one rather than the other, since you must of necessity choose. This is one point settled. But your happiness? Let us weigh the gain and the loss in wagering that God is. Let us estimate these two chances. If you gain, you gain all; if you lose, you lose nothing. Wager, then, without hesitation that He is. "That is very fine. Yes, I must wager; but I may perhaps wager too much."—Let us see. Since there is an equal risk of gain and loss, if you had only to gain two lives, instead of one, you might still wager. But if there were three lives to gain, you would have to play (since you are under the necessity of playing), and you would be imprudent, when you are forced to play, not to chance your life to gain three at a game where there is an equal risk of loss and gain. But there is an eternity of life and happiness. And this being so, if there were an infinity of chances, of which one only would be for you, you would still be right in wagering one to win two, and you would act stupidly, being obliged to play, by refusing to stake one life against three at a game in which out of an infinity of chances there is one for you, if there were an infinity of an infinitely happy life to gain. But there is here an infinity of an infinitely happy life to gain, a chance to gain against a finite number of chances of loss, and what you stake is finite. It is all divided; wherever the infinite is and there is not an infinity of chances of loss against that of gain, there is no time to hesitate, you must give all. And thus, when one is forced to play, he must renounce reason to preserve his life, rather than risk it for infinite gain, as likely to happen as the loss of nothingness.

For it is no use to say it is uncertain if we will gain, and it is certain that we risk, and that the infinite distance between the *certainty* of what is staked and the *uncertainty* of what will be gained, equals the finite good which is certainly staked against the uncertain infinite. It is not so, as every player stakes a certainty to gain an uncertainty, and yet he stakes a finite certainty to gain an uncertainty, without transgressing against reason. There is not an infinite distance between the certainty staked and the uncertainty of the gain; that is untrue. In truth, there is an infinity between the certainty of gain and the certainty of loss. But the uncertainty of the gain is proportioned to the certainty of the stake according to the proportion of the chances of gain and loss. Hence it come that, if there are as many risks on one side as on the other, the course is to play even; and then the certainty of the stake is equal to the uncertainty of the gain, so far is it from fact that there is an infinite distance between them. And so our proposition is of infinite force, when there is the finite to stake in a game where there are equal risks of gain and of loss, and the infinite to gain. This is demonstrable: and if men are capable of any truths, this is one.

"I confess it, I admit it. But, still, is there no means of seeing the faces of the cards?"—Yes, Scripture and the rest, etc. "Yes, but I have my hands tied and my mouth closed; I am forced to wager, and am not free. I am not released, and am so made that I cannot believe. What, then, would you have me do?"

True. But at least learn your inability to believe, since reason brings you to this, and yet you cannot believe. Endeavor then to convince yourself, not by increase of proofs of God, but by the abatement of your passions. You would like to attain faith, and do not know the way; you would like to cure yourself of unbelief, and ask the remedy for it. Learn of those who have been bound like you, and who now stake all their possessions. These are people who know the way which you would follow, and who are cured of an ill of which you would be cured. Follow the way by which they began; by acting as if they believed, taking the holy water, having masses said, etc. Even this will naturally make you believe, and deaden your acuteness. — "But this is what I am afraid of." — And why? What have you to lose?

But to show you that this leads you there, it is this which will lessen the passions, which are your stumbling-blocks.

The end of this discourse. Now, what harm will befall you in taking this side? You will be faithful, honest, humble, grateful, generous, a sincere friend, truthful. Certainly you will not have those poisonous pleasures, glory and luxury; but will you not have others? I will tell you that you will thereby gain in this life, and that, at each step you take on this road, you will see so great certainty of gain, so much nothingness in what you risk, that you will at last recognize that you have wagered for something certain and infinite, for which you have given nothing.

"Ah! This discourse transports me, charms me," etc.

If this discourse pleases you and seems impressive, know that it is made by a man who has knelt, both before and after it, in prayer to that Being infinite and without parts, before whom he lays all he has, for you also to lay before Him all you have for your own good, and for His glory, that so strength may be given to lowliness. (233)

423. The heart has its reasons which reason does not know. We feel it in a thousand things. I say that the heart naturally loves the Universal Being, and also itself naturally, according as it gives itself to them; and it hardens itself against one or the other at its will. You have rejected the one, and kept the other. Is it by reason that you love yourself? (277)

424. It is the heart which experiences God, and not the reason. This, then, is faith; God felt by the heart, not by reason.

512. *The difference between the mathematical and the intuitive mind.* In the one the principles are palpable, but removed from ordinary use; so that for want of habit it is difficult to turn one's mind in that direction; but if one turns it thither ever so little, one sees the principles fully, and one must have a quite inaccurate mind who reasons wrongly from principles so plain that it is almost impossible they should escape notice.

But in the intuitive mind the principles are found in common use, and are before the eyes of everybody. One has only to look, and no effort is necessary; it is only a question of good eyesight, but it must be good, for the principles are so subtle and so numerous, that it is almost impossible but some escape notice. Now the omission of one principle leads to error; thus one must have very clear sight to see all the principles, and in the next place an accurate mind not to draw false deductions from known principles.

All mathematicians would then be intuitive if they had clear sight, for they do not reason incorrectly from principles known to them; and intuitive minds would be mathematical if they could turn their eyes to the principles of mathematics to which they are unused.

The reason, therefore, that some intuitive minds are not mathematical is that they cannot at all turn their attention to the principles of mathematics. But the reason that mathematicians are not intuitive is that they do not see what is before them, and that, accustomed to the exact and plain principles of mathematics, and not reasoning till they have well inspected and arranged their principles, they are lost in matters of intuition where the principles do not allow of such arrangement. They are scarcely seen; they are felt rather than seen; there is the greatest difficulty in making them felt by those who do not of themselves perceive them. These principles are so fine and so numerous that a very delicate and very clear sense is needed to perceive them, and to judge rightly and justly when they are perceived, without for the most part being able to demonstrate them in order as in mathematics: because the principles are not known to us in the same way, and because it would be an endless matter to undertake it. We must see the matter at once, at one glance, and not by a process of reasoning, at least to a certain degree. And thus it is rare that mathematicians are intuitive, and that people of intuition are mathematicians, because mathematicians wish to treat matters of intuition mathematically, and make themselves ridiculous, wishing to begin with definitions and then with axioms, which is not the way to proceed in this kind of reasoning. Not that the mind does not do so, but it does it tacitly, naturally, and without technical rules; for the expression of it is beyond all men, and only a few can feel it.

Intuitive minds, on the contrary, being thus accustomed to judge at a single glance, are so astonished when they are presented with propositions of which they understand nothing, and the way to which is through definitions and axioms so sterile, and which they are not accustomed to see thus in detail, that they are repelled and disheartened.

But dull minds are never either intuitive or mathematical.

Mathematicians who are only mathematicians have exact minds, provided all things are explained to them by means of definitions and axioms; otherwise they are inaccurate and insufferable, for they are only right when the principles are quite clear.

And men of intuition who are only intuitive cannot have the patience to reach first principles of things speculative and conceptual, which they have never seen in the world, and which are altogether out of the common. (1)

513. *Mathematics. Intuition.* True eloquence makes light of eloquence, true morality makes light of morality; that is to say, the morality of the judgment, which has no rules, makes light of the morality of the intellect.

For it is to judgment that perception belongs, as science belongs to intellect. Intuition is the part of judgment, mathematics of intellect.

To make light of philosophy is to be a true philosopher. (4)

599. But is it *probable* that *probability* gives assurance?

Difference between rest and security of conscience. Nothing gives certainty but truth; nothing gives rest but the sincere search for truth. (908)

601. The causits submit the decision to the corrupt reason, and the choice of decisions to the corrupt will, in order that all that is corrupt in the nature of man may contribute to his conduct. (907)

628. *Antiquity of the Jews.* What a difference there is between one book and another! I am not astonished that the Greeks made the Iliad, nor the Egyptians and the Chinese their histories.

We have only to see how this originates. These fabulous historians are not contemporaneous with the facts about which they write. Homer composes a romance, which he gives out as such and which is received as such; for nobody doubted that Troy and Agamemnon no more existed than did the golden apple. Accordingly he did not think of making a history, but solely a book to amuse; he is the only writer of his time; the beauty of the work has made it last, every one learns it and talks of it, it is necessary to know it, and each one knows it by heart. Four hundred years afterwards the witnesses of these facts are no longer alive, no one knows of his own knowledge if it be a fable or history; one has only learnt it from his ancestors, and this can pass for truth.

Every history which is not contemporaneous, as the books of the Sibyls and Trismegistus and so many others which have been believed by the world, are false, and found to be false in the course of time. It is not so with contemporaneous writers.

There is a great difference between a book which an individual writes, and publishes to a nation, and a book which itself creates a nation. We cannot doubt that the book is as old as the people. (628)

691. Skepticism is true; for, after all, men before Jesus Christ did not know where they were, nor whether they were great or small. And those who have said the one or the other, knew nothing about it, and guessed without reason and by chance. They also erred always in excluding the one or the other.

What therefore ye ignorantly seek religion declares unto you [Acts 17:23].

693. The easiest conditions to live in according to the world are the most difficult to live in according to God, and vice versa. Nothing is so difficult according to the world as the religious life; nothing is easier than to live it according to God. Nothing is easier, according to the world, than to live in high office and great wealth; nothing is more difficult than to live in them according to God, and without acquiring an interest in them and a liking for them. (906)

822. *History of China.* I believe only the histories, whose witnesses got themselves killed.

Which is the more credible of the two, Moses or China?

It is not a question of seeing this summarily. I tell you there is in it something to blind, and something to enlighten.

By this one word I destroy all your reasoning. "But China obscures," say you: and I answer, "China obscures, but there is clearness to be found; seek it."

Thus all that you say makes for one of the views, and not at all against the other. So this serves, and does no harm.

We must then see this in detail; we must put the papers on the table. (593)

832. *The beginning.* Miracles enable us to judge of doctrine, and doctrine enables us to judge of miracles.

There are false miracles and true. There must be a distinction, in order to know them; otherwise they would be useless. Now they are not useless; on the contrary, they are fundamental. Now the rule which is given to us must be such, that it does not destroy the proof which the true miracles give of the truth, which is the chief end of the miracles.

Moses has given two rules; that the prediction does not come to pass [Deuteronomy 18], and that they do not lead to idolatry [Deuteronomy 13], and Jesus Christ one.

If doctrine regulates miracles, miracles are useless for doctrine.

If miracles regulate. . . .

Objection to the rule. The distinction of the times. One rule during the time of Moses, another at present. (803)

833. Every religion which is false, which as to its faith does not worship one God as the origin of everything, and which as to its morality does not love only God as the object of everything. (487)

834. *Reasons why we do not believe.*

[John 12:37] *But though he had done many miracles before them, yet they believed not on him, that the saying of Esaias the prophet might be ful-*

filled . . . He hath blinded their eyes. These things said Esaias when he saw his glory and spake of him.

For the Jews require a sign and the Greeks seek after wisdom, but we preach Christ crucified [I Corinthians 1:22].

[Pascal's commentary] *But full of signs and full of wisdom.*

But you preach Christ not crucified and a religion without miracles and without wisdom.

What makes us not believe in the true miracles, is want of love [John 10:26]. *But ye believe not because ye are not of my sheep.* What makes us believe the false is want of love [II Thessalonians 2].

The foundation of religion. It is the miracles. What then? Does God speak against miracles, against the foundations of the faith which we have in Him?

If there is a God, faith in God must exist on earth. Now the miracles of Jesus Christ are not foretold by Antichrist, but the miracles of Antichrist are foretold by Jesus Christ. And so if Jesus Christ were not the Messiah, He would have indeed led into error. When Jesus Christ foretold the miracles of Antichrist, did He think of destroying faith in His own miracles?

Moses foretold Jesus Christ, and bade to follow Him. Jesus Christ foretold Antichrist, and forbade to follow him.

It was impossible that in the time of Moses men should keep their faith for Antichrist, who was unknown to them. But it is quite easy, in the time of Antichrist, to believe in Jesus Christ, already known.

There is no reason for believing in Antichrist, which there is not for believing in Jesus Christ. But there are reasons for believing in Jesus Christ, which there are not for believing in the other. (834)

835. The prophecies, the very miracles and proofs of our religion, are not of such a nature that they can be said to be absolutely convincing. But they are also of such a kind that it cannot be said that it is unreasonable to believe them. Thus there is both evidence and obscurity to enlighten some and confuse others. But the evidence is such that it surpasses, or at least equals, the evidence to the contrary; so that it is not reason which can determine men not to follow it, and thus it can only be lust or malice of heart. And by this means there is sufficient evidence to condemn, and insufficient to convince; so that it appears in those who follow it, that it is grace, and not reason, which makes them follow it; and in those who shun it, that it is lust, not reason, which makes them shun it. (564)

836. I suppose that men believe miracles. You corrupt religion either in favor of your friends, or against your enemies. You arrange it at your will. (855)

837. If there were no false miracles, there would be certainty. If there were no rule to judge of them, miracles would be useless, and there would be no reason for believing.

Now there is, humanly speaking, no human certainty, but we have reason. (823)

842. Our religion is wise and foolish. Wise because it is the most learned, and the most founded on miracles, prophecies, etc. Foolish because it is not all this which makes us belong to it. This makes us indeed condemn those who do not belong to it; but it does not cause belief in those who do belong to it. It is the cross that makes them believe. *Lest the Cross of Christ should be made of none effect* [I Corinthians 1:17]. And so Saint Paul, who came with wisdom and signs, says that he has come neither with wisdom nor with signs, for he came to convert. But those who come only to convince, can say that they come with wisdom and with signs. (588)

887. Descartes useless and uncertain. (78)

889. *Thoughts. With all these I sought for rest* [Ecclesiasticus 24:7]. If our condition were truly happy, we would not need diversion from thinking of it in order to make ourselves happy. (165)

890. *Weakness.* Every pursuit of men is to get wealth; and they cannot have a title to show that they possess it justly, for they have only that of human caprice; nor have they strength to hold it securely. It is the same with knowledge, for disease takes it away. We are incapable both of truth and goodness. (436b)

905. *Skepticism.* Every thing here is partly true and partly false. Essential truth is not so; it is altogether pure and altogether true. This mixture dishonors and annihilates it. Nothing is purely true, and thus nothing is true, meaning by that pure truth. You will say it is true that homicide is wrong. Yes; for we know well the wrong and the false. But what will you say is good? Chastity? I say no; for the world would come to an end. Marriage? No; continence is better. Not to kill? No; for lawlessness would be horrible, and the wicked would kill all the good. To kill? No; for that destroys nature. We possess truth and good only in part, and mingled with falsehood and evil. (385)

Bibliography

WORKS BY PASCAL

French Texts

Oeuvres complètes, publiées suivant l'ordre chronologique. . ., 14 vols., Leon Brunsch-vicg, P. Boutroux, and F. Gazier (eds.). Paris: Hachette, 1904–1914.

Oeuvres complètes, Louis Lafuma (ed.), New York and Paris: Macmillan, 1963. Fine one-volume edition with Lafuma's reordering of the text of the *Pensées*.

Ouevres complètes, 2 vols., Jean Mesnard (ed.). Paris: Descleé De Brouwer, 1964–78. An extended revision by the leading present Pascal expert in France.

English Translations

Great Shorter Works, translated, with an introduction, by Emile Caillet and John C. Blankenagel. Westport, Ct.: Greenwood, 1974. Includes all of Pascal's important works except the *Pensées* and the *Provincial Letters*.

Pensées and The Provincial Letters, translated by W. F. Trotter and Thomas M' Crie. New York: Modern Library, 1941.

Pensées, translated by W. F. Trotter, with an introduction by T. S. Eliot. New York: E. P. Dutton, 1975.

Pensées, translated by A. J. Krailsheimer, based on the Lafuma text. New York: Penguin, 1966.

Physical Treatises of Pascal, Frederick Barry (ed.). New York: Octagon, 1973.

Works about Pascal

Abercombie, Nigel, *Pascal and St. Augustine*. Oxford: Oxford University Press, 1938.

Bishop, Morris, *Pascal: The Life of Genius*. Westport, Ct.: Greenwood, 1970. A very good intellectual biography.

Boutroux, Emile, *Pascal*. Paris: Hachette, 1922. Standard French study of Pascal.

Brunschvicq, Leon, *Descartes et Pascal, lecteurs de Montaigne*. New York: Brentano's, 1944. Important French study of how Descartes and Pascal used ideas from Montaigne.

Caillet, Émile, *Pascal: The Emergence of Genius*. Westport, Ct.: Greenwood, 1975. A reissue of an important full-length biography.

Chevalier, Jacques, *Pascal*. New York: Longmans Green, 1930. Lectures given by a leading French interpreter.

Coleman, Francis, X. J., *Neither Angel nor Beast*. New York and London: Routledge Kegan Paul, 1986.

Costabel, P., *Oeuvres scientifiques de Pascal*. Paris: Presses Universitaires de France, 1964. Papers by leading French scholars on Pascal's scientific works.

Davidson, Hugh M., *Blaise Pascal*. Boston: Twayne series, 1983. A good overview by a leading American Pascal scholar.

————, *The Origins of Certainty: Means and Meaning in Pascal's Pensées*. Chicago: University of Chicago Press, 1979. An interesting exposition and interpretation.

Flew, Anthony, "Is Pascal's Wager the Only Safe Bet?" *Rationalist Annual*, 1960, pp. 21–25. A criticism of the merits of Pascal's wager argument.

Goldmann, Lucien, *The Hidden God*. London: Routledge Kegan Paul, 1976. Translation of an important French Marxist interpretation of Pascal and Jansenism.

Gouhier, Henri, *Blaise Pascal, Commentaires*. Paris: J. Vrin, 1966. Commentary by leading French scholar of 17th century philosophy.

Julien-Eymard d'Angers (Charles Chesenau), *Pascal et ses precurseurs*. Paris: Nouvelles éditions latines, 1954. On Pascal's place in the Christian apologetic tradition of the time.

Krailsheimer, A., *Pascal*. New York: Oxford University Press, 1980. A survey of Pascal's writings and ideas in the "Past Masters" series.

Lafuma, Louis, *Histoire des Pensées de Pascal, 1656–1952*. Paris: Éditions de Luxembourg, 1954. The results of Lafuma's fundamental researches into the history of the text.

Mackie, J. L., *The Miracle of Theism*. Oxford: Oxford University Press, 1982. The chapter on "Belief without Reason" offers a critical evaluation of Pascal's wager argument.

Mesnard, Jean, *Pascal, His Life and Works*. Translation of study by the leading French expositor of Pascal. New York: Philosophical Library, 1952.

Miel, Jan, *Pascal and Theology*. Baltimore: Johns Hopkins University, 1970.

Mortimer, Ernest, *Blaise Pascal: The Life and Work of a Realist*. Westport, Ct. Greenwood, 1976. Reissue of a basic biography and interpretation.

Orcibal, Jean (ed.), *Les Origines du Jansenisme*, 5 vols. Louvain and Paris: J. Vrin, 1947–1962. Basic study of the development of Jansenism.

Patrick, Denzil G., *Pascal and Kierkegaard, A Study on the Strategy of Evangelism*. London: Lutterworth, 1947. A comparison of the techniques used by these two polemical apologists for Christianity.

Popkin, Richard H. "Pascal," *Encyclopedia of Philosophy*. New York: Macmillan, 1967, vol. 6, pp. 51–55.

Rescher, Nicholas, *Pascal's Wager: A Study of Practical Reasoning in Philosophical Theology*. South Bend: University of Notre Dame Press, 1985. Examination of one of Pascal's famous arguments by a leading contemporary philosopher.

Steinmann, Jean, *Pascal*. New York: Harcourt, Brace. Study by a French leading liberal churchman.

Strowski, Fortunat, *Pascal et son temps, 3 vols*. Paris: Librarie Plon, 1907. Major study of the background and development of Pascal's views.

Waterman, M., *Voltaire, Pascal and Human Destiny*. New York: Octagon, 1973. A study of the differences and similarities of these two great thinkers.